Advanced Studies in
Physical Education
and Sport

Edited by Paul Beashel and John Taylor

Contributors: John Alderson, Paul Beashel, John Coghlan,
Angela Cumine, Conor Gissane, Paul Grimshaw, Kathleen Kerr, John Kremer,
Bill McLoughlin, Elizabeth Pike, Mahmoud Saleh EL-Sayed, Deidre Scully,
John Taylor, Eric Wallace, John White

Nelson

Thomas Nelson and Sons Ltd
Delta Place
27 Bath Road
Cheltenham
GL 53 7TH
United Kingdom

ISBN 0-17-4482345
NPN 9 8 7

Printed in China

Acquisitions: Roda Morrison, Steve Berry
Administration: Jenny Goode
Concept design: Eleanor Fisher
Design and layout: Claire Brodmann
Editorial: Melanie McRae
Marketing: Jane Lewis
Production: Liam Reardon

CONTENTS

INTRODUCTION

The growth in the number of candidates sitting examination in A-level Physical Education and Sport Studies has been phenomenal. This development was only made possible through the foresight and pioneering work of the AEB and the teachers involved.

The establishment of Physical Education as a popular GCSE subject taught throughout the country has, of course, provided the impetus for many pupils to carry their studies through to A-level. Our experience in providing a text book for the GCSE examination led us naturally to this book.

Our objective has been to present the academic expertise and teaching skills of a number of eminent experts to A-level students of Physical Education in a readable, friendly and coherent manner. In doing so, we believe we have produced a book which will be of interest to all serious students of sport, whether in schools or colleges, laboratories or offices, homes or clubs.

No task of this complexity can be achieved without the cheerful goodwill of the contributors. We are proud to have been part of such an outstanding team, full details of all of its members are contained elsewhere in the book. We must also acknowledge our grateful thanks to the Department of Sport Science and Physical Education at St Mary's University College, Doug Neate, Ken Hardman, Janet Kendrick and most importantly of all, to our wives, Marilyn and Liz.

Chapter 1

John Anderson qualified in Physical Education at Carnegie College, Leeds University. He continued his studies in PE gaining a Ph.D. specialising in the psychology of skill acquisition. He taught and lectured in Physical Education, Sport Studies and Recreation Management and was instrumental in the development of the AEB A-level in Sport Studies. He is currently employed as the Head of Academic Quality in the School of Leisure and Food Management at Sheffield Hallam University.

Chapter 2

Kathleen Kerr qualified as a physiotherapist at the Northern Ireland School of Physiotherapy and practised in a number of hospitals. She then lectured at the Ulster Polytechnic in the Department of Occupational Therapy and Physiotherapy before moving to the University of Nottingham School of Physiotherapy. She lectures on Research and Evaluation, Movement Studies and Sports Medicine and has been awarded a Ph.D.

Chapter 3

Mahmoud Saleh EL-Sayed studied at the University of Helwan, Alexandria before lecturing at the University of Salford where he was awarded his Ph.D. specialising in exercise physiology. He then taught and researched at a number of universities and colleges. He is currently Reader in Sport Sciences at the Liverpool John Moores University.

Chapter 4

Angela Cumine trained at I M Marsh College, Liverpool before starting her teaching career in a comprehensive school. She gained an M.A. at Leeds University and is a Chartered Physiotherapist. Currently she is Programme Director for Sport Rehabilitation at St Mary's University College. She has been fitness adviser to international and professional sports teams and is an ex-international hockey player.

Conor Gissane studied at St Mary's University College, Twickenham where he gained a B.Hums. in Movement Studies and Geography. He continued his studies at Purdue University, Indiana, whader in Human Performance and Health Studies at The University of Ulster and is currently Senior Lecturer in Health Promotion at the University of Nottingham at the Queen's Medical Centre.

Chapter 5

Eric Wallace qualified in Physical Education at Queen's University, Belfast. He than studied and lectured at the University of California before gaining a D.Phil. in Bio-engineering at the University of Ulster. At present he lectures in Sports Mechanics in the School of Leisure and Tourism at the University of Ulster. His main research areas are sports and rehabilitation biomechanics, sports medicine and exercise physiology.

Paul Grimshaw trained as a mechanical engineer with the Ministry of Defence before graduating in Sport Studies at Carnegie College and gaining a Ph.D. in Biomedical Engineering at the University of Salford. He was a lecturer at Edinburgh University before becoming Senior Lecturer in Biomechanics at the West London Institute where he is reseaching into movement patterns of young children.

Chapter 6

Deidre Scully qualified in Physical Education at Ulster Polytechnic and then commenced her teaching career. She studied and taught at the University of Illinois where she was awarded a M.Sc. in Physical Education and a Ph.D. in Kinesiology. She has since held a lecturing post at the University of Ulster in the Department of Pre-Service Education specialising in psychology, information management and research.

Chapter 7

John Kremer studied social psychology at Loughborough University where he was awarded a Ph.D. He has specialised in two areas, equal opportunities at work and sport. He has acted as a consultant sports psychologist to a wide range of sporting bodies, as well as continuing to teach and research. He is currently Senior Lecturer in Psychology at Queen's University. Belfast.

Deidre Scully also contributed to this chapter.

Chapter 8

Paul Beashel and **John Taylor** qualified in Physical Education at St Mary's College Twickenham and Cardiff College, respectively. They have both had a wide range of teaching responsibilities in comprehensive schools and completed their Master's Degrees while teaching. They have considerable experience in teaching and examining Physical Education at secondary level. Paul is currently Headteacher of The Deanes School in Essex. John was a Deputy Headteacher in the London Borough of Hillingdon.

Chapter 9

John Coghlan MBE studied at Birmingham University and Loughborough College. He then taught Physical Education at school and college level before moving to be the Sports Council Director for the West Midlands. He became Director General of the Sports Council and Director of International Affairs representing the Government on the Committee for the Development of Sport at the Council of Europe. In retirement he is a visiting professor to a number of colleges at home and overseas.

Chapter 10

Elizabeth Pike gained a B.A. in Movement Studies at the University of Kent before completing an M.Sc. in Sport Science at Loughborough University. She is currently Senior Lecturer in the Department of Sport Science and Physical Education at St Mary's University College, Strawberry Hill. She specialises in the sociology of sport and qualitative research methods and directs a course in exercise and health science.

Chapter 11

Bill McLoughlin qualified as a teacher at St Luke's College, Exeter. He then specialised in exercise physiology at the University of Oregon and was awarded an M.Sc. Following teaching in Huddersfield, he lectured in Physical Education at St Mary's University College, acting as Head of Department at the time of his recent retirement. He has taken part and coached gymnastics at both national and international level and is an international judge.

John White studied at St Mary's College Twickenham before teaching. Following research at Purdue University, Indiana, he was awarded his Ph.D. He has since held lecturing posts at a number of colleges and universities including Reader in Human Performance and Health Studies at The University of Ulster and is currently Senior Lecturer in Health Promotion at the University of Nottingham.

1 SPORT ACTIVITY ANALYSIS

Objectives

To understand

- different definitions and interpretations of sport within our society
- that there are many different sport activities which provide people with a variety of challenges, experiences and roles
- how to group sport activities into categories according to certain 'family resemblances'
- how to analyse sport activities to illustrate the physical and mental demands they make of the sports performer

Figure 1.1

Definitions and interpretations of 'sport'

Think of someone taking part in a game of hockey, climbing a rock face, performing a gymnastic floor sequence, and running a marathon. Which images come to your mind?

In hockey, do you see the power of the flick at goal; the understanding between two players as they play a 'one-two'; the controlled aggression as a defender makes a hard, but legal tackle; the satisfaction for a player who knows that she has the skill to control the ball effectively?

Do you see the power and balance of the rock climber; his ability to cope with the exposure of an overhang; his ability to read the holds on the route ahead; the satisfaction that comes from knowing he can master the intricate moves required by the climb?

Do you admire the flexibility, power and grace of the gymnast; her ability to 'know' what her body is doing as she twists and turns in the air; the satisfaction of knowing that she is capable of performing the sequence of movements perfectly?

Can you imagine the relentless determination required of the marathon runner to maintain the rhythm associated with steady power output, mile after mile; the mental ability to concentrate on his running action for a minimum of two and a quarter hours, often in physical discomfort; the satisfaction of knowing that his physical and mental training is allowing him to achieve his own time target for the event.

In 1964, the International Council for Sport & Physical Education (ICSPE) defined sport as *'any physical activity which has the character of play and which takes the form of a struggle with oneself or involves competition with others…'*

The Council of Europe and the British Sports Council have identified four main categories of sporting activity:

- **Competitive Games and Sports**, such as netball and hockey.
- **Outdoor and Adventure Activities**, such as climbing and sailing.
- **Aesthetic Movement**, such as dance and figure skating.
- **Conditioning Activities**, such as weight training and aerobics.

However, some problems emerge if we were test out these definitions and categories of sport in a logical way. For example, gardening can be a very physical activity involving a struggle with oneself, and can lead to competition in the context of a horticultural show, but it would not normally be understood as sport. Darts is generally recognised as a sport, but is not very 'physical'.

If something is 'aesthetic', it means that it has some characteristic that can be recognised as 'beautiful'. We can all appreciate quality of movement or style in competition sports like tennis or hurdling, so should these sports be in the aesthetic category? Top class sports competitors have to train hard in order to compete effectively. Does this mean that all competitive sports should also be considered in the 'conditioning' category?

Interpretations of 'sport'

There are two main meanings or interpretations of the word 'sport'. The first meaning refers to activities in which people participate voluntarily, and which almost always provide a challenge of some kind. This challenge usually involves physical exercise, the execution of skill, or both.

The second interpretation of sport refers to the experience of pleasure or satisfaction gained by an individual through participating in these activities. At the most obvious level, there is the satisfaction of finishing the marathon, getting to the top of the climb and of beating the opponents in the hockey match or in the gymnastic competition.

There are other levels of pleasure and satisfaction, however. There is the pleasure of knowing that you can cope with the difficulty of a particularly tricky move on the climb; the satisfaction of knowing that you have sent an accurate pass to a team-mate in the hockey game; the pleasure of feeling your body performing a complicated tumbling sequence and making a perfect landing within the gymnastic routine; the elation of finishing the marathon in a respectable time. At yet another level, there is the satisfaction of knowing that you have mastered the skills required, or achieved the level of physical fitness demanded by your choice of activity.

Many sport activities are intensely competitive, but these descriptions of the pleasures arising from sports participation, demonstrate that winning is not everything. Much of the satisfaction comes from the preparation for, and from the attempt to meet, the challenge that a particular sport sets, whether the individual or the team wins or not.

The characteristics of participation in sport can be summarised as follows:

- Sport is usually a recreational activity undertaken voluntarily in the participant's own time.
- Sport is usually undertaken for fun.
- Sport usually implies a challenge of a physical nature and demands skilful performance.

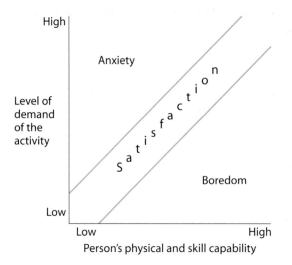

Figure 1.2 The relationship between the ability and capacity a person brings to a sports situation and the demand it places on him or her. (After Cziksentmihalyi)

If winning was the only aim, then a great number of regular sports participants would have stopped participating long ago!

The level of challenge within sports is variable. This variation arises from differences among the individuals regarding their physical capacities and skills, and from the variety of challenges which the sports themselves can present. For example, think of a group of children playing 'football' on a piece of waste ground with old bricks for goal posts. Contrast that image with the FA Cup Final at Wembley Stadium. Compare the demands of a summer hill walk in Britain with an attempt on Mount Everest in the high Himalayas, or of canoeing a gentle English river as compared with an expedition through the Grand Canyon.

The satisfaction that the individual should get from his participation in sport can be lost if there is a mis-match between the level of skill and physical capability, and the level of challenge provided by the sport. This idea has been represented in diagram form in Figure 1.2. In order to illustrate this idea, imagine a player turning up to play in a county tennis tournament for the very first time, and finding herself matched against the number one seed in the first round. Interpreting the model, the newcomer would have a low skill capability when compared with that demanded by the contest with the top seed. She would most likely feel out of place and possibly embarrassed. These feelings would result in anxiety, as shown in the model. By contrast, the highly skilful top seed, finding herself playing the beginner in the first round would quickly realise the inadequacy of the opponent's skills. The expert player would not experience the expected demands at county level and might quickly become bored with the lack of challenge provided by this particular match.

Sport, play, leisure, recreation and physical education

The concepts of sport, play, leisure, recreation and physical education are all related to each other. Although we can see a connection between sport and play, it is important to note that play can refer to a wide range of activities in addition to sport. We use the word 'play' to describe participation in some sports. For example, we would speak of someone 'playing' badminton or hockey. However, this use of the word seems to be specific to games, including board games like chess or scrabble. The word is not used in relation to other kinds of sport activities. For example, we would not speak of going to the track to 'play' sprinting, or to the sports hall to 'play' trampolining. Play usually refers to activity which is non-serious and therefore done 'for fun'. We often think of play as the opposite of 'work'. In this sense play is often associated with children's behaviour. The association of play with sport emphasises sport's essentially voluntary and non-serious nature, and refers to the manner in which people involve themselves with sport. Much sports participation might be said to be playful.

Leisure is generally understood to refer to time free from obligations such as work, attendance at school or college, sleeping, eating, or other necessary tasks. Leisure represents the time available to people to take part in sport activities, if they so choose. Think of a typical week in your life. How many hours are used up in obligatory activities and how many are free for leisure activities? People fill leisure time with a wide range of different activities, of which sports are but a few.

Recreation is generally understood as a process of refreshment of the mind and of the body. Literally, it means 'to re-create'. The word derives from the idea that after a number of hours of commitment to work or other obligatory activity, a person becomes fatigued or jaded and so needs to change to an activity which does not carry the same level of responsibility. This notion is well represented by the saying '*all work and no play makes Jack a dull boy*'. The word 'recreation' is associated with the idea of well-being, both physical and mental. People use sport activities to re-create themselves. Indeed, 'sports participation' sometimes means the same as 'physical recreation', describing people's involvement in activities which are in some way physically demanding.

It is important to note that the discussion in this section centres on the idea of 'amateur' participation in sport. The word 'amateur' originally meant someone who does something for the love of it (it has the same root in Latin as the word 'amorous'). Nowadays, an amateur is someone who involves him or herself in an activity as a recreation, rather than professionally; that is, rather than for money. The idea of amateurism is not restricted to sport. People can be amateur musicians, artists or astronomers. The important distinction to make is that professional sportspeople are contracted to perform for money. Consequently, professional participation in sport involves obligation and therefore cannot have the same quality of playfulness as amateur sport. Since the professional sportsperson goes to work at his or her sport, it does not take place in leisure time and cannot be seen as recreation.

Physical education is a term which refers to a subject within the school curriculum. Since attendance at school is compulsory, physical education lessons are obligatory and hence, do not directly meet the descriptions of sport, play, leisure and recreation offered above. However, physical education clearly does relate to sport in that it is concerned with the development of general physical capability, including that required for participation in sport activities. Students are introduced to a whole range of sport activities within national curriculum physical education. What is more, physical education spills out of formal curriculum time into after-school sport and community recreation. In this way, physical education does provide some opportunities for recreative, playful sport in leisure time.

We can link the ideas of **sport**, **play**, **leisure** and **recreation** together in the following way, that '*people usually participate in sport activities in a playful manner during their leisure time in order to re-create themselves.*'

Sebastian Coe:

'*For the vast majority of us, sport kindles memories of triumphs and tragedies in childhood, adolescence and adulthood: it cloaks a field of dreams. Be it competitive or social, organised or impromptu, a team game or a solo pursuit; whether we dedicate our lives to it or from time to time dip our toes in it, sport touches us all.*'

[Coe S, Teasdale & Wickham, 1992]

Sport and society

People have always played in their leisure time. Many play activities have become formalised into sports, firstly, through local festivals and holidays and later, into local and international competitions and leagues. As communications systems have developed, sport has become more and more influential as a spectator product. Events like the Olympic Games and the soccer World Cup now have enormous world-wide influence, socially, politically and economically.

Given these interpretations of the word 'sport', we can see that it is a part of our culture and our society. There are all kinds of different sport activities to provide us with challenges and satisfactions. Sport is something which most of us have some involvement with at some time in our lives.

Consumer roles and sport activity: performer, official, administrator, coach, teacher, spectator

Sport exists primarily because people want to participate actively in it. We might therefore say that the performer is the central consumer role in sport. If nobody wanted to play volleyball or badminton, bounce on a trampoline, pole vault or navigate through forests on a mountain bike, sports activities would cease to exist and there would be no sport to watch on television.

However, people do participate in a great variety of sports activities. Their involvement subsequently creates other important sport roles. People are involved in sport as officials, such as umpires, linesmen or judges. The national governing bodies of sport would not be able to organise sport events, coaching courses or the training of officials, if some people did not undertake the role of sports administrators. Young people would not be introduced to sport were it not for physical education teachers; others would not be able to develop their sporting talent without the help of sports coaches. People have an interest in sport as spectators, supporters and fans. Some of these may be 'students' of a sport, in the sense that they regularly study all aspects of that sport through the media of radio, television, newspapers and the growing number of highly-specialised sports magazines.

There are many ways in which people both consume sport and contribute to it. There are active roles, those which have a direct involvement with a sporting performance in some way, and passive roles, those which receive the sport experience at second-hand in sport. We, in sport differentiate between amateur and professional involvement, on the basis of whether the person gets paid for their role or not.

The impact of sport within the culture of this country can been summarised as:

- Sport plays a vital role in everyday life.
- We recognise its importance to people, and in the national and international scene.
- At home, sporting activity provides a healthy and enjoyable leisure pursuit.
- Sport promotes civic and national pride.
- It can assist social and community aims.
- It has a significant impact on the economy.
- Internationally, sport can extend British influence and prestige and promote trade and stability.

[Nicholas Ridley, Minister for the Environment 1988. *School Sport Forum*, The Sports Council]

Figure 1.3 The difference between 'amateur' and 'professional'

	Amateur	Professional
Active	Amateur Participant / Performer Voluntary Official & Administrator Unpaid Coach	Professional Performer Professional Official & Administrator Paid Coach PE Teacher
Passive	Spectator Fan Supporter 'Student'	Commentator Reporter Author

Kinds of sport activities

Classification of sport activities

We have defined sport activities as providing a challenge for the participant, involving physical exercise, or the execution of skill, or both. There are hundreds of activities that meet this definition. In order to analyse sport activities, we need to classify them into family groups or categories. The principle of any classification process is that members of each category within the classification bear a clear resemblance to one another, while remaining distinct from all other categories.

The classification presented in the section below is based on that of the Sports Council, but with some refinement. However, there is another issue to do with sport that needs to be addressed first.

Ways of moving around

Many sports involve people moving around. The most obvious, and perhaps the most natural, way of moving around is 'on foot'. Soccer and hockey players run, jog or walk around the pitch; athletes run around a track; a gymnast creates speed for a vault take-off through the run-up to the box. However, we can move around other than by walking and running. In addition to moving over land by running, we also move:

- over land by cycling.
- over water by water skiing.
- through water by swimming.
- over water by rowing.
- over water by canoeing.
- over ice by skating.
- over snow by skiing.

So we can see that it is not strictly accurate to call running or swimming or skating 'sports'. Running, swimming and skating are all ways of moving around; the technical term is 'locomotion,' which literally means 'movement of place'. Most of these forms of locomotion involve a person in some kind of rhythmical action which allows the body to be propelled along as a result of appropriate contact between the moving person and the medium through which the movement is taking place. Think of the driving action of the leg as a result of foot contact with the ground in running and with the ice in skating; the driving action of the canoe paddle and oar blade in water; the pedalling action acting through the chain and the rear tyre's contact with the ground in cycling. Downhill skiing is rather different because we use gravity to slide down the mountain, though skiers need to use certain, often rhythmic techniques, to control their speed and direction.

Within sport activities we use all the means of locomotion in a variety of different ways. For example, can use walking and running:

- to compete in races, as in athletics.
- as a way of getting fit, as in jogging.
- to negotiate a natural obstacle, such as climbing a mountain.
- to mount an attack, or to organise a defence in a game, as in soccer and basketball.

Figure 1.4 Moving through different sports media

Similarly, we can use canoeing to:

- compete in races on flat or white water.
- as a way of getting fit on a canal, river, lake or on the sea.
- to negotiate a natural obstacle, such as getting across a bay, or a lake, or getting down a set of rapids on a river.
- to mount an attack, or to organise a defence in a game, as in canoe polo.
- to demonstrate specific movement patterns, as in surf canoeing.

Similarly, we can use swimming to:

- compete in races in a pool or in natural water, such as a lake.
- as a way of getting fit, usually in a pool.
- to negotiate a natural obstacle, such as getting across a bay, or a lake, or a stretch of sea.
- to mount an attack, or to organise a defence in a game, such as water polo.
- to demonstrate specific movement patterns, as in synchronised swimming.

This analysis demonstrates that each form of locomotion is used in a variety of different sports. However, there are similarities. Each form of locomotion is associated with races; each with a way of getting fit, each with a game of some kind, and so on.

Movement through the air, or movement in the air?

Sports performers, such as a high jumper, diver, trampolinist, gymnast and ski jumper, also move through the air. This form of locomotion is different from the others because we cannot fly. We can only move through the air for a short period of time as a result of a take-off procedure, such as diving, leaping, or bouncing.

Once in the air, we cannot alter our flight path at all (see chapter 5 on principles of movement), but we can change our shape as we move through the air. Think of the body shape variations within the Fosbury flop technique once in the air, and of those of the diver or gymnast performing a back somersault.

Figure 1.5 The flight path of a projectile

Figure 1.6 The Fosbury flop technique

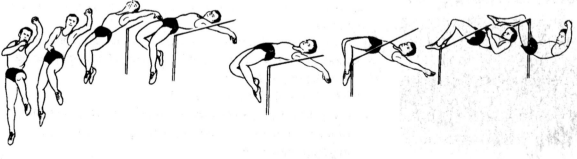

Competition sport, adventure activities and conditioning activities

Competition sport

Competition sports involve participants, as individuals or in teams, who compete with each other to find out who is best at the activity. Sports like netball, hockey, track and field athletics, swim racing, gymnastics and diving all fall into this category of sport.

The idea behind this category of sport is a pure test of skill and physical condition. Athletes running or swimming in lanes, changing ends at half-time in a football match, and a system of punishments for rule breakers, all illustrate the idea of making everything as equal and fair as possible for competitors, so that the competition can be a pure test of the participant's abilities. However, as we saw earlier, competition sports can be participated in and enjoyed at a variety of different levels.

The challenge and potential source of satisfaction for participants in competition sports, includes:

- the particular nature of the sport problem chosen: netball, pole vaulting and trampolining, for example, provide very different problems.
- the 'head to head' competition with other competitors.
- an environment in which other variables are kept to a minimum so that the focus is on the skills and level of preparation of the individual or team.

Adventure activities

These activities are concerned with journeying over 'wild' terrain and overcoming natural obstacles. The difficulty of such journeys is affected by the seasons and the weather. Hill-walking and mountaineering, rock climbing, caving and pot-holing, white-water and sea-canoeing, cross-country skiing and sailing 'voyages' have traditionally fallen into this category of sport. In recent years some new activities have been added to this list, sometimes as a result of technological developments. Examples of these activities would be river rafting, wind-surfing, mountain biking, hang-gliding and some forms of parachuting.

There are no rule structures as such for adventure activities; there are no winners and there are no behaviours which an official says can or cannot be done. However, there are conventions about how participants should behave in order to participate in the activities safely, with consideration for other people and for the natural environment.

The potential combination of difficult natural obstacles and bad weather means that some people regard adventure activities as dangerous and associated with risk. Although there is obviously a risk if someone capsizes a canoe, or falls from a rock face, this kind of danger is not the essential characteristic of these activities. Rather, it is a part of

Competition sport activities are characterised by a set of rules which:

- define the problem or challenge for the participants to test themselves against.
- incorporate a scoring system to determine who performs the best.
- allows participants to compete with one another, as far as is possible, on an equal basis.
- defines how competitors may or may not behave while trying to win.
- defines sanctions or punishments for participants who break rules.
- defines the activities of the officials who are responsible for seeing that the rules are administered effectively during the competition.

Figure 1.7   Adventure sports

the skill of a canoeist to be able to read the weather conditions and to right a capsized boat safely, and that of rock-climbers to be able to protect themselves against injury through a fall.

The challenge and potential source of satisfaction for participants in adventure activities, include:

- the particular nature of the activity and the type of 'terrain' being negotiated. Rock climbing, canoeing and mountain biking are all very different.
- the appropriate navigational skills.
- concern for safety and self-protection against injury.
- an environment which can change dramatically, including the weather.

Adventure activities have developed from our natural curiosity to explore. However, some of them have been developed into well-defined competition sport forms. White-water slalom races, downhill skiing, dinghy racing and speed climbing are all examples of activities which have lost their original adventure form, and have become competition sports with all the rules, regulations and scoring systems which characterise that category of sport activities.

Conditioning activities

These activities are designed primarily to maintain or improve physical working capacity, or 'fitness'. Conditioning activities can develop flexibility in the skeleto-muscular system, strength in muscle groups, and cardio-vascular or endurance fitness. Activities like aerobics, circuit training, weight training and jogging fall into this category. Some people would argue that conditioning activities can apply to mental fitness as well as to physical fitness. The concentration and effort of persevering with a formal physical training programme could be said to involve mental discipline. There are some activities, like yoga and the non-competitive elements of the martial arts, which have a specifically mental training aspect to them.

Some of these activities, weight training for example, developed from participants' efforts to prepare themselves for the specific physical demands of their own competition sports. Some have been borrowed from other cultures and adapted to western ideas, yoga and aspects of karate, for example. Others, like aerobics, have been developed specifically for general health purposes.

Figure 1.8 Conditioning sports

Like adventure activities, conditioning activities differ from competition sports by not having a set of rules; they are not about winning. However, they do have a structure in the sense that participants will set a training programme for themselves, or follow one designed by someone else. This programme will require the participant to undertake a level of work high enough and of sufficient regularity to develop his or her fitness to a desired level. Like adventure activities, conditioning activities also have conventions of behaviour which are designed to protect the individual from overwork or injury, to save equipment from damage and to ensure that other members of a training session are able to complete their work-out without interference.

Like competition sports and adventure activities, conditioning activities can be enjoyed over a range of levels and work rates. At one end there is light exercise with minimal conditioning benefit. At the other end, participants undertake the extremely strenuous training regimes which are needed to produce the pinnacle of strength, endurance fitness or mobility.

The challenge and therefore the potential source of satisfaction for participants in conditioning activities, includes:

- the particular nature of the type of conditioning activity. Aerobics, weight training, jogging and yoga are all very different.
- the targets set and levels of work undertaken.
- concern for safety and self-protection against injury.

Conditioning activities have developed in response to our natural desire to maintain or improve different aspects of fitness. However, as with adventure activities, some conditioning activities have further evolved into well-defined competition sport forms, for example, weight-lifting and body-building. These activities have lost their original conditioning form and become competition sports with all the rules, regulations and scoring systems which characterise that category of sport activities.

SUMMARY

- Competition sports, adventure activities and conditioning activities all fit the broad definition of sport given above. The three categories of activities are all accepted by the Sports Council as sport.
- The explanation of competition, adventure and conditioning undertaken in the previous section shows that there are real differences between these three categories of sport. Each offers the participant a different kind of experience. The participant will have different expectations of activities in the three categories and will be motivated in different ways to take part in them.

Example

Suppose you had just been given a mountain bike for your birthday. There would be a different way of using it that would fit each of the three categories of sport.

- If you wanted to ride in a competition sport, you could enter a race that might take the form of five laps of a two-mile circuit over paths and tracks in a forest. In this event you would be competing directly against other riders for as high a place as possible in the finishing order. The way would be well marked so that you could not get lost. There would be stewards at points along the course to help you if you got into mechanical difficulty or were injured. There would be an ambulance standing by in case of serious injury.

- If you wanted an adventure activity, you might plan a 20-mile route over green lanes and bridleways in the Yorkshire Dales National Park. On this ride, you would have to negotiate whatever difficult hills or rocky sections you might find on the route and you would need to navigate your way around it using map and compass. It would not be advisable to undertake this journey alone. If the weather was bad, you might have to deal with wet and cold, and possibly not being able to see well in low cloud on the tops of the moors. You would need to carry spare clothing, food and water, tools and a first aid kit. You would need to be able to deal with minor mechanical problems, particularly punctures, and should have first aid skills. If someone was hurt, some members of the party would have to go and raise the alarm while the others stayed with the injured person.

- If you wanted to participate in a conditioning activity to improve your general fitness, and in particular your cardiovascular fitness, you might decide to ride round a defined circuit within a park, on heath land or on an old railway line maintained for the purpose. You would select the route to provide the duration and level of exercise appropriate to your training target. You could undertake the training alone or with someone else. You would not be competing against anyone else directly, but would need to maintain the discipline required to make the training effective. You would need to be careful not to push yourself too hard and risk injury. You would need to be aware of other people using the paths and tracks for their own recreation.

Figure 1.9 Different uses for a mountain bike

Sport and art

You may have noticed that the classification of sport presented in this section makes no reference to dance, despite its inclusion under the Sports Council's 'aesthetic movement' category of sport.

It is important that art is not confused with sport. It is necessary here to distinguish between dance as a form of art, and dancing as a form of sport. For example, when formally presented to the spectating public, classical ballet and jazz dance are art forms, while ballroom dancing and ice dancing are forms of competition sport.

When audiences watch a ballet, they pay to see an artistic performance; that is, the dancers' expressions of a particular idea, theme or story. There is no competition; nobody awards marks and there are no 'winners'.

By contrast, spectators go to a ballroom or ice arena to watch a competition take place. In this case, the dancers must conform to the rules of the competition, just like the competitors in any other competition sport. The audience is keen to see how well the dancers perform relative to one another; to find out who will win.

It is, of course, true to say that 'dance as art' and 'dancing as sport' are similar, in that the controlled movement of the body is the essential medium for the activity. However, that does not mean that sport is art, or vice versa. The essential purposes of the two kinds of activities are different. After all, 'dance as art' is the domain of the Arts Council, whereas 'dancing as sport' is regulated by the Sports Council.

Competition sport

A definition

The remainder of this chapter is focused on competition sport. Competition sports are those in which participants compete with one another to find out who is best at the activity, at the time of the competition.

Another definition is given as:

' a sphere of human performance which is selected by participants as a means of trying to prove ascendancy over an opponent/s through the attempted solution of an arbitrary problem.'

[after Brackenridge & Alderson, 1986]

Sphere: suggests a boundary, an identity, a recognisable form of behaviour.

Example: sphere

If you turned on the television, and saw a competition sport going on, you would be able to see immediately if the behaviour of the performers fitted your idea of 'pole vault', or of 'high hurdles' or of 'javelin'. Each of these events has an instantly recognisable form.

Performance: implies positive action whose 'quality' or 'effectiveness' is important.

Example: performance

If you saw a high jump competition on television, you would be able to appreciate the difference between the performance of a competitor who clears the bar successfully and the performance of one who touches the bar and brings it down. You would also understand the implications for these two different jumps for the competitors in their quest to progress in the competition.

Ascendancy: illustrates the 'competitive' nature of sport; that the competitors strive to 'win'.

Example: ascendancy

While watching the sprint finish of a 5000 m track race, you would be left in no doubt that the runners were trying to beat each other to the tape.

Problem: all sport activities consist of a particular problem to be overcome in order to win. This problem is the same for all competitors participating in a particular sport, but different from that in all other sports.

Example: problem

Competitors in all track races have the same kind of problem: to finish the race before the others do. However, the precise nature of the problem varies between a 'flat' race (no obstacles on the track), high hurdles and steeplechase. Similarly, all throwing events have the same kind of problem: the longest distance wins. However, the precise problems facing the javelin thrower, shot putter and hammer thrower vary significantly.

Arbitrary: illustrates that the nature of the sport 'problem' has no significance in itself. It is simply the means by which the sport experience is made available to participants.

Example: arbitrary

International athletics races are run over distances of 800 m, 1500 m, 3000 m and 5000 m. There is no special signifiance to these distances. Races could be run at 750 m, 2500 m and 4000 m just as easily, but they are not. Similarly, high hurdles could be five centimetres lower, or a hockey goal could be half a metre wider. If they were, the nature of the sport problem would be slightly different, but the essential experience of hurdling or playing hockey would not change significantly.

Trying and **attempted**: these two words illustrate that the competitor takes on the sport problem with a view to performing well. However, success and winning are not guaranteed.

Example: trying and attempting

Only one competitor wins at the sprint finish of the 5000m race.

Figure 1.10   Reference list of competition sports

Archery	Football (Canadian)	Paddleball	Swim racing
Badminton	Football (Rugby League)	Polo	Synchro swimming
Baseball	Football (Rugby Union)	Pool	Table tennis
Basketball	Golf	Racquetball	Tennis
Bobsleigh racing	Gymnastics	Rowing	Tenpin bowling
Boxing	Handball (Court)	Shooting	Track & field athletics
Canoeing	Handball (Team)	Skating (figure)	Volleyball
Cricket	Hockey (field)	Skating (speed)	Water polo
Cycle Racing	Hockey (ice)	Skiing	Weightlifting
Diving	Judo	Skiing (biathlon)	Wrestling
Equestrianism	Lacrosse (men's)	Snooker	Yacht racing
Fencing	Lacrosse (women's)	Soccer	
Football (American)	Luge toboggan racing	Softball	
Football (Australian)	Modern Pentathlon	Squash	[after The Diagram Group, 1984]

The 'contract to compete'

Competition sports are considered to be a pure test of skill and physical condition, and are controlled by a set of rules. The rules are there to ensure equal opportunities for all competitors and fair play in terms of competitors' behaviour to one another.

Whenever competitors agree to participate in a competition, they enter into an agreement with the other competitors to strive to perform to their best standard, and to abide by the rules. We call this 'agreement' the contract to compete.

Normally this agreement is an informal one, in the sense that there is no written contract. However, the contract to compete is symbolised in many sports events. You may be familiar with the shake of hands between captains at the beginning of a hockey match, and with the swearing of the Olympic Oath by a representative competitor at the opening ceremony of the Games.

Breaking the contract to compete

The contract to compete is about each competitor's responsibility to do his or her best to win the competition, within the rules. This responsibility has two dimensions. One is a commitment to the principle of competition sport; the other is a commitment to fellow competitors. If a competitor deliberately breaks this contract, then the whole point and meaning of the activity is spoilt for others.

- If a track athlete takes drugs and so gains an unfair advantage in a race, then the principles of equal opportunity and fair play are not upheld.
- If a squash player does not try his or her best in a game, the whole idea of an equal contest breaks down and the opponent has a reduced opportunity to test his or her own skills and abilities on the court.
- If a basketball defender breaks the rules by obstructing the advance of an attacker to the basket, the principles of fair play and opportunity to demonstrate skilfulness have not been upheld.

Recreation, representation and elite levels of sport performance

Competition sport is always based on the contract to compete. We might say that participants' acceptance of this contract is the 'hallmark' of competition sport. However, we noted that sport allows people to participate at different levels of skill and ability. In line with this idea, competition sport can be thought of as allowing people to enter the contract at different points along a scale of competitiveness which ranges from the 'recreational', through the 'representative', to the 'elite'. This idea is expressed in the table in figure 1.11. Examples of different levels of competition along the scale, all taken from the game of squash, are given below.

Recreational competition

Recreational competition refers to competitions between people which are informal and friendly. If you were to book a court at your local squash club and have a game with a friend, it would be described as 'recreational'. You would play the game according to the rules, although you would not have an official marker and referee to control the game. You would score properly, keeping the score yourselves, and at the end of the game one of you would be the winner.

This kind of game of squash is informal and friendly because the result has no significance to anyone other than the two opponents, and possibly little significance for them. Recreational players accept the contract to compete and play to win, but are usually not concerned about who the winner is, as long as they have had a good game.

Representative competition

Representative competition refers to competitions between people that are formal in the sense that they are set up and administered by an official sports organisation of some kind, such as a local area league or a national governing body. Competitors usually represent a club, district or perhaps a town. Formal squash competitions take the form of leagues and tournaments. All matches within a league or a tournament are played according to the official rules, with a marker to control the matches.

A squash match of the representative kind is characterised by rivalry, because its result has significance beyond the game itself. In a tournament, the winner of a match will progress to the next round, whereas the loser will be 'knocked out'. In a league match, the result of an individual game will affect the league points earned by the whole team, and so, the team's standing within the league. A player who has won will feel that he or she has contributed to the team result, whereas one who has lost may feel some disappointment and responsibility for not having been able to make a more positive contribution to the team score.

Elite competition

Elite competition refers to competitions of the representative kind, but at the very highest level. In squash, this would mean county, national, international and open championships. The organisation of elite competitions is, in principle, exactly the same as for the rest of representative sport. The difference is in the significance of the results of such matches. At this level of competition sport, the demand on the participants is so high that a great deal of time and money has to be devoted to training and preparation for events. Consequently, much elite sport has become professional by nature, if not by name (see Chapter 10). Once elite sport occurs at the international level, national pride is also at stake. Successful international sportspeople are national heroes and heroines. Those less successful are sometimes seen by others as having let their country down!

Grass roots participation in sport, involving relatively large numbers of participants is concentrated towards the recreational end of the scale presented in figure 1.11. As individuals with the talent and the motivation move across the scale from left to right, the level of sport performance demanded of them rises all the time. As the level of demand increases, fewer individuals can match it. Consequently, only the very few, very talented and very dedicated performers ever make it to the extreme right hand end of the scale. At this level, competition sport tests the best. In any particular activity there can only be one team or individual who, at any one time, can claim the title of world champion. Despite this, thousands of people compete happily at the lower levels of the competition scale, regularly achieving satisfaction from their involvement in competition sport in the ways discussed earlier.

Figure 1.11 Scale of sports participation: recreational to elite.

RECREATIONAL	—	REPRESENTATIVE	—	ELITE
Informal				Formal
'Friendly'				'Rivalry'
Nothing hangs				Result has meaning or value
on the result				outside the 'event' itself

This idea of a scale of involvement in competition sport has been presented in a different way by the Sports Council. Their model takes the form of a pyramid.

The base of the pyramid, the foundation level, refers to peoples' first introduction to sports activities. Much of this happens within the physical education programme in schools, though clubs and leisure centres play their part too. When someone gets involved in a sport, and takes part regularly, they are said to be at the participation level of the pyramid. Not everyone who is introduced to a given sport decides to take it up on a regular basis, so the pyramid is narrower at the participation level than it is at the foundation level. Most involvement at the participation level is of a recreational nature, at the left hand end of the scale shown in figure 1.11. Some, but not all, of those who participate regularly move into representative sport.

The demands of representative sport, the middle of the scale in figure 1.11, mean that competitors have to commit to performing as well as they can. Hence, the third level of the Sports Council's pyramid is labelled 'performance'. Finally, the uppermost section of the pyramid, involving very few people by comparison with the foundation level, refers to excellence in sport: it is broadly comparable with the elite end of the scale in figure 1.11.

In elite sport the stakes can be high in terms of both money and fame. The growing impact of television has heightened the stakes considerably in recent years. Top-class spectator sport has become very big business. Consequently, the pressure on individuals to be successful in elite sport can be very high indeed. Unfortunately, there are times when winning becomes more important than trying to win, and the contract to compete is broken. We are all familiar with such behaviour, which ranges from the

Figure 1.12 The sports pyramid

Excellence

Performance

Participation

Foundation

'professional foul' to the problem of drug abuse by competitors. These ideas are further developed later in the book.

Amateurism and professionalism

Both the scale of sports participation (figure 1.11) and the pyramid model of sports participation illustrate that relatively few people reach the top in sport. All recreational sport and most representative sport up to national level is amateur. This means that people get involved with their sport for the love of it. We have also noted earlier in this section, that top class sport demands a great deal of commitment from participants in order for them to do the necessary amounts of practice and training to compete effectively. This means that they often do not have the time to undertake normal employment in addition to their sport, and therefore, turn professional.

Professionals may rely on one of three forms of income, or may use a combination of them. A professional may be someone just breaking into the top-class ranks, who earns just enough to survive. By contrast, some professionals make a fortune from their involvement with sport. However, there are relatively few who really make a lot of money.

Some sports, including snooker, soccer, golf, tennis, cricket and rugby league are openly professional at the top levels. Other sports, notably athletics, would say they are not professional. Nevertheless, at the top level, these sports demand a professional approach. Consequently, performers do receive either direct or indirect sponsorship.

Sub-categories of competition sport

All competition sports provide a 'problem' for participants to solve in order to demonstrate their skills and abilities. The scoring or judging system used to decide the winner of a competitive event relates to the nature of the sport problem. The nature of the sport problem and the associated scoring system for lacrosse, for example, is very different from that for trampolining.

There are many different competition sports for people to participate in, all with their own sport problems and scoring systems. However, these sports may not all be as different as at first appears. The section below identifies three sub-categories of competition sport. While the three sub-categories demonstrate quite different types of sport problems and associated scoring systems, members of each sub-category share 'family' resemblances. Each sub-category typifies a particular type of competition sport problem, although each member of a sub-category differs from the others to some extent.

Sports have developed to include different ways of moving around, through or over different 'media' (land, snow, water, ice, air). You will find that these different forms of locomotion, like running, swimming, skating and canoeing, are represented in all three sub-categories of competition sport.

A professional sportsperson is one who earns his or her living through sport performance, in one of three ways:

- The sportsperson signs a contract to play professionally for a club and is paid a wage. An example of this form of professionalism would be a soccer player who signs up to play for a club in the Premier Division of the Football League.
- The sportsperson earns a living, at least in part, from prize money. An example of this form of professionalism would be a professional golfer who tours the world playing in tournaments like the British, Australian or American Open Championships.
- The sportsperson receives money from sponsors who wish to have their sports equipment or clothing associated with him or her. Alternatively, the sportsperson is paid to advertise products which may have nothing to do with sport, for example, a car or a soft drink.

Athletics category

In this category of competition sports, the sport problem is to perform better than other competitors in terms of time taken to cover a certain distance, height jumped, weight lifted, distance thrown, or distance jumped. All forms of 'racing' fall into the athletics category of competition sports, including track athletics, swim races, cycle races, rowing, canoe races, ski races, speed skating and speed climbing. Other members of the athletic category include field athletics and weight lifting.

The judging procedures determine which performance is the fastest, longest, highest or strongest. Athletic sports, therefore, match the Olympic motto *citius, altius, fortius*, which means 'fastest, highest, strongest'. Performance in this category of competition sport is measured quantitatively, in terms of time (s), distance (m) or weight (kg), using standard measuring instruments such as electronic timing and steel tapes. For these reasons, the judging of athletic events is said to be objective.

The essential demand on the performer in athletic sports is the generation of power in either explosive or sustained forms, produced through rhythmic locomotor actions (for example, running or swimming), or specialised techniques (for example, discus or pole vault). Sprints, throws, jumps and lifts all require explosive power production, while all kinds of long distance racing require sustained delivery of power at lower rates. In middle- and long-distance races, competitors often have to produce explosive sprinting power at the finish, after a period of more sustained power delivery. Some athletic techniques are relatively simple, for example, running or skating; others are complex, for example, pole vaulting or triple jumping. However, in all athletic events the performer has relatively few technical skills to learn and develop.

Athletic activities are designed to emphasise the competitor's ability to deliver power through the appropriate technique. Consequently, competitors are not allowed to interfere with one another's performances. In many activities, competitors take it in turns to perform, so keeping out of each other's way. Weight lifting and field athletics work in this way. In many races, the participants are required to perform in separate lanes, so keeping them apart. Swimming and short distance track athletic events are like this. In longer distance racing, which does not take place in lanes, there are strict rules about competitors not obstructing their opponents' progress.

Gymnastics category

In this category of competition sports, the sport problem is the reproduction of complex movement patterns and sequences. Artistic gymnastics, sport acrobatics, trampolining, diving, synchro swimming, figure skating, ski aerials, water ski tricks, BMX bike tricks and surf canoeing all fall into the gymnastic category of competition sport.

The international governing bodies for these sports set out how the various movements should be performed and how they should be scored. In some gymnastic sports, like trampoline and diving, certain movements (or techniques) carry a tariff according to how difficult they are to perform. Judges are trained to observe a competitor's performance and to give it a score according to how well the movements match up to the set patterns. This kind of judging is said to be qualitative, and to a certain extent, subjective. This means that the gymnast's movements cannot be measured exactly and that there is a degree of interpretation taking place in the judges' minds. When you watch figure skating on television, how often do the six judges agree exactly on the marks for technical merit?

The essential demand on the performer in any gymnastic sport is to learn and to be able to reproduce the complex movements and sequences demanded by that particular activity. Some of these movements take place in direct contact with:

- **the ground:** elements of the floor routine in artistic gymnastics.
- **ice:** spins, turns and balances in figure skating.
- **water:** water ski tricks and surf canoe techniques.
- **apparatus:** the men's rings or the women's beam in artistic gymnastics.

However, many gymnastic sports use movements in the air. In some, like diving, trampoline and ski aerials, movements in the air predominate. In others, like floor gymnastics and figure skating, movements in the air are only a part of the repertoire of techniques used. Some movements are common to different members of the category. For example, you will see somersaults performed by trampolinists, divers, floor gymnasts, aerial skiers and even BMX bikers. Where athletes usually have only one movement pattern to learn, gymnastic category performers have many movements to learn.

Gymnastic activities are designed to emphasise the competitor's ability to reproduce set technical movement patterns. Consequently, competitors are not allowed to interfere with each other's performances. In all these activities, competitors take it in turns to perform, so keeping out of one another's way.

Games category

In this category of competition sports, the sport problem is that of achieving territorial domination over the opposition in some way. All ball games are members of this category, along with fighting sports like judo and target sports like archery. Scoring procedures in this category determine which player or team achieves most territorial domination, and so wins, through goals, runs, touchdowns, points, hits on target, etceteras. In some cases, the scoring systems are quantitative and objective, for example, successful baskets in basketball or 'pots' in snooker. In other games, like boxing or wrestling, the judgement of hits on target or 'pin falls' by an official, is more subjec-

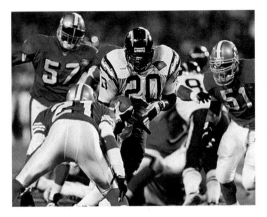

Figure 1.13 The video camera can 'catch' foul play which the field umpire does not notice

tive and open to a degree of interpretation. The same applies to some behavioural rule transgressions in team games, especially those involving contact between players. In recent years, technology has been used to try to make judging more objective in some game type sports. For example, the development of electronic systems to record hits in fencing and the introduction of a third umpire using video-taped evidence in cricket and American football.

The major difference between games and the athletic and gymnastic categories of competition sport lies in their interactive nature. In almost all games, opponents interact with one another directly in both attacking and defensive situations. The only exceptions to this general rule are a minority of target sports like golf, darts, archery and shooting, where opponents are not allowed in any way to interfere with the performance of other players. In team games, like doubles tennis, netball, volleyball, cricket and soccer, players also have to interact with other members of their own team.

The essential demand on the performer in a game sport is for control of the body in respect to movable or moving objects, and other players. Games players have to demonstrate accuracy in relation to targets of many different kinds. Sometimes the target is stationary, as with a hockey goal, the hole on the golf green or the dart board. In other cases the target is moving, as in passing to a team-mate in rugby, or trying to hit the opponent in boxing or fencing. In ball games, the player may have to deal with a stationary ball, as in golf or snooker, and a dead ball situation like a place kick in rugby or a penalty in soccer. In many situations however, the player has to deal with a moving object, as in receiving a pass in almost all team games, returning a ball in net games like badminton and in dealing with an incoming attack in judo.

We have already seen that the majority of games are interactive. As a result, games also demand that participants make decisions and organise responses to the behaviour of opponents and team-mates. These may be instant decisions, for example, deciding what return to play to a tennis service that has just been struck towards you at great speed. Alternatively, they may be of a more tactical nature, for example, a scrum-half deciding what kind of play to set up as the ball becomes available from the back of the set scrummage, or a hockey captain deciding what set play to use from a dead ball situation 20 metres from the opponents' goal.

There appear to be a lot more games than there are athletic and gymnastic kinds of competition sports. As a result, the games category can be further sub-divided into five distinct groups. Each of these demonstrates a different form of the essential game problem of territorial domination.

Invasion games

Invasion games are essentially a contest between two teams, over a set period of time. The contest is known as a match. More than two teams can be involved in a tournament or league which involves many matches. The playing area (territory) is normally rectangular, with a centre line to divide the territory and a goal placed at each end of the pitch or court. Field hockey and basketball provide examples of this type of playing area. There are some minor variations. For example, in ice hockey, rugby and lacrosse the playing area extends behind the goal, and in ice hockey the pitch has curved corners.

Teams are allowed to invade their opponents' territory. Each team tries to get a ball (or equivalent) through the opponent's half of the pitch or court to score in their goal. In most invasion games, like soccer and hockey, there is only one way of scoring; in others, like rugby, there is more than one way of scoring points. In basketball, a player can only score by getting the ball through the basket, but the basket is worth a different number of points depending on the game situation. In all invasion games the winning team is decided by the number of goals scored or points awarded.

Possession is a key aspect of invasion games, since an attack on goal can only arise when a team is in possession of the ball (or equivalent). A match is made up of a succession of 'possessions' which alternate between the two teams. A team can have possession at the beginning of a period of play or be awarded possession as a result of a rule infringement. A defending team (not in possession) can get the ball from the attacking team (in possession) in a number of ways. It can collect a loose ball, intercept a pass, or tackle an attacker in possession. The rules about permissible behaviour in this last case are very strict. They lead to the distinction between those invasion games which allow direct contact of some kind between opposing players, like American football, rugby union, rugby league, men's lacrosse, soccer and ice hockey, and those which do not, like field hockey, basketball and netball.

Invasion games

- American football
- Basketball
- Field Hockey
- Ice Hockey
- Netball
- Lacrosse
- Rugby Football
- Rugby League
- Soccer

Net games

Net games, like invasion games, are a contest between two opponents, are played with a ball, and have a rectangular court which is divided into equal halves. Net games vary in the number of players involved. For example, racket-based net games like badminton and tennis are played as 'singles' or 'doubles', whereas volleyball has a team of six players. Singles and doubles racket matches can contribute to team events where each individual or pair plays against his or her opposite number. More than two volleyball teams can be involved in a tournament or league involving many matches.

Net games do not have a fixed playing period. Instead, the game continues until one team achieves a winning result determined as the best of a number of 'rubbers', 'games' or 'sets'. For example, a tennis match over the best of five sets, would be won by the first player or pair to win three sets.

In most of these games, the rectangular playing area is divided by a net. There are no goals and players are not allowed to enter the opposite half of the pitch. Instead, players try to dominate the opposition's territory symbolically, with the ball. An opponent is temporarily 'dominated' when he or she cannot return the ball over the net. Consequently, the attacking player tries to strike the ball into a part of the court which will make it difficult for the opponent to return. There is some variation within the net game group as to the result of temporarily dominating territory in this way. In some cases the successful player or team wins a point which contributes directly to the score, for example, in tennis or American rules for squash. In other net games a point is only added to the score if the successful player or team served the rally which resulted in the point, for example, squash and volleyball. If a non-serving side wins the rally, then they win the right to serve the next one, rather than a point. The service is seen as important because it is the only 'dead ball' situation in net games, where the server has time to organise the service action.

There is one group of net games which do not have a net. The common members of this group are squash and racquetball, though the older games of rackets and fives are also included. These games are identical in principle to tennis, table tennis and badminton. The difference is that there is really only half a court available. Instead of the ball going over a net, in these games it is reflected back into the same half-court. In reality, the opponents take turns to occupy the half-court.

Volleyball is the only net game in which the ball can be retained and moved about by members of a team within their half of the court before it is returned over the net. This enables them to set up an attack and requires good understanding between the players in each team.

The rally, in which players attempt to hit the ball into the opposition's territory alternately, is the key aspect of all forms of net game. In racket games players use the rally to manoeuvre the opponent(s) into positions which 'open up the court', so creating space into which a winning, non-returnable ball can be hit. In invasion games a player can 'hold' the ball for a time while making a decision about what to do with it, but in net games this is not possible. The ball has to be struck cleanly, and not held. This is true of all net games, including volleyball, and emphasises the demand on players to read the game situation and make instantaneous decisions and responses to the incoming ball.

Net games

● American squash	● Rackets	● Table Tennis
● Badminton	● Racquetball	● Tennis
● Fives	● Squash Rackets	● Volleyball

Innings games

Innings games are like invasion and net games in that they are a contest between two teams. Like invasion games, innings games can be organised into tournaments or leagues involving more than two teams over many matches. Innings games are different from invasion and net games in the way the playing area (territory) is divided. Instead of two identical halves of a pitch or court, the innings games field has two distinctly different areas: the infield and the outfield. The infield is used for striking at a pitched or bowled ball with a bat of some kind, and for the striker to run within a designated area to score. The outfield is used to defend against the strikes, and field the ball to cut short the opportunity for the striker to run.

In cricket, the striking area is known as the wicket, whereas in rounders, baseball and softball it is called the diamond. An innings is the opportunity a team has to score. Batsmen or strikers go 'in' to bat, and stay there until the fielding side gets them 'out'. The way this is done varies from game to game. All the players on a team take it in turns to bat, and the innings goes on until they are all 'out'. Teams take it in turns to go 'in' to bat, or, to have their innings. A match may have more than one innings per team, depending on the rules of the particular game. When there are more than one innings per team, the scores accumulate across innings.

A key idea when analysing innings games is the battle between the bowler or pitcher on the fielding side and the batsman or striker on the striking side. Bowlers and pitchers vary their delivery in order to make it difficult for the batsman to make a scoring strike, or to force an error and so get the striker out. In cricket, where the ball bounces on the wicket as it is delivered, this battle can be much affected by the state of the pitch and the weather.

Innings games

● Cricket   ● Softball   ● Rounders   ● Baseball

Fighting games

Fighting games are contests of the most direct kind between two individuals. Matches can also contribute to team events in which each member fights his or her opposite number. Many of these modern sport activities have evolved from older forms of fighting disciplines, some of which would have been used in war. Boxing, fencing and some of the martial arts fall into this category, while judo is a relatively modern creation associated more directly with physical education in Japan. All modern forms of fighting have strict rule structures to limit physical damage to opponents. You may be aware of the current controversy about the safety of professional boxing.

Domination in these sports is achieved through successful attacks upon the opponents themselves. Boxing, fencing and some martial arts use a system of points for hitting well-defined target areas of the body. Wrestling and other martial arts use the 'hold' as a means of expressing dominance, since the held opponent is powerless to counter-attack. In all these fighting games, the action must take place within a confined area, for example, the boxing ring, judo mat or fencing piste, and within a set time period.

Fighting games

● Boxing   ● Judo   ● Fencing   ● Wrestling

Target games

Target games are territorial contests in which the essential game demand of accuracy is taken to a very high level, for example, snooker or darts. These games all demand precision in aiming skills. Participants are required to dispatch an object at a target. It is often a ball of some kind, though it may be an arrow, a dart or even a bullet. Invariably the object is stationary, rather than moving, prior to being despatched. Usually the target is still too, allowing the performer time to prepare for the aiming task. However, there are some exceptions to this rule, like clay pigeon shooting. Scoring systems in these games always reflect the accuracy of the performer, though they vary considerably from one activity to another. In pistol shooting and archery, accuracy is recorded in terms of being 'close to the bull'. In darts, the scoring rewards players who can reduce their score quickly and finish on the appropriate 'double' through accurate placement of the darts. In golf, the 'hole' is won by the player who takes the least number of strikes at the ball to get it from the tee into the hole on the green.

Target games can be sub-divided into two types. One type is interactive. Snooker, billiards, croquet, bowls and curling all allow one player to use his or her ball to spoil the efforts of an opponent, or make their next action more difficult. The 'snooker' is the classic example, but the bowls player who uses his bowl to knock an opponent's away from the jack is another. However, this type of interaction is different from that in other ball games, in that players take turns to perform. A player cannot interfere while an opponent is taking his or her turn to play. In this type of target sport there is no time limit on a person's performance.

The other type of target game does not allow interference from opponents at all. Darts, archery, shooting, ten-pin bowling and golf all belong to this category. In effect, players play against the target, the skittles or the golf course rather than directly against opponents. In archery and static target shooting, competitors have a time limit within which to loose off their shots.

Target games

● Archery	● Clay pigeon shooting	● Darts	● Ten Pin Bowling
● Billiards	● Crocket	● Golf	● Pistol shooting
● Bowls	● Curling	● Snooker	

Analysis of competition sports

The various categories of competition sport are similar in some ways and different in others. Because of a focus on the principle of category groupings in this chapter, we have not looked at any one sport in any detail. However, most of us are interested in a particular sport at some time, perhaps because we participate in that sport ourselves, follow a team, or because we want to help someone else to improve their performance.

Given this interest, we need to be able to analyse a particular sport in order to understand what the sport demands of someone who wishes to participate in it at a given level, and to decide what it is about someone's performance that could be improved.

Since there are so many different sports, it is helpful to have one way of analysing sport, a template, that will apply to them all.

Method of analysis

The method presented here for the analysis of competition sport activities has four levels. These are:

1   the structural level
2   the strategic level
3   the technical level
4a the physical level
4b the psychological level.

The levels of the analysis are hierarchical. This means that they relate to one another as shown in the diagram in figure 1.14. An explanation of the different levels of analysis and the way they relate to one another is given in the next section.

Levels of the sports analysis template

This section explains the four heirarchical levels of the sports analysis template. Examples of its use for an athletic, and a game example of competition sport are provided below. The sports analysed are sprint swim racing and rugby football.

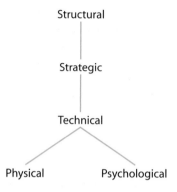

Figure 1.14 The hierarchical structure of sport analysis

LEVEL	EXPLANATION
1 Structural	This level of analysis refers to the nature of the 'sport problem', the scoring system, the rules that govern participants' behaviour, the roles of officials and the penalties imposed for rule infringements by performers.
	Potential participants cannot function properly in competition until they understand the 'structure' of a sport. They simply do not know what to do, or even what not to do!
	Think of a complex game like American football. When you first saw it on television, did you really understand what all the players were doing? Do you now?
2 Strategic	This level of analysis refers to the planning and decision-making aspects of sport performance. The strategies required by a sport are directly related to the nature of the sport problem defined at the structural level above.
	Strategy in gymnastic sports is all about selecting moves or designing sequences which are more technically difficult and demonstrate better artistic interpretation than those of potential competitors. This strategic activity takes place well in advance of the competition.

25

By contrast, much of the strategy in net games is about using a series of shots within a rally to manoeuvre an opponent out of position, in order to be able to play an irretrievable winner, or force an error from the attempt at retrieval. This strategy may be pre-planned in theory, but has to be controlled and varied in response to the quality of the player's own shots and those of the opponent as the rally progresses.

Neither of these strategies has any value whatsoever in the other sport form because the nature of the two sport problems are so different.

3 Technical

This level of analysis refers to the motor skills required to perform successfully at a particular sport. Techniques are used to carry out strategies, as defined above.

The gymnast uses techniques such as a somersault and a handstand in order to execute the planned sequence. The badminton player uses techniques such as the smash or the high clear to achieve certain strategic objectives in the course of a rally.

It is worth looking at the difference between technique and skill. Technique may be thought of as the perfect movement and its outcome, as defined by the requirement of the sport. You can picture a technically-perfect double back somersault, or the drop shot in squash that hits the 'nick' and rolls out along the court floor. Skill may be thought of as the sport performer's learned capacity to reproduce the technique. It may be more or less exact. Someone early in the process of learning a double back somersault may have an understanding of the technique, but would not be able to produce the perfect movement. Similarly, even the expert squash player will not hit the 'nick' very often.

Skill, and how people develop it, is a central topic for anyone studying sport. Chapter 6 analyses skill in more detail.

Sport techniques require controlled movement of the body to produce specified patterns or outcomes. Think again of the double back somersault, or of the angle of release and trajectory of the shot putt. These movements involve the application of forces generated by the muscles. Our understanding of sport technique is, thus, helped by the study of applied anatomy in chapter 2 and the principles of movement in chapter 5.

4a Physical

This, as part of the fourth level of analysis, refers to the body conditions required for successful performance at sport. The physical condition required varies with the sport, or in some cases, the specific event or positional role within a sport.

Different sports require different combinations of physical condition or fitness. These requirements can be defined in terms of strength in particular muscle groups, their ability to cope with repeated use (local muscular endurance), mobility or flexibility in particular joints, and stamina of the cardio-vascular system.

The required physical condition is absolutely necessary for successful sport performance and for its improvement. Without the necessary strength and flexibility, gymnastic skills, for example, would be impossible. Similarly, there would be no point in a tennis player deciding to adopt a baseline strategy in a match if he or she was not sufficiently fit to keep the rally going and wear down the opponent.

Because the physical demands of different sports vary, it is important to develop the right kinds of fitness for the event. The guiding idea here is known as the Specificity of Fitness Principle.

Your understanding of flexibility will be improved by reading chapter 2, while energy systems and the principles of training and fitness are dealt with in chapters 3 and 4.

4b Psychological This aspect of the fourth level of analysis refers to the mental and psycho-social conditions required for successful performance at the sport. Different sports place different mental demands on performers.

Competition sport means that performers are usually involved in a mental battle with their opponents in some way or another. It is therefore virtually impossible to compete without being assertive. Some sports, like fighting games and contact invasion games, require the performer to use controlled aggression. These sports, together with endurance racing, may well involve performers having to cope with a degree of pain without letting it interfere with their strategic and technical skill.

Performing well in any competitive sport requires concentration. Watching an archer or a high jumper in the preparation phase for their activity shows this requirement particularly well.

Interactive team games require quick thinking, the development of strategic understanding between team-members and the ability to anticipate what opponents are going to do. Team games also require some players to adopt leadership roles, while others must be prepared to conform to the leader's authority.

Endurance events can require participants to perform on their own for long periods of time without getting bored and losing their concentration. Gymnastic performers such as figure skaters for example, can find themselves literally under the spotlight, having to perform alone in front of a large audience and the television cameras. In all these events the performer has to be able to shut everything out of his or her mind except the performance itself.

We can think of the psychological level of analysis as being parallel with the physical level. Performers have to be 'fit' mentally as well as physically. Chapter 7 on sport psychology will help you improve your understanding of this area of sport.

Figure 1.15   Analysis of an athletic sport activity — sprint swim racing

LEVEL OF ANALYSIS	CHARACTERISTICS OF THE ACTIVITY
Structural	Athletic activity involving no direct physical contact /interference from other competitors.
	Simple rule structure which:
	- defines time over distance as the means of judging performance;
	- defines legal means of starting, swimming, turning & finishing.
Strategic	Little strategic demand. (Essentially it's flat out from start to finish!) Have to 'read' the wall for approach to turns.
Technical 'Closed' skills	Little variety required. One 'stroke', plus relevant start and turn techniques only. Emphasis lies in the control of the stroke in such a way as to enable maximum power delivery over the duration of the event.
	This implies a high level of technical perfection and consistency in a rhythmic locomotor skill.
Physical	Highly specific anaerobic and strength requirements, implying demanding physical training programmes.
Psychological	Individual (usually) involvement, implying 'limelight' role, especially if fancied to win. Competitive stress potential.
	High level need to shut out extraneous information and concentrate on stroke rhythm and power delivery.
	Need to cope with demands of long, arduous and 'stimulus poor' training regimes.

Figure 1.16   Analysis of a game sport activity — rugby football

LEVEL OF ANALYSIS	CHARACTERISTICS OF THE ACTIVITY
Structural	Invasion Game involving direct, physical contact and interference in performance from opponents.
	Complex rule structure which:
	- defines different means of scoring;
	- defines 'behaviour' of players and penalties for rule infringements..
Strategic	Highly tactical sport involving:
	- decisions about style of tactical approach;
	- set plays from specifically defined situations;
	- individual and instant decision-making;
	Variations in positional strategic roles.
	Requires skills of reading the game, anticipating the behaviour of both team-mates and opponents.
	Preparing for specific opponents.
Technical	Technical skills required in a variety of areas:
	Individual:
'Open' skills	- Ball-handling skills;
	- kicking skills;
	- tackling skills;

	- running skills and dodging skills;
	High reliance on consistency and 'outcome accuracy' in dealing with moving people and the ball.
Group:	- scrummaging, line-out;
	- rucking and mauling;
	- three-quarter line play;
	- etc.
	Individual varations/combinations to meet specific positional requirements
Physical	Specific combinations of speed, strength and agility/flexibility relating to positional responsibilities within the game.
	Implications for both aerobic and anaerobic fitness training programmes.
	Positional specificity so great that there are implications for players' physical size and shape at competitive levels.
Psychological	This is a hard physical contact sport, sometimes played in 'uncomfortable' conditions. Hence, physical stress potential.
	Aggression and its control are features of participation. Hence strict refereeing.
	Requires team commitment and appropriate leadership / 'followship' behaviour.
	Some positions imply 'limelight' roles.
	Competitive stress potential.

SUMMARY

- The word sport refers both to certain activities and the kinds of experiences they generate for people. Sport activities always provide participants with a challenge of some kind, usually of a physical nature or demanding skillful performance.
- People get involved in sport actively as performer, official, coach or administrator. There are also passive roles as spectator and fan.
- The competition, adventure and conditioning categories of sport activities provide people with different kinds of challenges and experiences.
- Competition sport is based on an unwritten contract to compete. Competition can occur at different levels, reflecting the skills and fitness of the participants.
- Competition sports can be grouped into athletic, gymnastic and game sub-categories, according to the nature of their sport problems and the associated scoring systems.
- Games can be sub-divided into invasion, net, innings, fighting and target sub-categories, according to their different rule structures and scoring systems.
- Any competition sport can be analysed at structural, strategic, technical, physical and psychological levels, illustrating what a person must be able to do in order to compete effectively.

Questions

1   Explain why both players in a tennis match might experience pleasure from their involvement, despite the fact that one won and the other lost.

2   What are the similarities and differences between amateur and professional sport?

3   How might canoes be differently used to provide competition sport, adventure activity and conditioning activity?

4   Explain what is meant by 'the contract to compete' within competition sport, relating your explanation to the rules governing the behaviour of participants. With reference to a sport of your choice, investigate the idea that there is a scale of penalties to reflect the seriousness of breaking the rules.

5   Find out and write down the nature of the sport problem and the scoring system for baseball, pursuit cycling, and rhythmic gymnastics. To which sub-categories of competition sport do these three activities belong?

6   With reference to the sub-categories of games, explain and compare what is meant by a possession in hockey, a rally in badminton, a frame in snooker, a round in boxing and an innings in rounders.

7   With reference to the different levels of sport analysis, and using figures 1.15 and 1.16 as a guide, prepare an analysis of trampoline as an example of a gymnastic type of competition sport.

8   Using the sport analysis template, contrast the demands of playing in goal in hockey with those of a middle-distance track athlete.

9   Illustrate the differences between representative sport, recreation sport, and physical education in the game of golf.

References

Alderson & Crutchley *Towards a National Curriculum*, in Armstrong (Ed) *New Directions in PE*. (1991)

Coe, Teasdale & Wickham *More than a Game: Sport in our time*, BBC Books. (1992)

Davis, Bull, Roscoe & Roscoe *Physical Education and the Study of Sport,* Wolfe.(1991 and 1994)

The Diagram Group *Sports Laws*, Dent & Sons.(1983)

The Official Rule Handbooks of the National Governing Bodies of Sport (various).

Sports Coaching Manuals (various).

School Sport Forum *Sport and young people: Partnership in action*, The Sports Council. (1988)

2 ANATOMY AND PHYSIOLOGY

To understand how the human body performs at all levels of sports activity, it is necessary to know the basic structure of the body and how it functions under different conditions.

The aim of this chapter is to provide information which will encourage the student to learn about and understand the anatomical structure of the human body, and how the body systems function under conditions of rest and physical activity.

The two major branches of science which relate to the structure and function of the human body are anatomy and physiology. The structure and function of body parts are inextricably linked. Each structure of the body is designed for a particular function, the structure often revealing the function.

This chapter will consider both the anatomical structure and physiological function of the following systems:

- the skeletal system – bones
- the skeletal system – articulations
- the nervous system
- the muscular system
- the cardiovascular system
- the respiratory system
- the endocrine (hormonal) system.

Although these systems will be described in separate sections, it is important to remember that they are interlinked. The interaction/function of all systems is essential for the effective working of the body.

Before looking at the individual systems, it is perhaps useful at this stage to consider a mechanism which influences the functioning of all systems, the concept of homeostasis.

Each of the body systems consists of specialised cells, which require relatively stable conditions in which to function effectively. They contribute to the survival of the body as a whole. This essential maintenance of stable conditions for the cells is known as homeostasis.

It is important to control both the internal composition of the cells, and that of the fluid which surrounds the cells (the extra-cellular fluid, which is referred to as the internal environment, and which provides the medium in which the cells carry out their vital activities). Among the substances which are found in the extra-cellular fluid are gases, nutrients, and electrically-charged particles (ions), all of which

Anatomy is the study of the overall organisation of the body, the structure of individual organs and systems, and the relationship among structures.

Physiology is the study of the function of body systems and how they work.

Homeostasis can be defined as a condition in which the body's internal environment remains within certain physiological limits.

Homeostasis is said to exist when the internal environment:

- contains the optimal concentration of gases, nutrients, ions and water.
- has an optimal temperature.
- has an optimal volume for the health of the cells.

are essential to maintain life. They must be controlled to maintain the balance of the internal environment.

Examples of variables which require control through homeostatic mechanisms include body temperature, blood pressure, ionic composition of blood plasma, blood glucose levels and the oxygen and carbon dioxide content of the blood.

Homeostatic mechanisms are regulated by the nervous system and the endocrine (hormonal) system, working together or independently. Basically, the nervous system detects changes from the normal homeostatic condition, and sends messages to the appropriate organ (e.g. heart, lungs) to counteract or enhance the cause of the change. This response usually occurs rapidly. The endocrine system acts in a similar way. The hormones are released to influence the cause of the change, but the hormonal response usually acts more slowly than the nervous response.

The system by which the homeostatic mechanisms operate is known as a feedback system (loop). This is a cycle of events in which information about the internal environment of the various systems and organs of the body are continually monitored and fed back to a central control system. A feedback system consists of three basic elements – a control centre, a receptor, and an effector.

Homeostatic mechanisms control the internal environment of all systems in the body. They will be considered in a variety of conditions affecting the individual body systems.

Part 1   The structure of muscle and bone

The first part of this chapter will look at the locomotor system, considering the basic skeletal framework, arrangement and function of muscles, and how the system works to produce normal movement.

Objectives

To understand
- the structure, development and function of bone
- the arrangement and major features of bones in the axial and appendicular skeleton
- the structural and functional classification of joints
- the axes and planes of movement
- the classification, characteristics and functions of major joints
- the structure, functions and division of the nervous system
- the nature of reflex activity
- the structure and function of muscle
- the central and peripheral control of movement
- the position and action of major muscles/muscle groups

Figure 2.1 The feedback (loop) system

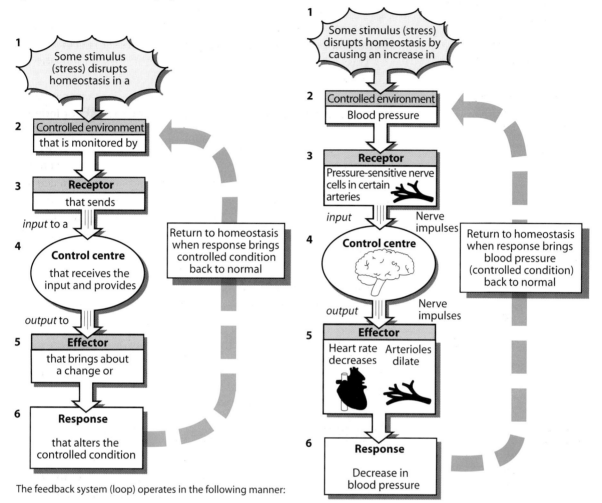

The feedback system (loop) operates in the following manner:

1 A stimulus or stress (which may originate either inside or outside the body) creates an imbalance in the internal environment.

2 This results in a disruption of homeostasis in a specific controlled environment (e.g. heart rate, blood pressure, body temperature).

3 The changes in the controlled environment are monitored by receptors.

4 The receptors send information about the change in the controlled environment to the control centre.

5 The control centre determines the point at which the changes in the controlled environment require action to limit the degree of disruption or imbalance.

6 When action is required, the control centre sends information to the effectors, which are the organs which carry out the required action or response.

7 The response alters the controlled environment. The most common response is to reverse the original stimulus, and return the controlled environment to its original balance. For example, when body temperature (controlled environment) increases, the sweat glands (effectors) increase activity to produce a cooling effect (response) and return body temperature to normal limits. This is known as a negative feedback system (loop). A positive feedback system (loop) has the effect of enhancing the original stimulus, and is usually destructive, resulting in malfunction. However it is occasionally beneficial, as in the clotting of blood to stop bleeding from a wound.

The mature skeletal system forms the rigid framework of the body. It consists primarily of bone (osseus) tissue, but also of some cartilagenous tissue. The most obvious functions of the skeletal system are to provide support, protection and to allow movement to occur.

This section will describe the structure, development and function of bone and the structure of the skeleton.

Bone – structure, development and function

Bone is hard, with a certain amount of resilience. The hardness is provided by large amounts of calcium salts deposited in the bone. The resilience is provided by the connective tissue framework of the bone. The result is that bone is not only exceptionally strong, but it is also light.

Classification of bone

There are four types of bone in the body, all classified according to shape.

- Long bones are found within the limbs, and consist of a shaft (diaphysis), and two expanded ends (ephiphyses), between which are the metaphyses.
- Short bones are found in the wrist (carpus) and the foot (tarsus).
- Flat bones are found in the skull and shoulder blade (scapula). They are thin and tend to be curved.
- Irregular bones are those which do not fit into the other categories. They include the vertebrae, hip bones and facial bones.

Gross structure of bone

The overall gross structure of bone consists of four major elements.

Periosteum

Each bone is enclosed in a dense layer of fibrous tissue, known as periosteum, which consists of two layers. The outer fibrous layer contains blood vessels and nerves which pass into the bone. The inner osteogenic (bone developing) layer contains elastic fibres, blood vessels and various types of bone cells. The periosteum is essential for growth in the diameter of the bone, and for its repair and nutrition.

Spongy or cancellous bone

Systems of trabeculae, or thin plates of bone are arranged in a lattice-like network, giving a spongy appearance to the bone. Spongy or cancellous bone makes up most of flat, short and irregular bones, and of the ends of long bones. The trabeculae are aligned along lines of stress in the bone. This arrangement gives strength to the structure, without unnecessary weight.

The spaces between the trabeculae are filled with red bone marrow which produces both red and white blood cells; the prime sites for this are the hip bones, vertebrae, sternum (breast bone), ribs and skull. Osteocytes (mature bone cells) are also found within the trabeculae.

Compact bone

Compact bone is dense and has few spaces. It forms the external layer of the bones of the body, and the bulk of the shaft (diaphysis) of long bones. Compact bone provides protection and support and helps the long bones resist the stresses of weight placed upon them.

Medullary cavity

The medullary or marrow cavity is the space within the shaft (diaphysis) of long bones, surrounded by a layer of compact bone and lined with endosteum. In the infant, the spaces in both spongy or cancellous bone and the medullary cavities of long bones contain red bone marrow. This produces both red and white blood cells. In the adult, the medullary cavities of long bones contain yellow fat marrow. This consists primarily of adipose (fat) cells, and a few scattered bone cells.

Cellular structure of bone

There are four types of bone cells. They are distributed throughout both compact and spongy bone.

Osteogenic cells

These are found in the inner part of the periosteum and in the bony canals which contain blood vessels. They are capable of mitosis (division) and develop into osteoblasts.

Osteoblasts

Derived from osteogenic cells, osteoblasts are the true bone-forming cells, but have lost the ability to divide. They produce collagen and the mineral components of bone.

Osteocytes

Osteocytes are mature bone cells derived from osteoblasts. They are the principal cells of bone tissue. They are not capable of division or bone formation, but maintain the daily cellular activities of bone tissue.

Osteoclasts

These are thought to develop from a type of white blood cell (monocyte), and their main function is absorption (destruction) of bone. Bone is constantly developing and remodelling in response to the stresses placed upon it. Osteoclasts have an important function in this respect, being, with osteoblasts, involved in the development, growth, maintenance and repair of bone. The correct balance between osteoblast (bone forming) and osteoclast (bone absorption) activity is crucial for maintaining bone strength, without unnecessary bulk and weight.

Figure 2.2 Cellular structure of bone

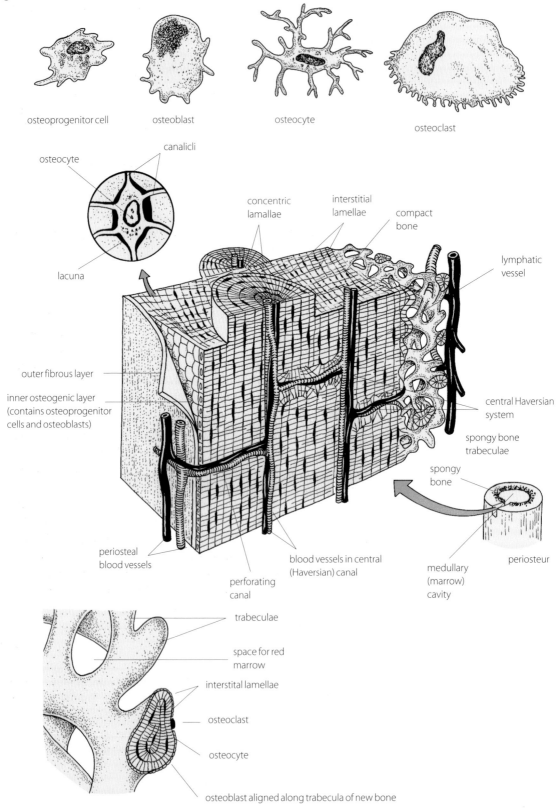

osteoprogenitor cell

osteoblast

osteocyte

osteoclast

osteocyte

canalicli

concentric lamallae

interstitial lamellae

compact bone

lymphatic vessel

lacuna

outer fibrous layer

inner osteogenic layer (contains osteoprogenitor cells and osteoblasts)

central Haversian system

spongy bone trabeculae

spongy bone

periosteal blood vessels

blood vessels in central (Haversian) canal

perforating canal

medullary (marrow) cavity

periosteur

trabeculae

space for red marrow

interstital lamellae

osteoclast

osteocyte

osteoblast aligned along trabecula of new bone

Compact bone has a concentric ring structure of lamellae (rings of hard calcified matrix) arranged around central canals (Haversian canals) containing blood vessels and nerves, which run longitudinally through the bone. Between the lamellae are small spaces (lacunae), from which radiate narrow canals (canaliculi). Osteocytes lie in the lacunae, and can link with each other via their long finger-like projections through the caniculi. This permits the passage of material from one cell to another. The canaliculi are filled with extracellular fluid, and form an intricate canal network throughout the compact bone, linking to the central canals. This network allows nutrients and oxygen to reach the osteocytes, and waste products to diffuse away.

In spongy bone, the trabeculae also consist of lamellae. These are arranged less formally than in compact bone. Osteocytes lie in the lacunae of the trabeculae, and a similar arrangement of canaliculi radiate from the lacunae. The osteocytes in spongy bone receive nutrition directly from the blood which circulates through the marrow cavities.

> The arrangement of lamellae and canals is known as a **Haversian System.**

The growth of bone

During the period of growth from birth to early adulthood, bone grows in all dimensions. In a long bone, growth in diameter is a function of the periosteum, and growth in length is a function of the epiphyseal plate which is a band of multiplying cartilage cells between the shaft (diaphysis) and end (epiphysis) of the bone.

The growth in diameter occurs as osteoblasts from the periosteum add new bone tissue to the outer surface, firstly in the form of spongy bone, but is eventually replaced by compact bone. At the same time, to prevent the bone becoming too heavy, and to maintain the relative size of the medullary cavity, osteoclasts destroy the bone which lines the cavity, and thus increasing its diameter.

During growth, cartilage cells multiply on the epiphyseal side of the epiphyseal plate, and are replaced by bone on the diaphyseal side, so that while the bone increases in length on the diaphyseal side, the thickness of the epiphyseal plate remains constant. The rate of growth is controlled by the growth hormones and the sex hormones.

Damage or injury to the epiphyseal plate may result in abnormalities in bone growth. If the entire width of the plate is affected, bone growth in length will be retarded, or will cease. If part of the plate is affected, bone growth will be unequal across the plate, resulting in abnormal shape or deformity.

When maturity or adulthood is reached, the cartilage cells in the epiphyseal plate stop dividing, and are replaced by bone. The resulting bony structure is called the epiphyseal line.

Exercise and bone

Bone has the ability to alter its strength in response to mechanical stress. By the process of bone formation and resorption, there is increased deposition of minerals and increased formation of collagen fibres. Both contribute to increased strength in the bone.

The deposits of minerals and collagen fibres align themselves along the lines of stress produced by the external mechanical force, such as the force of gravity and the pull of muscles. Thus the bone is strengthened to withstand specific mechanical forces.

Some people (athletes and heavy manual workers), subject their bones to high levels of repetitive mechanical stress. Their bones respond by becoming thicker and stronger. However, if the stress and repetition is excessive, bone resorption may exceed formation. In specific sites (foot, lower leg), stress fractures (painful weakened areas of bone) may occur. These are common in endurance athletes, such as distance runners and race walkers, who train regularly over long distances.

In the absence of mechanical stress, as occurs during periods of inactivity, immobility (as in a plaster cast) or bedrest, bone absorption outstrips formation. This results in weakened bone. This also occurs as a natural process in aging, when minerals are lost from bone. This process starts after the age of 30 in females, and accelerates rapidly after the age of 45 as oestrogen levels decrease, until up to 30% of calcium loss at 70 years. Typically, this process starts in males after the age of 60. Furthermore, there is a loss of collagen with ageing. This causes the bone to become brittle and lose its tensile strength. Fractures are more common in the elderly.

Bone – the skeletal system

Bones and cartilage are organised into a framework which protects organs and allows movement. This is known as the skeletal system. It is important to recognise the physical features of bone to understand how different movements occur. The shape of the bone ends and the points of attachment of the muscles on the bone determine the movements which occur at the joint.

The adult human skeleton consists of 206 bones, which are grouped into two major divisions. The axial skeleton consists of the bones which lie around the longitudinal axis of the body. The appendicular skeleton consists of the bones of the upper and lower limbs, and the shoulder and pelvic girdles which connect the extremities to the axial skeleton (Figures 2.3 and 2.4).

Figure 2.3 The appendicular skeleton

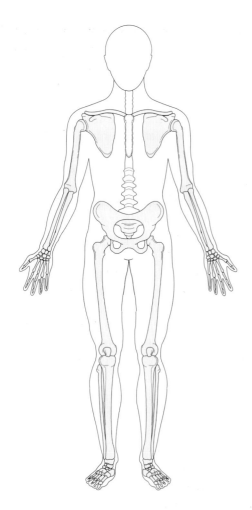

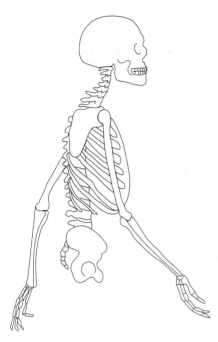

Features of bones

The shape and physical features of bones have developed in response to function, and provide a variety of surface markings. Long weight-bearing bones have large rounded ends to provide weight-bearing surfaces and stable joints. Raised roughened areas of bone serve as points of attachment for muscles, tendons and ligaments. Grooves provide a passage for blood vessels and nerves, and openings occur where blood vessels and nerves pass through the bone.

The axial skeleton

The axial skeleton consists of the bones which lie around the longitudinal axis of the body.

The skull

The skull is a complex bony structure consisting of many individual bones which are joined together edge-to-edge by fibrous interlocking joints known as sutures. The main function of the skull is to provide protection for the brain and the vital senses of sight, hearing and balance.

The mandible is the only truly moveable bone of the skull, and is the strongest facial bone. Its function is in the biting, tearing and mastication of food.

Figure 2.4   The axial skeleton

Figure 2.5   Features of bones

Marking	Description	Example
Condoyle	A large rounded prominence which forms part of a joint	Medial condyle of the femur
Crest	A prominent border or ridge	Iliac crest of the hip bone
Epicondyle	A prominence above a condyle	Medial epicondyle of the femur
Facet	A smooth flat surface	Articular facet of a vertebra for the tubercle of a rib
Fontanel	Dense connective tissue-filled space between skull bones at birth	Anterior fontanel between frontal and parietal bones
Foramen	An opening through which blood vessels, nerves or ligaments pass	Foramen magnum at the base of the skull, through which the spinal cord passes
Fossa	A depression in or on a bone	Olecranon fossa at the lower end of the humerus
Groove or sulcus	A furrow or depression for a soft structure such as a blood vessel, nerve or tendon	Intertubercular sulcus of the humerus
Head	A rounded articular portion, supported on a narrow portion (neck) of a bone	Head of femur
Spinous process	A sharp slender process	Spinous process of a vertebrae
Trochanter	A large projection found only on the femur	Greater trochanter of the femur
Tubercle	A small rounded process	Greater tubercle of the humerus
Tuberosity	A large rounded, usually roughened prominence	Ischael tuberosity of the hip bone

Figure 2.6   The skull

The top and most of the sides of the skull are formed by the parietal bones. They are joined together at the sagittal suture. The front of the skull is formed by the frontal bone. This joins the parietal bones at the parietal suture. The point at which these sutures meet is called the bregma, which at birth is not ossified. It can be felt as a soft diamond-shaped area (the anterior fontanel) on top of the baby's head. It gradually decreases in size, and disappears at 18 months.

The posterior part of the skull is formed by the occipital bone which joins the parietal bone at the lamboid suture. At birth there is another soft area at the junction of the lamboid and sagittal sutures (the posterior fontanel), which closes over at six to nine months.

The base of the skull consists of irregularly shaped bones, with several foramina. The largest (foramen magnum) is for passage of the of the spinal cord from the brain. The smaller ones allow the passage of the cranial nerves (of which there are 12 pairs), and blood vessels.

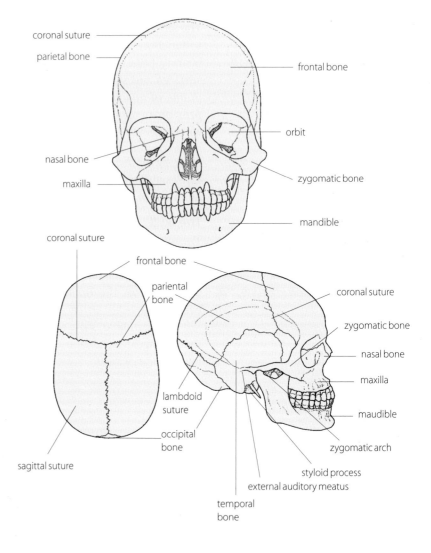

The vertebral column

Apart from the upper two cervical vertebrae, (the atlas and axis – which allow nodding and turning movements of the head, and have an atypical structure), all vertebrae have the same basic structure. This structure consists of a solid spherical body, two lamina and two pedicles, which encompass the vertebral canal, two transverse processes and a spinous process.

Variations to the basic structure of a typical vertebra, tend to be functional and regional in origin. In the cervical region the vertebrae are smaller and lighter. They also allow a wide range of movement and have a large vertebral canal as the spinal cord is thick in this region. The vertebrae in the thoracic region are adapted to form joints with the ribs. In the lumbar region the vertebrae are large to withstand the weight of the trunk above. They also permit a relatively small range of

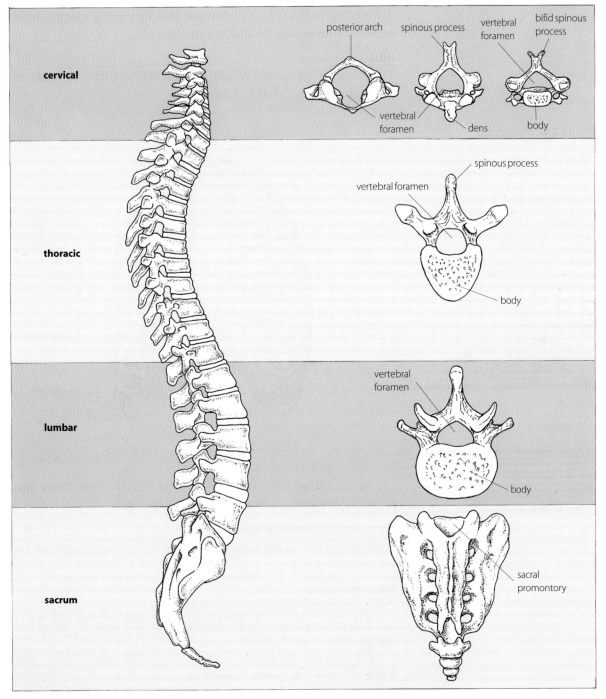

Figure 2.7 The vertebral column

The vertebral column consists of 33 bony segments, 24 of which are mobile. The lower nine are fused to form the sacrum (five bones) and the coccyx (four bones).

The mobile segments are distributed into three regions - seven cervical vertebrae (neck), 12 thoracic vertebrae (chest/ribcage) and five lumbar (low back).

movement and have a smaller vertebral canal, as the spinal cord is much reduced in size at this level.

The sacrum consists of five bones which are fused together to form a solid triangular structure. The coccyx comprises four fused bones, and is the lowest part of the vertebral column.

The main functions of the vertebral column are to protect the spinal cord, to provide points of attachment for the powerful muscles of the trunk, to provide a mobile framework for the trunk, and to form a relatively stable base for attachment of the ribs.

Ribs

The ribs, forming the thorax, provide a framework for the mechanism of breathing and protect the lungs.

Figure 2.8   The rib cage

Twelve pairs of ribs make up the thoracic cavity . The upper seven pairs of ribs (known as true ribs) attach directly to the transverse processes of the vertebrae behind, and to the breast bone or sternum in front, via a strip of cartilage (costal cartilage). The next three pairs (known as false ribs) attach to the vertebrae behind, but their costal cartilages join the costal cartilage of the rib above, and eventually indirectly join the sternum. The lower two pairs have no anterior attachment, and are known as floating ribs.

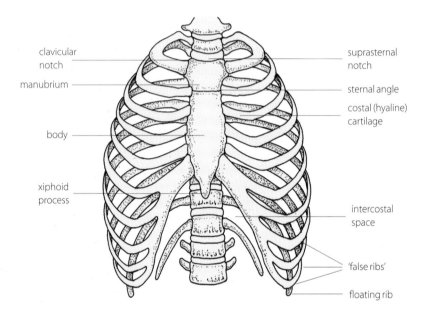

The appendicular skeleton

The appendicular skeleton consists of the bones of the limbs, the pectoral (shoulder) girdle and the pelvic (hip) girdle.

The pectoral (shoulder) girdle

The arrangement of the bones making up the pectoral girdle can be seen in figure 2.9.

The upper limb

The upper limb consists of three main regions – the arm (from the shoulder to the elbow), the forearm (from the elbow to the wrist) and the hand.

The arrangement and the major features of the bones of the upper limb are shown in figures 2.10 and 2.11.

The pelvic girdle

The pelvic girdle, unlike the pectoral girdle, consists of strong sturdy bones which form a complete bony ring. The bones which make up the pelvic girdle are the two hip (coxal) bones, and the sacrum of the vertebral column. Each of the hip bones consists of three bones (the ilium, ischium and pubis) which are fused together. They articulate with each other at the symphysis pubis in front and with the sacrum at the sacro-iliac joints behind. This arrangement provides a strong,

Figure 2.9 The pectoral girdle

The pectoral girdle forms the basis of attachment of the upper limb to the trunk. It consists of two clavicles (collar bones), which articulate with the sternum in front, and with two scapulae (shoulder blades) behind. The pectoral girdle does not form a complete bony ring, since the scapulae do not articulate with the vertebral column. They are attached to the back of the ribcage (thorax) by a complex arrangement of muscles. This arrangement of bony and muscular girdle increases the mobility of the shoulder girdle, and permits the upper limbs to move extensively in any direction.

Figure 2.10 Major bones and features of the upper arm

The humerus is the longest and largest bone of the upper limb, and is the only bone in the arm. It articulates with the glenoid cavity of the scapula above, and with the radius and ulna of the forearm below.

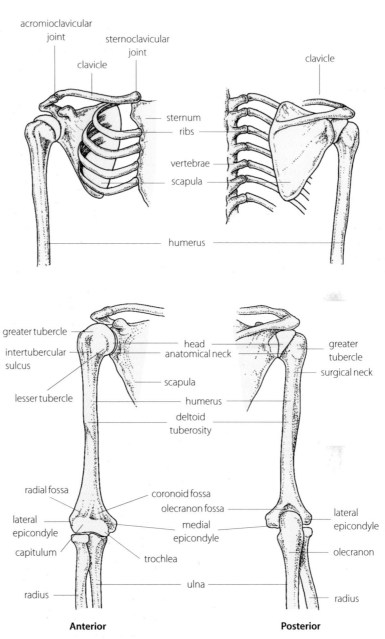

relatively immobile structure. This is important in the transmission of weight between the trunk and the lower limbs. The pelvis also functions to protect the internal reproductive organs and the bladder.

The major features of the hip bones, and the basic structure of the pelvis is shown in figures 2.12 and 2.13.

The lower limb

The basic structure of the lower limb is similar to that of the upper limb, consisting of the thigh (hip to knee), the leg (knee to ankle) and

Figure 2.11 Major bones and features of the lower arm

The radius and ulna are two long slender bones, arranged in parallel, and which can rotate around each other. Finally, the hand consists of eight small bones (carpal bones) arranged in two rows (the carpus). They articulate with the radius and ulna above, and with the five metacarpal bones (forming the palm of the hand) below. Each of the fingers consist of three phalanges, and the thumb two phalanges, making a total of 14 in all.

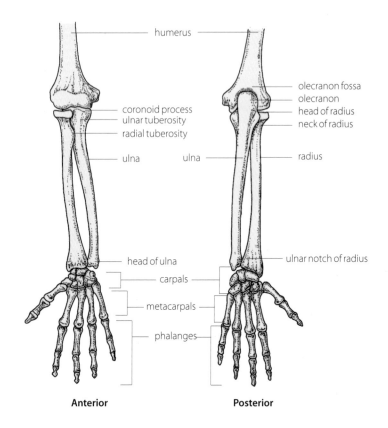

Anterior   **Posterior**

the foot. The thigh consists of a single long bone (the femur) which is the longest, strongest and heaviest bone in the body. It articulates with the acetabulum of the hip bone above, and with the tibia below. The patella (knee cap) is a small triangular bone in the tendon of the quadriceps femoris muscle, which lies on the front of the thigh.

Figure 2.12 Anterior view of the pelvic girdle

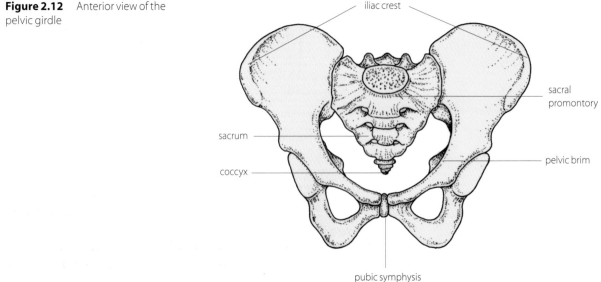

Figure 2.13 Major bones and features of the upper leg system

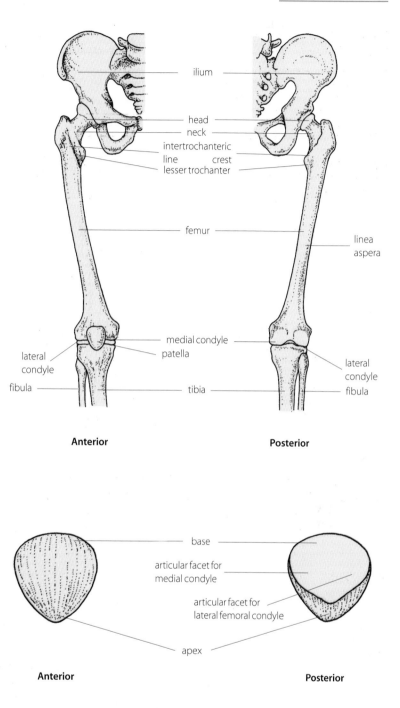

Figure 2.14 The patella

The leg, like the forearm, consists of two long bones (the tibia and fibula) arranged parallel to each other. However, unlike the upper limb, the bones are unequal in size. The tibia is thick and heavy and the fibula slender and light, and the bones cannot rotate around each other. The foot consists of seven tarsal bones arranged in two groups. There are five metatarsals, forming the major part of the arch of the foot, and fourteen phalanges, arranged in a similar manner to those in the hand. The great toe has only two phalanges, and the other toes three.

The major features and arrangement of the bones of the lower limb are shown in figure 2.15.

Figure 2.15 Major bones and features of the lower leg

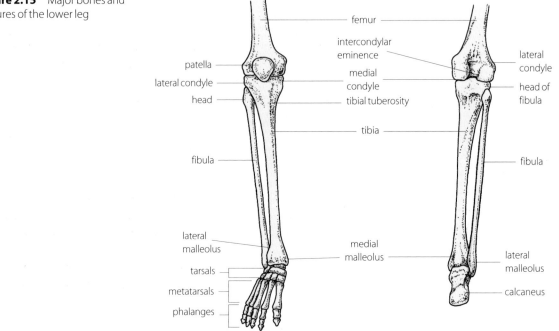

SUMMARY

- The homeostatic mechanisms which maintain the body's internal environment within certain physiological limits, depend upon the presence of three elements — a control centre, a receptor and an effector.
- Bones may be classified into long bones, short bones and irregular bones.
- The development (ossification) and growth of bone depends on the balance between osteoblasts (bone-forming cells) and osteoclasts (bone-absorbing cells). Osteocytes maintain the daily cellular activities of bone.
- The skeleton may be divided into the axial (head and trunk) and appendicular (upper and lower limbs) skeleton.

Questions

1 What is meant by a 'homeostatic loop'?
2 Describe the structure of a long bone.
3 How does a long bone grow in length and diameter?
4 What are the main divisions of the skeleton?
5 List and give examples of ten features of bones.

Articulations

An articulation (joint) is a point of contact between bones, or between cartilage and bones. All body movements occur at joints, and almost all joints permit movement. A few joints do not permit movement, but provide protection (for example, the sutures of the skull).

This section will describe the classification of joints, the movements which occur at joints, and will consider in some detail, the structure and movements which occur in some named joints.

Classification of joints

The amount and direction of movement at a joint depends on its structure (the shape of the articular surfaces) and on the position and length of the soft tissues (for example, muscle and ligaments) which surround it.

Joints may be classified on structure (based on the anatomical characteristics of the joint), or on function (based on the range and type of movement which occurs).

Structural classification of joints

Structural classification is based on the presence or absence of a space (the joint cavity) between the articulating surfaces of the joint.

Fibrous joints have no joint cavity, and the bones are held together by fibrous tissue. Examples of fibrous joints are:

- **Sutures** which occur only in the skull, where the broader surfaces of the bones meet. In the immature skeleton, the surfaces are separated by fibrous tissue, but when growth is complete this becomes transformed into bone. This does not occur until the late twenties.

- **Syndesmosis** which is an articulation in which closely opposed bony surfaces are bound together by an interosseous ligament. The only example in the body is the joint between the lower ends of the tibia and fibula (the inferior tibio-fibular joint). The joint between the sacrum and the ilium (the sacro-iliac joint) resembles a syndesmosis, but is not a true example, as a small amount of movement occurs at this joint.

Cartilagenous joints also have no joint cavity, and the bones which form the joint are held together by cartilage. Examples of cartilage-nous joints are:

47

- **Synchondrosis** which is a temporary cartilagenous junction between the diaphysis and epiphysis of bones in the immature skeleton. The connecting hyaline cartilage is eventually replaced by bone when growth ceases.

- **Symphysis** which is a fibro-cartilagenous articulation at which a limited range of movement is allowed by deformation of a connecting disc or pad of fibro-cartilage. The thickness of the disc determines the range of movement possible at the joint. All layers of the articulation are firmly bonded together – bone, hyaline cartilage and fibro-cartilagenous disc.

  All symphyses are confined to the axial skeleton – between the manubrium and body of sternum, the joints between the bodies of the vertebrae, and pubic symphysis between the anterior surfaces of the hip bones.

Synovial joints are freely moveable joints which make up the majority of joints in the body. They have a variety of shapes, and permit several different types of movement. In spite of individual differences, synovial joints all have the same basic structure. They consist of a joint cavity between the bone ends, and a capsule and ligaments which link the bones. The general characteristics and specific features of named synovial joints will be described later in this section.

Functional classification of joints

Functional classification is based on the functional characteristics of the joint, primarily the amount of movement permitted.

- **Synarthroses** are immoveable joints. Examples include the sutures of the skull, and the synchondroses of the immature skeleton.

- **Amphiarthroses** are slightly moveable joints, and include syndesmoses and symphyses.

- **Diarthroses** are the freely moveable joints, found primarily in the appendicular skeleton, and include the synovial joints.

Terminology

Before considering the general features and specific characteristics of joints, it is important to understand the terminology used to describe position and movement. Below are the definitions of terms commonly used in the description of joints and the movements which occur at them.

Movement

All movements are conventionally described as being started from the anatomical position. This is standing upright, with feet pointing forwards and the palms of the hands facing forwards. For ease of description, movements are related to planes and axes.

The following are general descriptions of movements occurring at joints, related to the axes and planes.

Figure 2.16   Planes of the body

There are three cardinal planes of the body; the sagittal plane which is a vertical plane which divides the body into right and left halves, the frontal (coronal) plane, which also is a vertical plane, and divides the body into front and back halves, and the horizontal (transverse) plane which divides the body into upper and lower halves.

   There are also three axes of movement which occur in the body:

  i) the frontal axis which runs from side to side across the body;

  ii) the sagittal axis which runs from front to back through the body; and

  iii) the vertical axis, an axis that runs from top to bottom (head to foot) along the body.

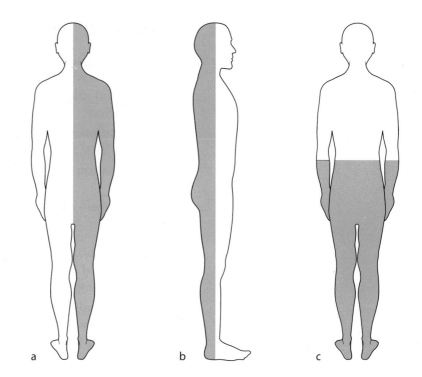

a   b   c

Movements in a sagittal plane about a frontal axis

These are best observed from the side.

- **Flexion** – the angle between the surfaces of two adjacent segments decreases as the joint is bent. Flexion is also said to occur when a segment or body part moves forward at a joint (moving the arm forward from the shoulder, bending the head forward at the neck).

- **Extension** – the angle between two adjacent segments increases as the limb is straightened. Extension also occurs when a segment or body part moves backwards from a joint (moving the arm backwards from the shoulder, stretching the head backwards at the neck). Extension is the opposite of flexion.

  An exception to this is flexion and extension of the thumb which takes place in the frontal plane.

- **Dorsiflexion** – the foot is pulled up towards the leg.

- **Plantarflexion** – the foot moves downwards from the leg.

Movements in a frontal plane about a sagittal axis

These movements are best observed either from in front or behind the person moving.

- **Abduction** – the segment moves away from the midline of the body.

- **Adduction** – the segment moves towards the midline of the body.

    An exception to this is in the movements of the digits. In the foot the midline is taken as the second digit; in the hand it is the third digit. Abduction and adduction of the thumb takes place in the sagittal plane.

- **Ulnar deviation** – the hand moves in the direction of the little finger at the wrist.
- **Radial deviation** – the hand moves in the direction of the thumb at the wrist.
- **Lateral flexion** – movement of the trunk or head and neck to the left or right.

Movements in a horizontal plane about a vertical axis

- **Medial/internal rotation** – the anterior surface of the segment turns inwards, towards the midline.
- **Lateral/external rotation** – the anterior surface of the segment turns outwards away from the midline.
- **Rotation to the left or right of the vertebral column.**
- **Supination** – the palm of the hand is turned anteriorly at the forearm.
- **Pronation** – the palm of the hand is turned posteriorly at the forearm

Circumduction

A combination of the movements of flexion, abduction, extension, and adduction are performed in sequence, so the segment traces out a conical shape.

Characteristics of diarthrodial (synovial) joints

There are several types of synovial joint. They differ according to the shapes of the articular surfaces and the movements which are permitted.

In all synovial joints the bony surfaces are in contact, but not joined, and are covered by a thin layer of hyaline cartilage. This is smooth and has a very low coefficient of friction (0.002 or less). This facilitates smooth gliding movements between the bone ends, with the minimum of resistance. Sliding contact between the bone ends is further helped by the presence of a viscous fluid – synovial fluid – which acts as a lubricant. Synovial fluid is also important in the mainte-nance and nutrition of living cells in the articular cartilage. The viscosity of the synovial fluid is greater when the joint is at rest, but it becomes less viscous when the joint is moved.

The bones are linked by a fibrous articular capsule and by ligaments. The capsule is in the form of a sleeve which surrounds the joint, enclosing it completely, with a few exceptions. It is lined with a synovial membrane. The synovial membrane is composed of areolar

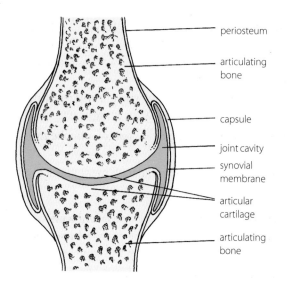

periosteum

articulating bone

capsule

joint cavity

synovial membrane

articular cartilage

articulating bone

Figure 2.17 Frontal section of typical synovial joint

connective tissue with elastic fibres and a variable amount of adipose tissue. It secretes synovial fluid, which lines the joint cavity, covering all surfaces except those involved directly with the articulation. Where ligaments and tendons pass through the joint capsule, these structures are covered with synovial membrane. The ligaments associated with synovial joints may be extracapsular (occurring outside the capsule), or intracapsular (inside the capsule). Ligaments are relatively inextensible structures. They consist of fibrous connective tissue and some elastic fibres, and are attached to each of the bones which make up the joint, close to the articular surfaces. They function to hold the bone ends together, to prevent excessive movement at the joint, and to guide the movement which occurs at the joint. Extracapsular ligamanents may be completely separate from the capsule, or may be integrated with the capsule, when they form a localised thickening of the capsule. Intracapsular ligaments lie completely within the joint capsule.

A 'typical' synovial joint is illustrated in figure 2.17.

Some joints have associated fibrocartilagenous structures, which function to improve the stability and mechanics of the joint. Articular discs or menisci intervene between certain articular surfaces, where they improve the degree of congruity (that is, how closely the articular surfaces 'match'). They consist of fibrocartilage, with the fibrous element predominating, and may be complete (as in the disc between the distal end of the ulna and the proximal row of carpal bones at the wrist), or incomplete (as in the menisci between the femur and the tibia at the knee joint). These structures tend to have a blood supply around the periphery, but centrally, they are avascular. This limits the potential for repair following injury. Functions of menisci or discs include:

- Provide shock absorption
- Improve the matching of the two bones
- Facilitate combined movements
- Limit translatory (gliding) movements
- Improve weight distribution
- Protect articular surfaces
- Facilitate rolling movements
- Distribute synovial fluid.

Some joints have a fibro-cartilagenous rim or lip, known as a labrum. This is a circular structure, usually triangular in cross section, and attached to the margin of an articular surface. Examples are the glenoidal labrum at the shoulder joint, and the acetabular labrum at the hip joint. The functions of a labrum include:

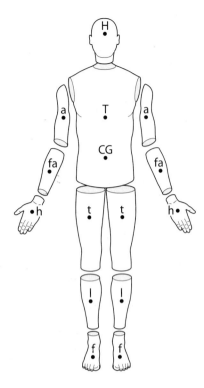

Figure 2.18 Centres of gravity of limb and trunk segments

- Increase the area of contact between the articulating bones.
- Deepen the socket, and add to stability.
- Assist in the distribution of synovial fluid.

Synovial joints may be classified in several ways.

Complexity of organisation

This refers to the number and complexity of the articulating surfaces.

- **Simple joints** possess only one pair of articulating surfaces.
- **Compound joints** possess more than one pair of articulating surfaces (the knee joint)
- **Complex joints** have an additional articular element.

Degrees of freedom of joints

Degrees of freedom refers to the imposition of one of a pair of articulating bones, in one, or more planes. The axis of a joint is basically the fulcrum about which the bones which make up the joint move. The movement occurs within a plane. Movement at axes are taken from the anatomical position, that is, standing upright, feet pointing forward, and the palms of the hands facing forward.

The principal planes of the body are the horizontal plane (parallel to the floor), the sagittal plane (vertical, in an antero-posterior direction) and the coronal or frontal plane (vertical, across the front of the body).

- **Uni-axial** (one degree of freedom) movement of a bone at a joint is limited to rotation about a single axis (inter-phalangeal joints of the fingers).
- **Bi-axial** (two degrees of freedom) or completely independent movements can occur about two distinct axes (carpo-metacarpal joint at the base of the thumb).
- **Multi-axial** (three degrees of freedom) movement of a bone occurs about the three main axes (shoulder joint).

The axis of movement of a joint continuously changes position as the movement progresses. This reflects the fact that the articular surfaces are not completely geometric in form, and that the degree of curvature changes at each point across any profile. The 'mean' position of the axes of movement is the reference position of the joint axis.

Almost all joints contain an element of translation – one joint surface sliding across the other – especially in joints which allow a large range of movement.

The shape of the articular surfaces

This is perhaps the most useful, and most descriptive classification of joints. Examples of these joint classifications are shown in figure 2.19.

Figure 2.19 Types of joints

Gliding joint between the navicular and second and third cuneiforms of the tarsus in the foot

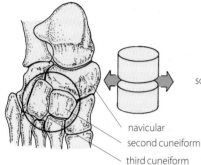

navicular
second cuneiform
third cuneiform

Ellipsoidal joint between radius and ulna and scaphoid and lunate bones of the carpus (wrist)

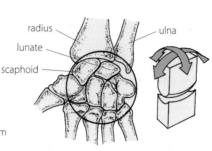

radius
lunate
scaphoid
ulna

Pivot joint between head of radius and radial notch of ulna

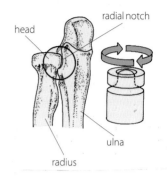

head
radial notch
ulna
radius

Plane joints have relatively flat articular surfaces. The movement is largely translatory as one articular surface slides or glides on the other (the carpal joints of the wrist and tarsal joints of the foot).

Ellipsoid joints are bi-axial joints formed by an oval convex surface and an elliptical concave surface (the joint between the distal end of the radius and the ulnar articular disc, and the proximal row of carpal bones at the wrist).

Condylar joints occur between two pairs of condyles. This is basically a uni-axial joint, in which the main movement occurs in one plane about a single axis. However, a smaller amount of movement occurs about a second axis, perpendicular to the first (the joint between the femoral condyles and the tibial condyles at the knee).

Pivot joints are uni-axial joints which consist of a central bony pivot surrounded by an osteo-ligamentous ring. Movement consists of rotation on a longitudinal axis about the pivot of the joint (the joint between the bony ring of the axis and the peg-like projection of the atlas in the neck and the superior radio-ulnar joint).

Hinge joint between trochlea of humerus and trochlear notch of ulna at the elbow

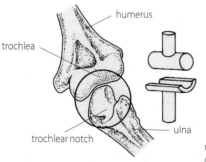

humerus
trochlea
trochlear notch
ulna

Saddle joint between trapezium of carpus (wrist) and metacarpal of thumb

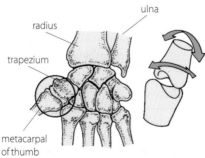

ulna
radius
trapezium
metacarpal of thumb

Ball-and-socket joint between head of the femur and acetabulum of the hipbone

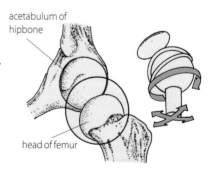

acetabulum of hipbone
head of femur

Hinge joints surfaces allow to-and-fro movement in one plane only. Usually these joints have very strong collateral ligaments situated at each side of the joint, to protect against abnormal movement in a different plane (the elbow joint between the hook-like projection of the proximal end of the ulna and the pulley-like lower end of the humerus).

Saddle joints are bi-axial joints, with concavo-convex opposing surfaces. Each surface is concave in one direction and convex at right angles to this (the joint between the proximal end of the first metacarpal and the distal surface of the trapezium or carpal at the base of the thumb).

Ball-and-socket joints are multi-axial joints in which a spherical head of one bone articulates with a cup-like concavity of the other (the joint between the spherical head of the femur and the cup-like acetabulum of the hip bone at the hip).

To complete this section, a few major joints will be described, with respect to their classification, structure and the movements which occur.

Shoulder joint

The shoulder joint is a synovial ball-and-socket joint between the spherical head of the humerus and the relatively shallow glenoid cavity of the scapula. Both surfaces are covered with hyaline cartilage, and the glenoid cavity is deepened by a fibro-cartilagenous rim, called the glenoid labrum. The joint is enclosed by a loose capsule, which is strengthened slightly in front by the gleno-humeral ligaments, and above by the coraco-humeral ligament.

Elbow joint

The elbow joint is a synovial hinge joint, between the trochlear notch of the ulna and the head of the radius inferiorly, and the trochlea and the capitulum of the humerus superiorly. The joint is surrounded by a capsule, which is strengthened medially by the ulnar collateral ligament and laterally by the radial collateral ligament.

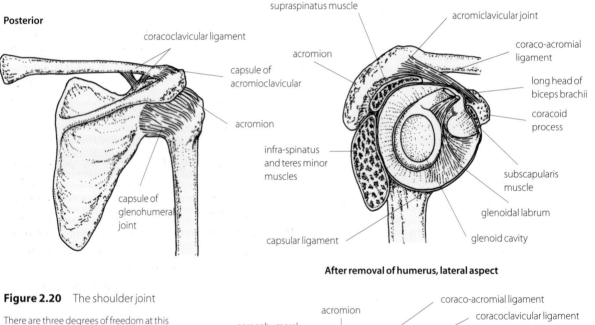

Posterior

supraspinatus muscle

acromiclavicular joint

coracoclavicular ligament

acromion

coraco-acromial ligament

capsule of acromioclavicular

long head of biceps brachii

acromion

coracoid process

infra-spinatus and teres minor muscles

capsule of glenohumeral joint

subscapularis muscle

glenoidal labrum

capsular ligament

glenoid cavity

After removal of humerus, lateral aspect

Figure 2.20 The shoulder joint

There are three degrees of freedom at this joint; the movements which occur at the shoulder joint are flexion, extension, abduction, adduction, medial rotation, lateral rotation and circumduction. Due to the relatively shallow glenoid cavity and the loose articular capsule, there is a large range of motion at the joint, but this, together with the fact that the gleno-humeral ligaments are not totally effective in strengthening the anterior part of the capsule, makes the joint prone to dislocation. The shoulder joint is the most commonly dislocated joint, and this injury often occurs in sport.

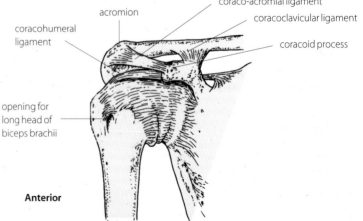

acromion

coraco-acromial ligament

coracoclavicular ligament

coracohumeral ligament

coracoid process

opening for long head of biceps brachii

Anterior

Figure 2.21 The elbow joint

The joint has one degree of freedom, allowing the movements of flexion and extension. The elbow joint is a very stable joint, but occasionally dislocation occurs in sports such as gymnastics.

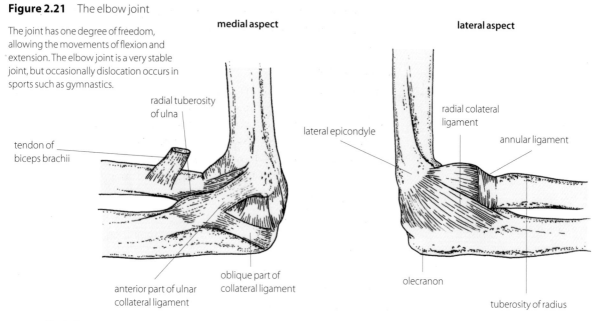

medial aspect

radial tuberosity of ulna

tendon of biceps brachii

anterior part of ulnar collateral ligament

oblique part of collateral ligament

lateral aspect

lateral epicondyle

radial colateral ligament

annular ligament

olecranon

tuberosity of radius

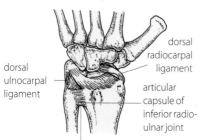

Posterior aspect

dorsal ulnocarpal ligament

dorsal radiocarpal ligament

articular capsule of inferior radio-ulnar joint

radial collateral ligament

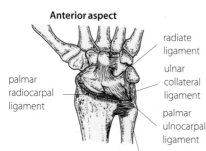

Anterior aspect

palmar radiocarpal ligament

radiate ligament

ulnar collateral ligament

palmar ulnocarpal ligament

capsular ligament

Figure 2.22 Carpals and metacarpals

There are two degrees of freedom at the wrist joint, allowing the movements of flexion, extension, radial deviation and ulnar deviation to occur. Overall movement at the wrist is increased by gliding movements which occur between the proximal and distal rows of carpal bones. The wrist is more likely to break (fracture) at the lower end of the radius or the scaphoid than to dislocate during falls on to the outstretched hand.

Wrist joint

The wrist joint is a synovial ellipsoid joint between the distal end of the radius and the articular disc which covers the distal end of the ulna superiorly, and the proximal row of carpal bones (scaphoid, lunate, triquetrum, pisiform). The joint is enclosed in an articular capsule, which is strengthened by medial and lateral collateral, and anterior and posterior ligaments.

Hip joint

The hip joint is a synovial ball-and-socket joint between the large spherical head of the femur, and the cup-shaped acetabulum of the hip bone. The acetabulum is further deepened by a fibrocartilagenous rim (the acetabular labrum). The joint is surrounded by an articular capsule, which is thickened substantially by the ilio-femoral and pubo-femoral ligaments anteriorly, and the ischio-femoral ligament posteriorly. The combination of the shape of the joint surfaces, the acetabular labrum and the strong capsule and ligaments makes the hip joint very stable.

Knee joint

The knee joint is probably the most complex joint in the body. It is basically a synovial condylar joint between the rounded femoral condyles at the distal end of femur, and the flattened tibial plateau on the superior surface of the tibial condyles. Additionally, within the knee joint, the patella (knee cap) articulates with the anterior surface of the femoral condyles. The relatively flat surface of the tibial articular surfaces is deepened by C-shaped fibrocartilagenous menisci attached to the outer margins of the articular surfaces, with the open borders towards the centre of the joint.

Figure 2.23   The hip joint

There are three degrees of freedom at the hip joint, the movements being flexion, extension, abduction, adduction, medial rotation, lateral rotation and circumduction. Due to the factors contributing to the stability of the joint, the range of motion at the hip joint is considerably less than that at the shoulder joint.

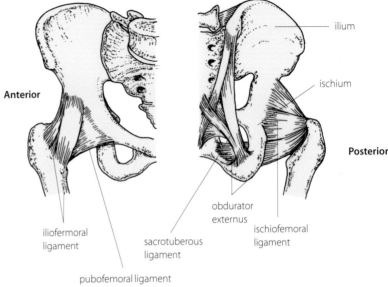

Anterior

ilium

ischium

Posterior

obdurator externus

iliofermoral ligament

sacrotuberous ligament

ischiofemoral ligament

pubofemoral ligament

Figure 2.24   The right knee joint

The knee joint is sometimes described as a 'modified' hinge joint. The main movements which occur at the knee are flexion and extension, which is characteristic of a hinge joint with one degree of freedom. However, when the knee is flexed, medial and lateral rotation are also possible (these movements cannot occur when the knee is in extension). In spite of the poor congruence of the articular surfaces, the knee joint is surprisingly stable, because of its strong ligaments and muscles. The most common injuries which occur at the knee joint are injuries to the ligaments (usually the medial collateral and/or the anterior cruciate) and the menisci (usually the medial meniscus).

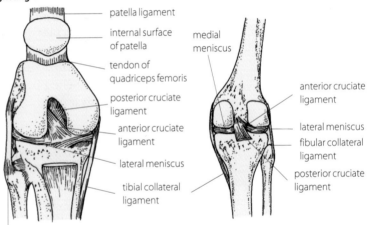

Anterior aspect. Patella and patellar ligament are turned upwards, femur is at right angles

Posterior aspect. Posterior part of capsule has been removed.

patella ligament

internal surface of patella

tendon of quadriceps femoris

posterior cruciate ligament

anterior cruciate ligament

lateral meniscus

tibial collateral ligament

capsule of tibiofibular joint

medial meniscus

anterior cruciate ligament

lateral meniscus

fibular collateral ligament

posterior cruciate ligament

Unlike the hip and the elbow, the shape of the joint surfaces does not provide much stability; the knee joint relies on the strong muscles and ligaments around the joint to maintain stability. On each side of the joint, the medial (tibial) and lateral (fibular) collateral ligaments prevent excessive lateral movement. In the centre of the joint the anterior and posterior cruciate ligaments prevent excessive antero-posterior gliding.

Ankle joint

The ankle joint is a synovial hinge joint between the mortice provided by the lower end of the tibia and the tibial malleolus, together with the fibular malleolus, and the superior surface and sides of the talus. The articular capsule is strengthened at the sides by the lateral (fibular) collateral ligament, and the medial (tibial or deltoid) ligament.

Medial aspect

medial ligament (deep part)

plantar calcaneocuboid ligament

medial ligament (superficial part)

calcaneocuboid ligament

plantar calcaneonavicular ligament

long plantar ligament

Lateral aspect

anterior tibiofibular ligament

posterior tibiofibular ligament

lateral malleolus

posterior talofibular ligament

anterior talofibular ligament

interosseus talocalcaneal ligament

calcaneofibular ligament

Figure 2.25 The ankle joint

There is one degree of freedom at the ankle joint, and the movements which occur are flexion (plantarflexion) and extension (dorsiflexion) Additional movements at the ankle region, inversion (turning the sole of the foot inwards) and eversion (turning the sole of the foot outwards) occur at the subtalar joint, and in small gliding movements at the tarsal joints.

The ankle joint is a relatively stable joint due to the shape of the articular surfaces and the strong ligaments. The most common injury to the ankle joint affects the lateral (fibular) collateral ligament. This is probably the most common single injury in sport, and is is usually referred to as a sprained ankle.

Intervertebral joints

There are two types of joints between adjacent vertebrae – cartilagenous joints between the bodies of the vertebrae, and synovial plane joints between the articular facets at the junction of the pedicles and laminae.

The joints between the vertebral bodies are in the form of a thick fibrocartilagenous intervertebral disc, which, especially in youth, has a high water content and is consequently quite compressible. Thus trunk flexion compresses the anterior part of the disc, trunk extension compresses the posterior part of the disc, and trunk side-flexion compresses the sides of the disc. Furthermore, the lattice-like arrangement of the fibrous elements of the disc permit small gliding (translatory) movements, and rotation to occur.

The joints between the facets (facetal joints) are small plane joints in which the upper facets of one vertebra articulate with the lower facets of the vertebra above. The facetal joints are enclosed by an articular capsule, and permit small gliding movements to occur; their function is to guide the movement occurring at the joint between the vertebral bodies, which they do by virtue of the direction of the articular surfaces.

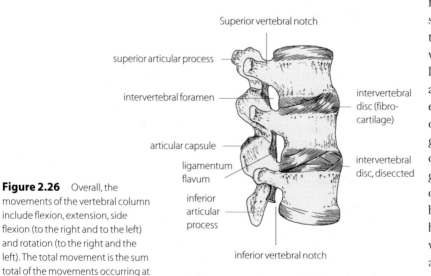

Superior vertebral notch

superior articular process

intervertebral foramen

articular capsule

ligamentum flavum

inferior articular process

inferior vertebral notch

intervertebral disc (fibro-cartilage)

intervertebral disc, disected

Figure 2.26 Overall, the movements of the vertebral column include flexion, extension, side flexion (to the right and to the left) and rotation (to the right and the left). The total movement is the sum total of the movements occurring at individual intervertebral joints.

SUMMARY

- Joints may be classified according to structure or function.
- Movement occurs in planes, about axes, which are at right angles to the planes.
- Movement in a sagittal plane occurs about a frontal axis.
  Movement in a frontal plane occurs about a sagittal axis.
- Movement in a horizontal plane occurs about a vertical axis.
- The most common joints in the body are the freely moveable synovial joints.
- All synovial joints have the same basic structure; the shape of the articular surfaces and the arrangement of ligaments determine the movements which occur at each joint.

Questions

1 Describe and explain the axes and planes of movement.
2 How may the joints of the body be classified (a) structurally (b) functionally?
3 What are the general features of a synovial (diarthrodial) joint? Describe and give examples of seven arrangements (shapes) of articulating surfaces in synovial joints. What movements can occur at each of these joints?
4 Compare and contrast the shoulder joint and the hip joint.
5 What determines the movements which occur in the vertebral column?

The nervous system

The nervous system has three basic functions:

- Sensory – the recording of certain changes (stimuli) both from the internal environment of the body (for example, stomach pain and discomfort) and from the external environment (for example, a blow from a hockey ball, or warmth from a fire).
- Integrative – the analysis of sensory information and consequently making the decision whether to store the information, or to respond to it.
- Motor – the response to stimuli, which may be by muscular action or by glandular secretion.

There are two principal divisions of the nervous system. The central nervous system (CNS) is made up of the brain and spinal cord. The peripheral nervous system is made up of the cranial nerves which arise from the brain and the spinal nerves which come from the spinal cord. The divisions of the nervous system may be compared to the axial and appendicular divisions of the skeletal system.

The peripheral nervous system is further divided into two subsystems. The somatic nervous system, is concerned mainly with receiving information from the skin, joints and muscles, and responding to these stimuli by action of the skeletal muscles. This activity is under conscious control, and is said to be voluntary. The autonomic nervous system (figure 2.27) receives information from the organs

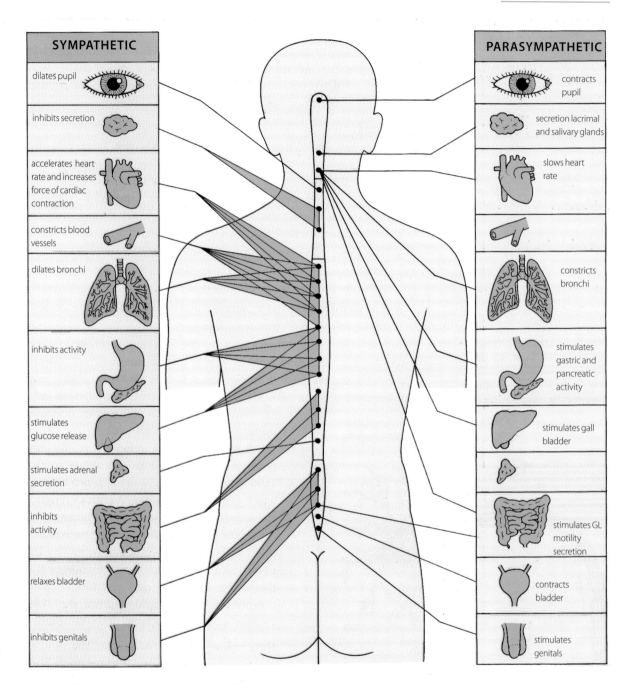

Figure 2.27   The autonomic nervous system

within the body (stomach, heart, intestines). It responds by sending impulses to the specialised muscle in the walls of these organs and to the glands.

This activity is not under conscious control, and is said to be involuntary. The autonomic nervous system is further divided into the sympathetic and parasympathetic branches, which in general tend to increase and decrease activity respectively.

Cellular structure of nervous tissue

Nervous tissue consists of two basic types of cell, the neuron which is responsible for the three basic functions of nervous tissue, and neuroglia which is essential for the support, maintenance and normal functioning of the neurons.

Neurons

Neurons consist of three parts: the cell body, the axon, and the dendrites.

- The **cell body** contains a neucleus, surrounded by cytoplasm which includes organelles (structures which are specialised for specific cellular activities) and neurofibrils, which provide shape and support for the cell.
- The **axon** is a long thin process coming from the cell body. It conveys nerve impulses from the cell body toward another neuron, muscle fibre or gland cell.
- The **dendrites** are short, tapered and highly branched processes of the cell body.

Neurons are responsible for most of the functions attributed to the nervous system. These include muscle activity, sensation, regulating glandular secretions and intellectual activities such as thinking and remembering. If the cell body of a mature neuron is injured, it has little capability for repair, as it does not normally undergo mitosis (division).

A nerve fibre is a general term for any neuronal process, but usually refers to the axon. A nerve is a bundle of many nerve fibres which travel along a common path to supply a structure or group of structures. For example, the sciatic nerve travels down the back of the thigh and into the lower leg to supply motor impulses to the muscles of the back of the thigh, the lower leg and the foot. It also transmits sensory impulses from the skin, muscles and joint structures of the same area.

Neuroglia

Neuroglial cells are found both in the central nervous system and the peripheral nervous system. In the CNS, they function to provide a supporting network, to produce a lipid and protein sheath around the axons, to protect the CNS from disease, to control the metabolism and levels of substances essential for transmission of nerve impulses, and to provide a lining for the ventricles (spaces that form cerebro-spinal fluid which bathes the brain and spinal cord).

Figure 2.28   The neuron

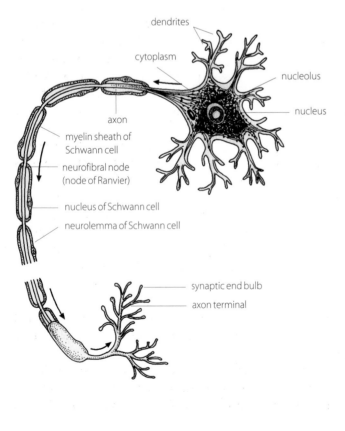

dendrites

cytoplasm

nucleolus

nucleus

axon

myelin sheath of Schwann cell

neurofibral node (node of Ranvier)

nucleus of Schwann cell

neurolemma of Schwann cell

synaptic end bulb

axon terminal

In the peripheral nervous system, specialised neuroglial cells (Schwann cells) produce a lipid and protein covering (the myelin sheath) for the axons. This protects the axon, and also determines the speed at which an impulse can travel along the axon. Myelinated fibres conduct more rapidly than unmyelinated fibres.

The presence of myelin gives the characteristic white colour to some areas of the brain and spinal cord (white matter), which indicates the aggregations of myelinated processes from several neurons. The grey matter represents the nerve cell bodies, or aggregates of unmyelinated processes. The cell bodies are concentrated on the surface of the brain, in specific areas (nuclei) deep in the brain, and in an H-shaped core in the spinal cord.

Gross structure of the nervous system

In functional terms, the nervous system consists of three parts – the brain, the spinal cord, and the peripheral nerves. At a simple level, the brain analyses, stores and processes information. The spinal cord functions primarily to transmit information from the periphery to the brain, and from the brain to the periphery, but by virtue of the presence of grey matter (cell bodies), is also capable of processing information from the periphery. The peripheral nerves function only to transmit information and are not involved in the processing element.

The brain contains both grey matter (cell bodies) and white matter (myelinated axons). The cell bodies receive information from other parts of the brain via the axons in the brain, and from the rest of the body via the axons in the spinal cord. The brain is one of the largest organs of the body, weighing about three pounds. It is mushroom-shaped, and is divided into four principal parts (the cerebrum, diencephalon, brain stem and cerebellum) which are concerned with the control of different functions and areas of the body.

The spinal cord is a solid cylindrical structure, which leaves the brain through the foramen magnum in the base of the skull. It consists of nerve cells (in the central H-shaped area) and nerve fibres (axons) which carry messages to and from all parts of the body and the brain (figure 2.29). Nerve fibres leave the spinal cord through the small foramina between the vertebrae (intervertebral foramina) to form the peripheral nerves. The nerve fibres (white matter) in the spinal cord are organised into groups or tracts. These may be ascending (carrying messages to the brain) or descending (carrying messages from the brain).

The peripheral (or spinal) nerves consist of groups of sensory and motor fibres which carry messages to and from the muscles, glands and organs of the body.

The endings of the axons which receive the information (stimuli) are called receptors, and the axons which transmit the information to the brain are called afferent neurons. If the information received in

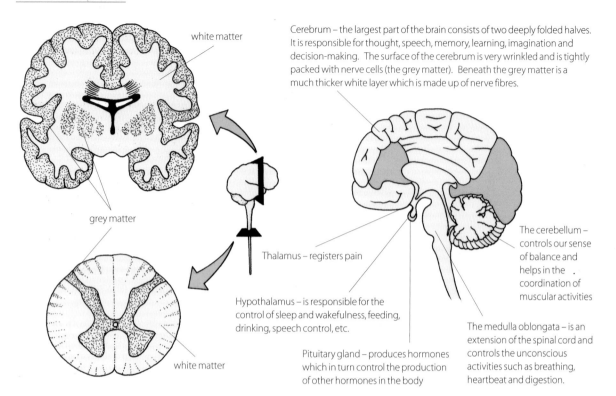

Figure 2.29 The brain

The right side of the cerebrum controls the activities and movements of the left side of the body and vice versa.

There are three types of receptors or sense organs, depending on where they are found.

- **Exteroceptors** receive information from outside the body (for example, eyes and ears).
- **Interoceptors** receive information from the organs inside the body (for example, the lungs and digestive system).
- **Proprioceptors** receive information from the muscles and joint structures to provide knowledge of the relative positions of the different parts of the body. Proprioceptors allow us to move our limbs accurately without having to watch them.

the cerebral grey matter requires action, impulses are sent via the axons in the spinal cord to muscle, gland or organ, which are known as the effector organs. The axons which transmit the information to the effectors are called efferent neurons.

Information processing by the central nervous system can take place at different levels. Lower regions of the brain, such as the brain stem, diencephalon and cerebellum control most subconscious activities of the body, such as regulation of blood pressure, respiratory rate, posture and balance, and muscle tone. At higher levels, the cerebrum integrates conscious activities, processes and stores information (learning and memory), provides circuits for abstract thought processes and initiates and controls voluntary movements.

Reflex actions

Reflexes are fast, predictable, automatic responses to changes in the environment. They can occur in the brain (cranial reflexes), in the internal organs of the body (visceral reflexes) where the autonomic nervous system operates at a subconscious level, and in the musculo-skeletal system (somatic reflexes), which involve contraction of skeletal muscles. Reflex actions are a form of homeostasis in which the body automatically responds to protect itself from dangerous or potentially harmful situations, and to prepare the body for change. Examples include blinking in response to a foreign object coming close to the eye, withdrawing your hand from a hot plate, and shunting blood away from the digestive system to the muscles to prepare for exercise.

Figure 2.30   The spinal reflex arc

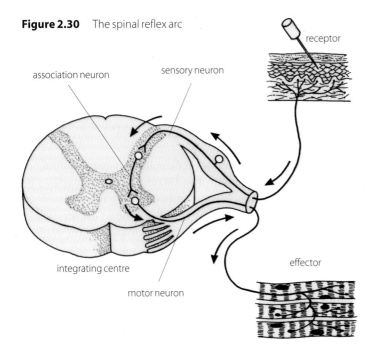

association neuron

sensory neuron

receptor

integrating centre

motor neuron

effector

The simplest example of a reflex involves the spinal reflex arc. A reflex arc includes five functional components:

1   A receptor responds to a specific stimulus (for example, the hand touching a hot plate).
2   Impulses are conducted from the receptor to the axon terminals of a sensory neuron located in the grey matter of the spinal cord.
3   The impulses are relayed to an integrating centre (the spinal cord) where the sensory neuron links with a motor neuron at a synapse.
4   Impulses pass through the synapse to a motor neuron, and along its axon to the part of the body which will respond (in this case to the muscles of the arm).
5   The muscles of the arm, the effector, contract, causing the arm to be withdrawn from the hot plate.

SUMMARY

- The nervous system has sensory, integrative and motor functions.
- The nervous system has two major divisions – the central nervous system (the brain and the spinal cord) and the peripheral nervous system. The peripheral system is further divided into the somatic and the autonomic nervous systems.
- The essential cell of the nervous system is the neuron.
- In functional terms, the nervous system consists of three parts- the brain, the spinal cord and the peripheral nerves.
- Reflex actions are fast, predictable and automatic responses to changes in the environment.

Questions

1   What are the three basic functions of the nervous system?
2   Describe the divisions of the nervous system.
3   What are the functions of the brain, the spinal cord and the peripheral nerves?
4   Name the three types of receptors. What information does each receive?
5   Describe a spinal reflex arc, giving an example.

The muscular system

Although the bones and joints provide leverage and the framework of the body, they cannot move the body by themselves. Movement results from alternate contraction and relaxation of muscles. When muscles contract and shorten, they produce movement. This measurement is only possible if at the same time appropriate muscles relax. Muscles are also involved in the support and normal functioning of various organs within the body.

There are three different types of muscle, which differ in structure, location and type of control.

- **Skeletal muscle** is attached to the skeleton, and is the means by which movement occurs. Skeletal muscle is also termed striated muscle because of the transverse light and dark bands which are visible under microscopic examination. It can be made to contract and relax under conscious control, and so is described as voluntary muscle.

- **Cardiac muscle** which forms most of the heart, is also striated, but is not under conscious control and is termed involuntary. Contraction of cardiac muscle is controlled by a pacemaker system within the heart, which may be influenced by hormones and neurotransmitters to either speed up or slow down the rate of contraction.

- **Smooth muscle** is located in the walls of hollow internal structures such as the stomach, intestines, blood vessels and bronchioles. This muscle is non-striated, and under involuntary control, and may also be influenced by hormones and neurotransmitters.

Functions of muscle tissue

By contraction (either sustained or phasic) and relaxation, muscle tissue fulfils three functions.

Movement

Through their attachment to bones, skeletal muscles can contract to produce movement, or relax to allow movement to occur. Although less obvious, cardiac muscle contracts and relaxes to produce movement, the heart beat. Smooth muscle will produce movement to transmit foodstuffs through the gastro-intestinal tract.

Stabilisation

Through sustained contractions, skeletal muscle can maintain the body in a stable position, for example, standing and sitting. Smooth muscle can produce sustained contractions to maintain or stabilise organ volume. For example, the temporary storage of food in the stomach occurs by contraction of the smooth muscle sphincter (valve) at the exit.

Heat generation

Contraction of skeletal muscle may perform work, a by-product of which is heat, which is used to maintain body temperature. It is thought that up to 85% of body heat is generated by skeletal muscle contractions.

Structure of skeletal muscle

As skeletal muscle is concerned primarily with voluntary activity and movement, this type of muscle only will be described in this section.

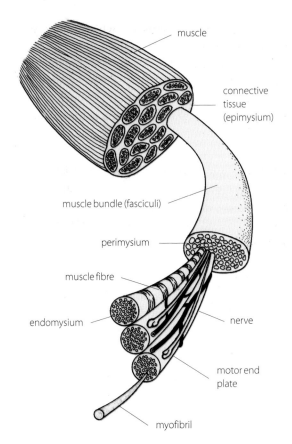

Figure 2.31 Structure of the skeletal muscle

Within the muscle, bundles of muscle fibres (10 to 100 in number) form fasciculi, which are also surrounded by connective tissue and the perimysium. Each individual muscle fibre is surrounded by the endomysium.

These connective tissue structures are strong and relatively inelastic, and form a supporting network for the muscle. They extend beyond the contractile part of the muscle to combine to form tendons which attach the muscle to bone. Usually the tendon is cord-like in shape, but when it forms a broad, flat sheet of connective tissue, it is called an aponeurosis.

Basically, a skeletal muscle consists of muscle tissue (the contractile elements), connective tissue which surrounds and supports the muscle tissue, together with nerves which carry information to and from the muscle, and blood vessels which supply nutrition and remove waste products.

Working from the largest units, muscles are organised into functional groups, which when working together, produce a specific movement (or movements). For example, the hamstring muscles, which are three in number and are situated on the posterior aspect of the hip and thigh, can flex the knee joint, and extend the hip joint. Working individually, the muscles can produce additional movements: biceps femoris (the lateral hamstring) laterally rotates the flexed knee, while semitendinosis and semimembranosis (the medial hamstrings) medially rotate the flexed knee.

Muscle groups are surrounded by a dense, irregular connective tissue, called the deep fascia. Each individual muscle is surrounded by a connective tissue sheath called the epimysium.

The muscle fibre is the basic cellular unit of muscle, and because of its long cylindrical shape, contains several nuclei positioned at the periphery of the cell, and mitochondria arranged in rows throughout the muscle fibre. When examined under a microscope, each muscle fibre can be seen to consist of smaller units called myofibrils, which extend lengthwise within the muscle fibre. They are characterised by alternating light and dark bands (cross-striations).

Within the myofibrils are three types of smaller structures known as filaments. Two of the filaments consist of contractile proteins, myosin (the thicker of the two filaments) and actin (thin filaments), which lie side

Figure 2.32 Electron micrograph of sarcomere

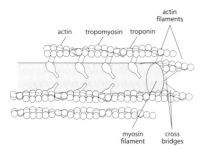

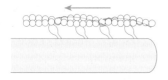

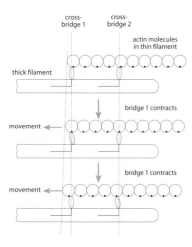

Figure 2.33 Arrangement of actin and myosin

ATP ————————- ADP +

P + energy for contraction

by side. The degree of overlap of these filaments causes the characteristic cross-striations of the myofibril, and the activity of these filaments sliding past each other results in the shortening and lengthening of the muscle. Additionally, elastic filaments are found in the myofibrils. These are thought to stabilise the position of the protein elements, and to assist in returning the muscle to its resting length following stretching.

Contraction of muscle

Originally it was thought that muscle shortened through a folding process, rather like closing an accordian. In the 1950s, Jean Hanson and Hugh Huxley proposed the sliding filament theory of muscle contraction.

The myosin filaments contain molecules which consist of a twisted tail section and two projecting heads (cross bridges), which extend towards the actin filaments. The tails form the core of the myosin filament, and the heads project all around the filament in a spiral fashion. The actin filaments are arranged parallel to and around the myosin filaments, and also consist of several molecules, arranged in a chain-like appearance. Each actin molecule contains a myosin binding site to which a cross bridge from the myosin filament can attach itself (Figure 2.33).

When the muscle is relaxed, the free ends of the actin filaments are separated. During muscle contraction, the myosin cross bridges attach to the binding sites on the actin filaments, and pull the actin filaments towards the centre of the myosin filament (the H zone). As the cross bridges pull on the actin filaments, the free ends of the actin filaments may meet or even overlap in the H zone. As the actin filaments slide towards each other, the Z discs to which they are attached also move towards each other, thus shortening each sarcomere or contractile unit. The sliding of filaments and shortening of the sarcomeres cause shortening of the whole muscle fibre, and ultimately the entire muscle (Figure 2.34).

This process is under the control of the cerebral cortex via a motor nerve which enters the muscle at the motor point. From the motor point, nerve fibres pass to each muscle fibre, and make contact at the motor end plate. When a motor nerve fibre delivers a stimulus or action potential to a skeletal muscle fibre at the motor end plate, the action potential quickly spreads over the entire sarcolemma and towards the interior of the fibre. The result of this action potential is to release calcium ions (Ca^{2+}) from the sarcoplasmic reticulum. When a muscle is relaxed (not contracting), the concentration of calcium ions is low, but for contraction to occur, calcium ions must bind to troponin molecules on the actin filaments in order for the myosin binding sites to be freed for cross bridge formation with the myosin filaments.

In addition to requiring calcium, muscle contraction also requires energy. The myosin heads are moveable, and the energy to produce this movement is provided by ATP (Adenosine triphosphate). ATP

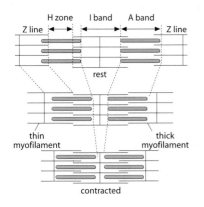

Figure 2.34 Structural rearrangement of actin and myosin filaments at rest and during contraction

Figure 2.35 Action of the sarcomere

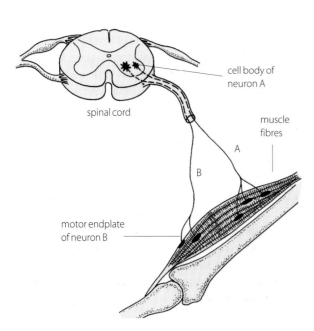

attaches to ATP-binding sites on the myosin heads, which activates movement, and the myosin heads can attach themselves to the freed sites on the actin filaments, thus forming the cross bridges. Once this occurs, myosin can act as an enzyme to split ATP into ADP (Adenosine diphosphate) plus P (phosphate) with the simultaneous release of energy to make the myosin heads swivel toward the centre of the A band and move the actin filaments in that direction.

Each time a myosin head moves the actin filament toward the centre of the A-band, hundreds of other myosin heads throughout the myofibril are making other attachments with actin filaments to assist in movement. Simultaneously, hundreds more are released from their attachment sites and are preparing to reattach at other sites to further pull the actin filaments toward the centre of the A-bands throughout the myofibril. This repetitive attachment, release and re-attachment of myosin heads to actin filaments is called cross bridge cycling, and because of the phased nature of the activity, the muscle does not have to relax for the cross bridge cycling to occur.

Types of muscle fibre

Skeletal muscles are adapted by heredity and activity for the work they must perform. For example, those leg muscle fibres which are involved in prolonged contractions to maintain the body in the upright posture have different characteristics to those involved in a 100-metre sprint. The differences in characteristics are classified according to the speed with which the fibres respond to an electrical stimulus. Three fibre types have been identified:

- **Slow twitch oxidative (type I) fibres** – these fibres contain large amounts of myoglobin (which releases oxygen in the fibre), many mitochondria (which generate ATP) and a concentrated capillary network. They split ATP at a slow rate and so have a slow contraction velocity. They are red in appearance, have a high resistance to fatigue, and are found in large numbers in the postural muscles (for example, in the posterior muscles of the neck which hold the head upright)

- **Fast twitch oxidative (type II A) fibres** – these fibres contain large amounts of myoglobin, many mitochondria and many capillaries. Like type I fibres, these fibres are red in appearance, and have a high capacity to generate ATP by oxidative processes. However, they split ATP at a rapid rate, and consequently have a rapid contraction velocity. They are relatively resistant to fatigue, but not to the same extent as type I fibres. Sprinters tend to have a high proportion of type II A fibres in their leg muscles.

● **Fast twitch glycolytic (type II B) fibres** – these fibres have a low myoglobin content, relatively few mitochondria, and relatively few capillaries. They contain large amounts of glycogen, which permits generation of ATP by anaerobic (without oxygen) processes (glycolysis). They are white in appearance, split ATP at a fast rate to produce rapid, strong contractions, but fatigue easily. The muscles of the arm contain many of these fibres.

Neural control of muscle strength

Obviously, not all activities which we perform require the same amount of muscular force. For example, it requires less force to lift a sheet of paper from a desk, than to lift a weighted bar-bell. The neuromuscular system has the capacity to produce just the required force, and so avoid at best, wildly excessive movements and at worst, potential injury. There are two ways in which the strength of muscle contraction may be varied. The total number of motor units, and hence the total number of muscle fibres, may be varied. The frequency with which a given number of motor units is activated may also vary.

Motor units

A motor unit consists of a motor nerve cell (neuron) that originates in the grey matter of the spinal cord, and all of the muscle fibres it supplies. The number of muscle fibres which may be triggered by a single neuron can vary from as few as five (in muscles which require very precise control, as in the eye muscles) to 1000 or more in the large muscles (such as the hip muscles) which do not require the same degree of control.

All the muscle fibres within any motor unit are the same fibre type (Type I, Type II A, or Type II B). They are usually located throughout the muscle and not found close together. Thus, each muscle will consist of a variety of fibre types, the relative distribution of which will depend on the function of the muscle. The motor neuron which supplies a motor unit determines to a large extent the fibre type of the fibres. Normally, slow twitch units are activated before fast twitch units, as the slow units are smaller and more easily activated.

When the motor neuron of a motor unit activates the muscle fibres within the unit, all the muscle fibres of that unit will contract, and they will contract maximally. This is the 'all or none law' which states that under a given set of conditions, the muscle fibres within a motor unit will contract maximally or not at all.

When this is applied to a muscle as a whole, it can be seen that the force or strength output of the muscle will depend on the size of the motor unit, and the number of motor units activated. Thus, activation of a small number of small motor units will produce less force than a large number of large motor units. The neuromuscular system has the ability to activate precisely the correct number, size and type of motor units for any given task.

Frequency of stimulation of motor units

All motor units do not fire at the same time except under conditions of maximal stimulation, and even in these conditions an inhibitory safety mechanism may come into play. This may prevent the simultaneous contraction of all fibres within a muscle to reduce damage to the muscle.

During sub-maximal contractions, some motor units are active, and some are inactive. Furthermore, the units may switch roles, so that previously inactive units may become active, and previously active units may become inactive. This exchange of roles means that fatigue can be avoided by limiting the duration of activity in any motor unit. Consequently, by shunting of activity among groups of motor units (asynchronous contraction), a muscle can maintain a state of contraction for a considerable period of time, depending on the level or intensity of contraction.

If the rate of firing of motor units is increased, the strength of contraction of the muscle increases. This is because the rest period between contractions is reduced, so more units are active simultaneously.

Smooth voluntary contraction

When skeletal muscle is stimulated briefly with an external electrical impulse, it responds by a single twitch, that is, it contracts briefly before returning to its resting state. If a second impulse is applied some time after the first, the muscle will again respond by a single twitch. Obviously, a series of single twitches of muscular activity will not provide the smooth controlled contraction which is essential for normal voluntary movement.

The internal stimulation of skeletal muscle by nerve works in much the same way. A single impulse carried along a motor nerve to the muscle fibres it supplies will result in a single twitch, and a second spaced impulse will have the same effect. However, if the second impulse is applied immediately following the first, before the muscle fibres have time to return to their resting state, a slightly larger contraction (or twitch) will result. This is known as wave (temporal) summation. If a succession of impulses are applied to the muscle fibres in quick succession, the twitches will become 'fused', and a continuous tetanic contraction results. A frequency of approximately 50 stimuli per

Figure 2.36 The frequency of stimulation of motor units

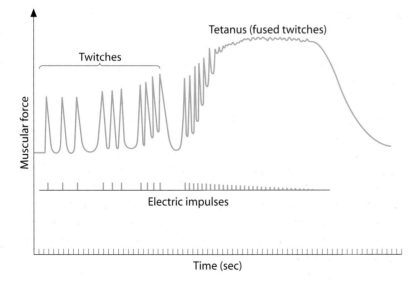

second is required to produce a tetanic contraction, which will last as long as the stimulus is applied.

If a tetanic contraction is maintained, the muscle fibres will eventually become fatigued, and unable to maintain the contraction. The phased (asynchronous) stimulation of different motor units in a muscle means that only the number of motor units required to perform the activity are active at any one time. As those motor units begin to fatigue, others are stimulated to take over. The co-ordination of this activity is such that the muscle contraction throughout the activity remains smooth, with no evidence of individual 'twitches'.

Excitatory and inhibitory neurons

All neurons send signals to each other by transmitting small amounts of chemical substances called neurotransmitters. Some of these neurotransmittors are excitatory and facilitate activity in the neuron, and others are inhibitory and reduce activity. Thus, the amount of activity in any neuron depends on the balance between the excitatory and inhibitory neurotransmittors. If the level of excitatory neurotransmittors is greater, the neuron will fire (and obey the all or none law). If the level of inhibitory neurotransmitters is greater, the level of activity in the neuron will decrease, and it will remain inactive.

While excitatory activity is obviously important to produce movement, inhibitatory activity is equally important to prevent excessive activity and over-reaction to the internal and external environment. For example, it is important that excitatory neurons act to make us pull a foot away from a painful stimulus such as that provided by standing on a nail. If we had the same response to everything which stimulated our feet, we would be unable to stand, as we would be constantly pulling our feet away from the ground!

The functional contact between two neurons or between a neuron and an effector organ (muscle or gland) is called a synapse. Certain synapses can modify the quantity of neurotransmitter released at other synapses. Presynaptic facilitation increases the amount of neurotransmitter released, whereas presynaptic inhibition decreases it.

When the amount of neurotransmitter released at a synapse by a single neuron is insufficient to cross the synapse, no activity will result. However, if the same amount of neurotransmitter is released from several neurons at the same synapse, the total amount may be sufficient to cross the synapse and produce activity. This build-up of neurotransmitter from several neurons is known as spatial summation.

Central modifiers of muscular force

The idea for a complex movement originates in the association areas of the cerebral cortex. The planning of the pattern of the activation of the motor units required to perform the movement involves other areas of the brain, namely the basal ganglia and the cerebellum, which are concerned with co-ordination. When the movement pattern has been programmed, the motor area of the cerebral cortex receives the appropriate information. This enables the movement to be started by sending signals via the motor nerves to the motor units of the muscles which will carry out the movement.

Peripheral modifiers of muscular force

A sophisticated feedback system is present in muscles and joints. This will provide information on the position of joints and degree of contraction, and link this information back to higher centres to enable modifications to be made to movement patterns if required.

The appreciation of the relative position of the limbs in space, and of how muscles are contracting is known as the kinaesthetic sense. This sense is obviously of vital importance in all human movements, but especially those involved in skills such as tumbling, diving and pole vaulting. A failure of kinaesthetic sense could easily result in severe injury or death. In general it is accepted that athletes who train regularly have a more highly developed kinaesthetic sense than those who do not exercise regularly.

Muscle spindles

Changes in the length of muscles and the rate of change in muscle length are sensed by receptors called muscle spindles. The spindles are situated among the muscle fibres. They are covered with connective tissue which is integral with that covering the regular (extrafusal) muscle fibres. Thus, if the muscle is stretched or shortened, the muscle spindle also is stretched, or shortened.

Inside the muscle spindle are a small number (2 – 12) of specialised muscle fibres, known as intrafusal fibres. The ends of these are capable of contracting and altering the length of the muscle spindle. The central part of the intrafusal fibre is sensitive to stretch. This central portion can be stretched by two actions. Firstly, if the extrafusal fibres (the main muscle) is stretched, due to the connective tissue attachments, the intrafusal fibres will also be stretched. Secondly, if the ends of the intrafusal fibres are contracted and shortened, a pull or stretch will be exerted on the central portion. There are two sets of sensory nerve endings supplying the central part of the intrafusal fibres The primary sensory ending senses not only stretch, but also the velocity of the stretch. The secondary sensory endings sense only stretch. The contractile ends of the intrafusal muscle fibres are supplied by gamma motor neurons. The operation of the muscle spindle will be explained in relation to the stretch reflex.

Figure 2.37 Muscle spindle

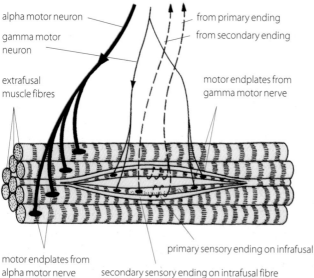

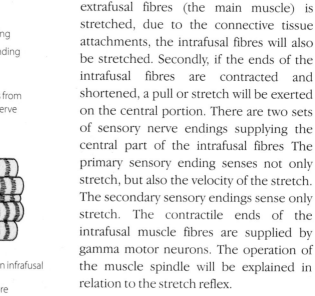

alpha motor neuron

gamma motor neuron

extrafusal muscle fibres

from primary ending

from secondary ending

motor endplates from gamma motor nerve

motor endplates from alpha motor nerve

primary sensory ending on infrafusal

secondary sensory ending on intrafusal fibre

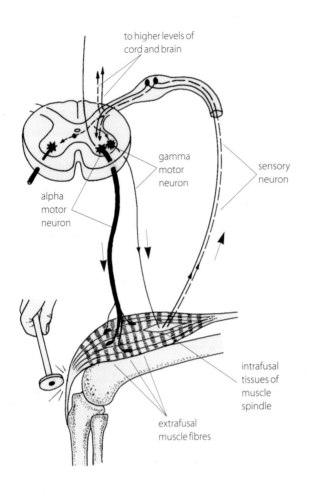

to higher levels of
cord and brain

gamma
motor
neuron

sensory
neuron

alpha
motor
neuron

intrafusal
tissues of
muscle
spindle

extrafusal
muscle fibres

Figure 2.38   The stretch reflex

The stretch reflex

If a muscle is suddenly stretched, the muscle almost instantaneously contracts to resist the stretch. This is a reflex action, and operates at the level of the spinal cord. Perhaps the most common example of the stretch reflex is the knee jerk, which is the test in which the patellar tendon is tapped by a reflex hammer. As the hammer strikes the patellar tendon, the quadriceps muscle is rapidly stretched. The stretch of the extrafusal fibres is transmitted via the connective tissue to the intrafusal fibres of the muscle spindle. The central portions of the intrafusal fibres are stretched, and the primary and secondary sensory endings are stimulated. Excitatory impulses are sent from the muscle spindle to the alpha motor neurons in the spinal cord. These neurons stimulate the extrafusal fibres of the same muscle (quadriceps) to contract, thus relieving the stretch. At the same time, inhibitory impulses are transmitted to the antagonistic muscles (the hamstrings, which produce the opposite movement) to cause them to relax to allow the movement to occur (reciprocal inhibition).

The contraction of the extrafusal fibres also relieves the stretch on the intrafusal fibres of the muscle spindle. Thus the stimulus to the sensory nerve endings is removed, and so the excitatory impulses to the spinal cord, and to the alpha motor neurons cease. The muscle relaxes. What is seen is that immediately after the tendon is tapped, the knee jerks rapidly into a few degrees of extension, and then returns to its original position.

This reflex is a protective mechanism, and occurs only in response to rapid stretch. Most muscle stretches are much less rapid. Consequently, they do not stimulate the primary sensory endings of the spindle, and a reflex contraction of the muscle does not occur. This is important, as there are many circumstances in which contraction of a muscle which is being stretched is undesirable, for example, during static stretching exercises for improving flexibility.

The gamma motor system

Small motor neurons called gamma motor neurons supply the intrafusal fibres of the muscle spindle. When stimulated, they cause the intrafusal fibres to contract. The primary and secondary sensory endings in the central part of the muscle spindle are stimulated only by stretch. Therefore, if the extrafusal fibres of the muscle contract,

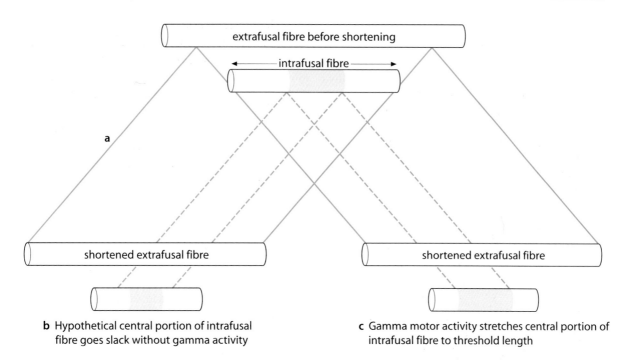

a

extrafusal fibre before shortening

intrafusal fibre

shortened extrafusal fibre

shortened extrafusal fibre

b Hypothetical central portion of intrafusal fibre goes slack without gamma activity

c Gamma motor activity stretches central portion of intrafusal fibre to threshold length

Figure 2.39 The gamma motor system

tension will be removed from the spindle, and the sensory endings will cease to fire. In this situation, the gamma motor neurons cause contraction of the intrafusal fibres. Thus a situation of stretch is created on the central part of the spindle, and the sensory nerve endings are stimulated. This in turn can link through the spinal cord to the alpha motor neurons, then to the muscle. This results in increased strength of contraction of the extrafusal fibres.

The ability of the intrafusal fibres to shorten means that the muscle spindle can adapt to any length of the extrafusal fibres. It will also remain in a state of readiness to register and respond to changes in length and speed of contraction.

Golgi tendon organs

Golgi tendon organs are peripheral sensory receptors located at the junctions of muscle and tendon. They are sensitive primarily to contractile force, although extreme stretch of muscle can also cause these receptors to fire. Their function is inhibitory. Increased activity of the Golgi tendon organs results in decreased strength of contraction of the muscle.

These tendon organs register the level of tension, and relay the information back to the spinal cord and brain so that the necessary adjustments in tension may be made. Increased tension in the muscle results in an increase in inhibitory stimuli to flow from the tendon organ receptors to the alpha motor neurons. Subsequently, the inhibitory stimuli flow to the muscle where they reduce the strength of contraction.

Figure 2.40 Golgi tendon organs

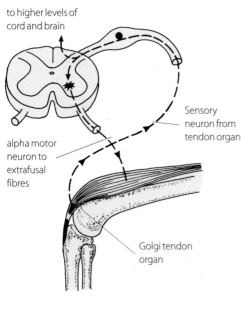

to higher levels of cord and brain

Sensory neuron from tendon organ

alpha motor neuron to extrafusal fibres

Golgi tendon organ

The Golgi tendon organs may be regarded as a safety mechanism which protects against the development of excessive muscle force. This force may cause damage to the muscle, or detach the tendon from its bony or muscular attachment. It also functions to feed back information about force levels in the muscle to the central nervous system.

Reduced levels of activity in the Golgi tendon organs will cause an increase in strength of muscular contraction. It is thought that strength training may reduce (that is, inhibit) the sensitivity of the Golgi tendon organs. Thus the inhibitory impulses are reduced and the amount of force increased.

Muscles and movement

Skeletal muscles produce movement by exerting force on tendons. Tendons in turn pull on bones or other structures such as skin. Most muscles cross at least one joint, and are attached to the articulating bones which form the joint. When a muscle or group of muscles contract and shorten, one articulating bone is drawn towards the other. The two articulating bones do not usually move equally. One tends to remain relatively fixed, and the other moves towards it. The 'fixed' bone is usually the proximal bone. For example, the radius and ulna usually move towards the humerus when the elbow is bent. The muscle attachments to the 'fixed' bone are called the origins. The muscle attachments to the distal moving bone are called the insertions. When the bones move in the opposite manner the muscles are said to be working with reversed origin and insertion. An example is when the humerus moves towards the radius and ulna as in a 'chin up' or in climbing a rope.

Lever systems

In producing body movement, bones act as levers, and joints as fulcrums for these levers. Levers are categorised into three types according to the relationship of the positions of the fulcrum, the effort (the point at which the force acts to produce the movement), and the resistance (the weight of the part of the body to be moved).

- **First class levers** – the fulcrum is between the effort and the resistance (like a see-saw).
- **Second class levers** – the fulcrum is at one end, the effort is at the other end, and the resistance is between them (like a wheel-barrow).
- **Third class levers** – the fulcrum is at one end, the resistance is at the opposite end and the effort is between them. (like lifting a drink in your hand by bending your elbow).

Muscles attached close to the fulcrum (joint) of a lever system will produce greater range and speed of movement. Muscles attached at a distance from the joint will produce greater force.

Examples of the application of lever systems within the body are illustrated in figure 2.41.

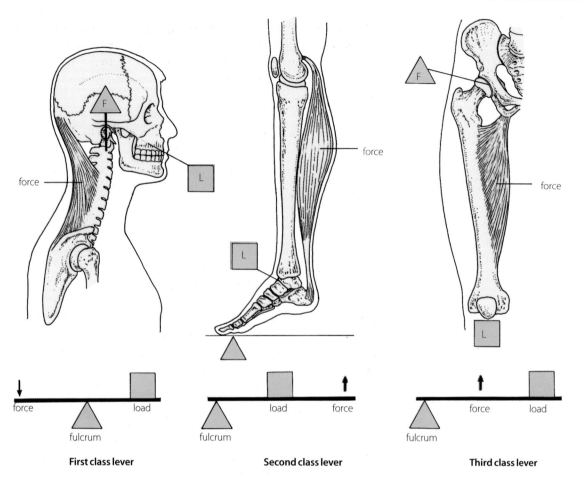

First class lever

Second class lever

Third class lever

Figure 2.41 Lever systems

- The muscles which produce the desired action are called the agonists or prime movers.
- The muscles which oppose the action are called the antagonists. The antagonists must relax and lengthen to allow the movement to occur.
- The muscles which stabilise the bone of origin of the agonists are called the fixators.
- The muscles which prevent unwanted movement and improve the efficiency of the agonists are called the synergists.

Arrangement of fasciculi

There are several patterns of the arrangement of fasciculi (groups of muscle fibres) within muscles, which determine the strength and range of muscle contraction. Muscles in which the fasciculi are arranged in a long strap-like fashion are capable of producing large ranges of movement. Muscles which contain short fasciculi arranged in a pennate (feather-like) fashion are capable of exerting great force, but over a smaller range of motion.

Group action of muscles

Skeletal muscles work together in groups to produce movement, and tend to be arranged in opposing pairs. Thus the muscles around a ball-and-socket joint (hip, shoulder) will be arranged into flexors/extensors, abductors/adductors and medial rotators/lateral rotators. The co-ordinated activity of all groups of muscles around a joint is essential to produce purposeful movement.

An example of how group action of muscles operates is when you make a fist. The agonists are the finger flexors, the antagonists are the finger extensors, the fixators are the muscles passing from the upper arm and shoulder which stabilise the forearm, and the synergists are the wrist extensors which prevent the wrist from flexing. To illustrate

Figure 2.42   Arrangement of fasciculi

Marking	Description	Example
Parallel	Fasciculi are parallel with longitudinal axis of muscle and finish at either end in flat tendons	Sartorius muscle 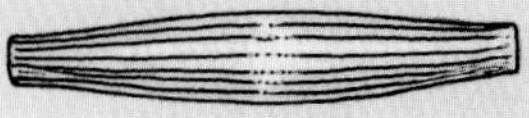
Fusiform	Fasciculi are nearly parallel with longitudinal axis of muscle and finish at either end in flat tendons, but muscle tapers towards tendons where the diameter is less than that of the belly.	Digastric muscle 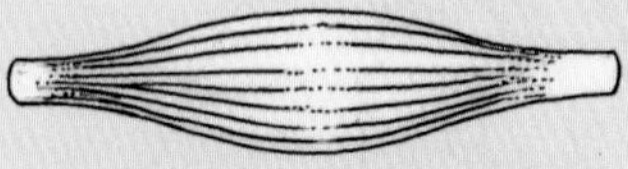
Pennate	Fasciculi are short in relation to muscle length and the tendon extends nearly the entire length of the muscle	
Unipennate	Fasciculi are arranged on only one side of tendon.	Extensor digitorum longus muscle 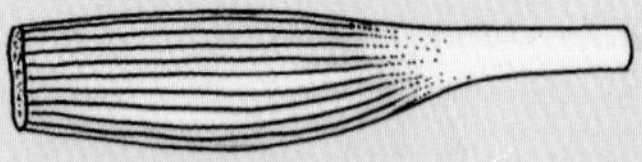
Bipennate	Fasciculi are arranged on both side of a centrally positioned tendon	Rectus femoris muscle 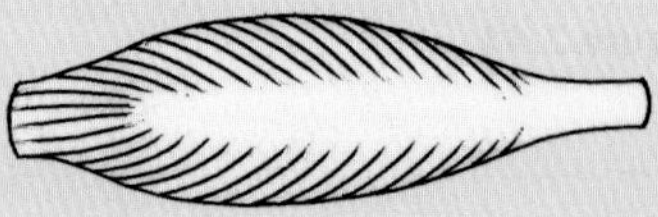
Multipennate	Fasciculi attach obliquely from many directions to several tendons	Deltoid muscle 
Circular	Fasciculi are arranged in a circular pattern and enclose an orifice (opening)	Orbicularis oris muscle 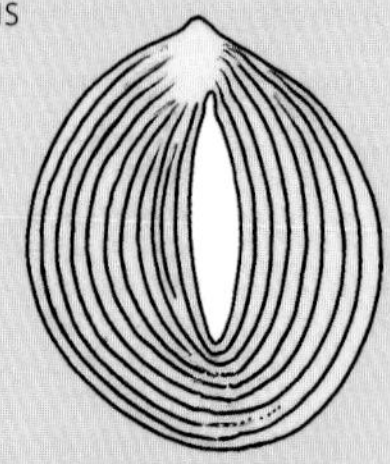

the importance of the synergists in this case, flex your hand at the wrist, and note how difficult it is to make a fist in this position. Extend your wrist and note the difference.

Types of muscle action

When a muscle contracts, it can shorten, remain the same length, or lengthen. In general terms, when a muscle shortens, it produces a movement, when it lengthens it controls movement, and when it remains the same, it stabilises.

When a muscle alters its length, either to shorten or to lengthen, the contraction is said to be isotonic. An isotonic contraction which shortens is called concentric and an isotonic contraction which lengthens is called eccentric. For example, when you bend your elbow to lift a weight, the elbow flexors are working concentrically; when you lower the weight, the elbow flexors are working eccentrically. If this eccentric activity did not occur, the weight would fall in an uncontrolled manner, which is potentially dangerous. You can demonstrate this by watching and feeling the biceps muscle as you lift and lower a weight such as a heavy book.

When a muscle contracts but does not lengthen or shorten, the contraction is called isometric. An example of isometric muscle work is when you push or pull against a structure which will not move, or hold a weight steadily.

A relatively recent addition to the types of muscle action is the concept of speed of movement produced by the muscle activity. Isokinetic muscle contraction occurs when the speed of movement produced by the muscle activity is constant throughout the movement. Obviously, isometric contraction may be viewed as a form of isokinetic muscle contraction, when the speed of movement produced is zero degrees/second (because no movement occurs). Apart from isometric contraction, other speeds of isokinetic muscle contraction are only possible using specific equipment (isokinetic dynamometers) which can control the speed of movement produced by a group of muscles at a joint throughout the entire range of movement. The speed of movement can be controlled to between 30 and 360 degrees per second, depending on the specific equipment.

To complete this section, the major muscle groups and muscles will be described with respect to their attachments and actions. Finally, a framework within which analysis of movement can be performed will be proposed.

It should be noted that muscles which have extensive attachments may perform several actions, depending on the part of the muscle which is active. In the tables below, the part of the muscle responsible for the action is indicated in brackets.

Figures 2.43 and 2.44 illustrate the overall arrangement of muscles throughout the body. Figures 2.45 to 2.51 name most of the major muscles, and indicate their attachments and actions.

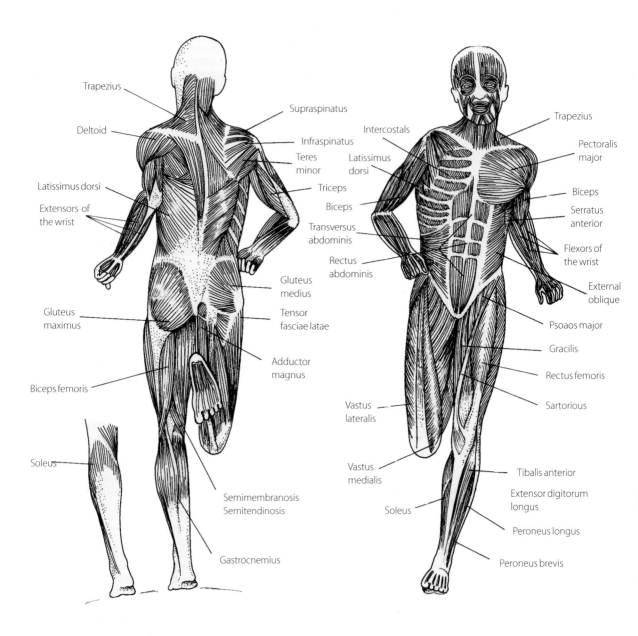

Trapezius

Deltoid

Latissimus dorsi

Extensors of
the wrist

Gluteus
maximus

Biceps femoris

Soleus

Supraspinatus

Infraspinatus

Teres
minor

Triceps

Biceps

Gluteus
medius

Tensor
fasciae latae

Adductor
magnus

Semimembranosis
Semitendinosis

Gastrocnemius

Intercostals

Latissimus
dorsi

Transversus
abdominis

Rectus
abdominis

Vastus
lateralis

Vastus
medialis

Soleus

Trapezius

Pectoralis
major

Biceps

Serratus
anterior

Flexors of
the wrist

External
oblique

Psoaos major

Gracilis

Rectus femoris

Sartorious

Tibalis anterior

Extensor digitorum
longus

Peroneus longus

Peroneus brevis

Figure 2.43   The arrangement of muscles throughout
the body (posterior view)

Figure 2.44   The arrangement of muscles throughout
the body (anterior view)

Range of muscle action

When a muscle contracts from its fully lengthened to its fully shortened position, it contracts through full range. Outer range is from fully lengthened to approximately one third shortened. Inner range is from approximately two thirds shortened to fully shortened. Middle range is from approximately one third shortened to approximately two thirds shortened.

Figure 2.45   Muscles of the shoulder region

Muscle	Origin	Insertion	Action
Trapezius	Occipital bone Ligamentum nuchae Spine of C7 Spines of T1 – T12	Clavicle Acromion and spine of scapula	Elevates shoulder girdle Laterally rotates scapula Adducts scapula
Deltoid	Lateral end of clavicle Acromion and spine of scapula	Deltoid tuberosity of humerus	Abducts arm Flexes arm (ant) Medially rotates arm (ant) Extends arm (post) Laterally rotates arm (post)
Latissimus dorsi	Spines of T6 – T12 Spines of L1 – L5 Lower four ribs Crest of ilium	Intertubercular sulcus of humerus	Adducts arm Medially rotates arm Extends arm
Pectoralis major	Clavicle Sternum Cartilages of ribs 2 – 6	Greater tuberosity of humerus Intertubercular sulcus of humerus	Flexes arm (ant) Extends arm (stern) Adducts arm Medially rotates arm
Muscles of rotator cuff			
Subscapularis	Anterior surface of scapula	Lesser tuberosity of humerus	Medially rotates arm
Supraspinatus	Supraspinus fossa of scapula	Greater tuberosity of humerus	Adducts arm (with deltoid)
Infraspinatus	Infraspinus fossa of humerus	Greater tuberosity of humerus	Laterally rotates arm
Teres minor	Inferior lateral border of scapula	Intertubercular sulcus of humerus	Laterally rotates arm
Serratus anterior	Upper 8 – 9 ribs	Medial border and inferior border of scapula	Draws (protracts) scapula forwards around chest wall
Rhomboid major Rhomboid minor	Spines of C7 – T5	Medial border of scapula	Adducts (retracts) scapula

Figure 2.46   Muscles of the upper limb

Muscle	Origin	Insertion	Action
Triceps	Infraglenoid tubercle Postero-lateral surface of humerus Posterior surface of humerus	Olecranon of ulna	Extends forearm at elbow Extends arm at shoulder
Biceps	Supraglenoid tubercle Coracoid process of scapula	Radial tuberosity	Flexes elbow joint Supinates forearm Flexes shoulder
Brachialis	Distal anterior surface of humerus	Ulnar tuberosity Coronoid process of ulna	Flexes elbow joint
Flexors of wrist			
Flexor carpi radialis	Medial epicondyle of humerus	Second and third metacarpals	Flexes wrist Abducts wrist
Flexor carpi ulnaris	Medial epicondyle of humerus Proximal posterior border of ulna	Pisiform Hamate Fifth metacarpal	Flexes wrist Adducts wrist
Extensors of wrist			
Extensor carpi radialis longus	Lateral epicondyle of humerus	Second metacarpal	Extends wrist Abducts wrist
Extensor carpi radialis brevis	Lateral epicondyle of humerus	Third metacarpal	Extends wrist Abducts wrist
Extensor carpi ulnaris	Lateral epicondyle of humerus Posterior border of ulna	Fifth metacarpal	Extends wrist Adducts wrist
Rotators of the forearm			
Supinator	Lateral epicondyle of humerus Radial notch of ulna	Lateral surface of proximal third of radius	Supinates forearm
Pronator teres	Medial epicondyle of humerus Coronoid process of ulna	Midlateral surface of radius	Pronates forearm Flexes forearm at the elbow
Pronator quadratus	Distal portion of shaft of ulna	Distal portion of shaft of radius	Pronates forearm

This is not a comprehensive list of the muscles of the shoulder girdle and upper limb; additionally there are several muscles connecting the scapula and trunk, and the long muscles which flex and extend the fingers and thumb and the short (intrinsic) muscles of the hand which produce the fine co-ordinated movements necessary for dexterity in manual function.

Figure 2.47 Muscles of the hip region

Muscle	Origin	Insertion	Action
Psoas major	Transverse processes and bodies of lumbar vertebrae	Lesser trochanter of femur	Flexes hip joint Laterally rotates hip
Iliacus	Iliac fossa	Tendon of psoas major	Flexes hip joint Laterally rotates hip
Gluteal muscles			
Gluteus maximus	Iliac crest Sacrum Coccyx	Iliotibial tract of fascia lata Gluteal tuberosity of femur	Extends hip joint Laterally rotates hip joint
Gluteus medius	Ilium	Greater trochanter of femur	Abducts hip joint Medially rotates hip joint
Gluteus minimus	Ilium	Greater trochanter of femur	Abducts hip joint Medially rotates hip joint
Tensor fascia lata	Iliac crest	Proximal lateral surface of tibia (via ilio-tibial tract)	Abducts hip joint Medially rotates hip joint
Adductor muscles			
Adductor magnus	Inferior ramus of pubis Inferior ramus of ischium	Linea aspera on posterior aspect of femur	Adducts hip joint Medially rotates hip joint
Adductor longus	Pubic crest Pubic symphysis	Linea aspera of femur	Adducts hip joint Medially rotates hip joint
Adductor brevis	Inferior ramus of pubis	Upper half of linea aspera	Adducts hip joint Medially rotates hip joint

There are also several short muscles which pass between the hip and femur which contribute to and control movements at the hip joint.

Figure 2.48 Muscles of the thigh

Muscle	Origin	Insertion	Action
Quadriceps			
Rectus femoris	Anterior inferior iliac spine	Upper border of patella	Extends knee joint Flexes hip joint
Vastus medialis	Linea aspera of femur	Tibial tuberosity through patellar ligament/tendon	Extends knee joint
Vastus lateralis	Greater trochanter of femur Linea aspera	Tibial tuberosity through patellar ligament/tendon	Extends knee joint
Vastus intermedius	Anterior and lateral surfaces of the femur	Tibial tuberosity through patellar ligament/tendon	Extends knee joint
Hamstrings			
Biceps femoris	Ischial tuberosity Linea aspera of femur	Head of fibula Lateral condyle of tibia	Flexes knee joint Extends hip joint
Semitendinosis	Ischial tuberosity	Proximal medial surface of tibia	Flexes knee joint Extends hip joint
Semimembranosis	Ischial tuberosity	Medial condyle of tibia	Flexes knee joint Extends hip joint

Figure 2.49 Muscles of the leg

Muscle	Origin	Insertion	Action
Tibialis anterior	Lateral condyle and proximal shaft of tibia	First metatarsal Medial cuneiform	Dorsiflexes ankle joint Inverts sub-talar joint
Peronei			
Peroneus longus	Head of fibula Lateral condyle of tibia	First metatarsal Medial cuneiform	Everts sub-talar joint Plantarflexes ankle joint
Peroneus brevis	Shaft of fibula	Fifth metatarsal	Everts sub-talar joint Plantarflexes ankle joint
Calf muscles			
Gastrocnemius	Lateral and medial condyles of femur	Calcaneus through tendo-achilles	Plantarflexes ankle joint Flexes knee joint
Soleus	Head of fibula Medial border of fibula	Calcaneus through tendo-achilles	Plantarflexes ankle joint Flexes knee joint

In addition, there are long muscles which act on the toes to flex or extend, and short (intrinsic) muscles in the foot which act to stabilise the foot and help it to adapt to uneven surfaces.

Figure 2.50 Muscles of the trunk

Muscle	Origin	Insertion	Action
Abdominal muscles			
Rectus abdominis	Pubic crest Pubic symphysis	Fifth to seventh costal cartilages Xiphoid process	Flexes vertebral column Compresses abdomen
External oblique	Lower eight ribs	Iliac crest Linea alba (midline aponeurosis)	Flexes vertebral column (both) Side flexes and rotates vertebral column (one) Compresses abdomen
Internal oblique	Iliac crest Inguinal ligament Thoraco-lumbar fascia	Sixth to tenth costal cartilages Linea alba	Flexes vertebral column (both) Compresses abdomen Side flexes and rotates vertebral column (one)
Transversus abdominis	Iliac crest Inguinal ligament Lumbar fascia Sixth to twelfth costal cartilages	Xiphoid process Pubis Linea alba	Compresses abdomen
Quadratus lumborum	Iliac crest Ilio-lumbar ligament	Twelfth rib Transverse processes of L1 – L4	Side flexes vertebral column (one)

Figure 2.51   Respiratory muscles

Muscle	Origin	Insertion	Action
Respiratory muscles			
External intercostals	Attached between adjacent ribs		Act on ribs during respiration
Internal intercostals			
Diaphragm	Xiphoid process	Central tendon	Forms floor of thoracic cavity
	Sixth to twelfth costal cartilages		Descends during inspiration
	Lumbar vertebrae		to increase vertical diameter
			of thorax

The extensor muscles of the back are a complex arrangement of layers of muscles passing between vertebra and vertebra, between vertebra and rib, and between rib and rib. The muscles are of varying lengths, the shortest passing between adjacent bony structures, and longer muscles spanning several bony structures. Their actions are to extend the vertebral column (when working bilaterally), and to side flex and rotate the vertebral column when working unilaterally.

Analysis of movement

Detailed analysis of movement is a complex activity, requiring sophisticated equipment which may include optoelectric systems, high speed filming, force plates, electromyographic equipment, and electrogoniometry (see chapter 5).

However, basic analysis of movement can be done visually, and should involve the following elements:

1 A description of the actual movements which occur at the joints involved.
2 The plane/s in which the movement occurs.
3 The muscles producing the movement.
4 The function of the muscles involved (agonists, antagonists, synergists, fixators).
5 The type of contraction (isotonic – concentric/eccentric, isometric).
6 The range of the muscle action (inner, middle, outer).

Consider a simple example, that of standing and lifting one foot off the ground by bending the knee. The movements of the leg being lifted will be analysed.

1 There is flexion at the hip joint, flexion at the knee joint and dorsiflexion at the ankle joint.
2 All movements are occurring in the sagittal plane.
3 The hip flexors (psoas major, iliacus, rectus femoris)

   The knee flexors (the hamstrings) – although gravity may be producing this movement.

   The dorsiflexors (tibialis anterior, extensor digitorum, extensor hallucis longus).

   Additionally, some of the short extensors of the toes will be working.

Figure 2.52   Movement at joints

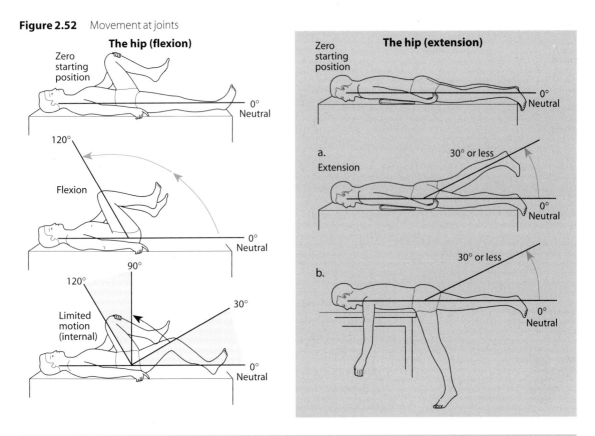

The hip (flexion)

Zero starting position

0° Neutral

120°

Flexion

0° Neutral

120°

90°

Limited motion (internal)

30°

0° Neutral

The hip (extension)

Zero starting position

0° Neutral

a. Extension

30° or less

0° Neutral

b.

30° or less

0° Neutral

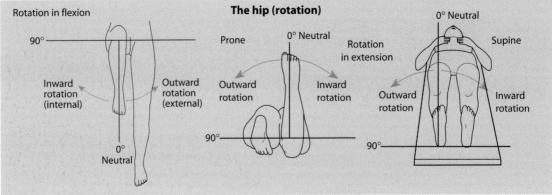

Rotation in flexion

90°

Inward rotation (internal)

Outward rotation (external)

0° Neutral

The hip (rotation)

Prone

0° Neutral

Outward rotation

Inward rotation

90°

Rotation in extension

0° Neutral

Supine

Outward rotation

Inward rotation

90°

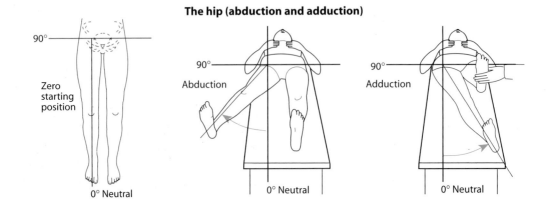

The hip (abduction and adduction)

90°

Zero starting position

0° Neutral

90°

Abduction

0° Neutral

90°

Adduction

0° Neutral

Figure 2.52 Movement at joints (continued)

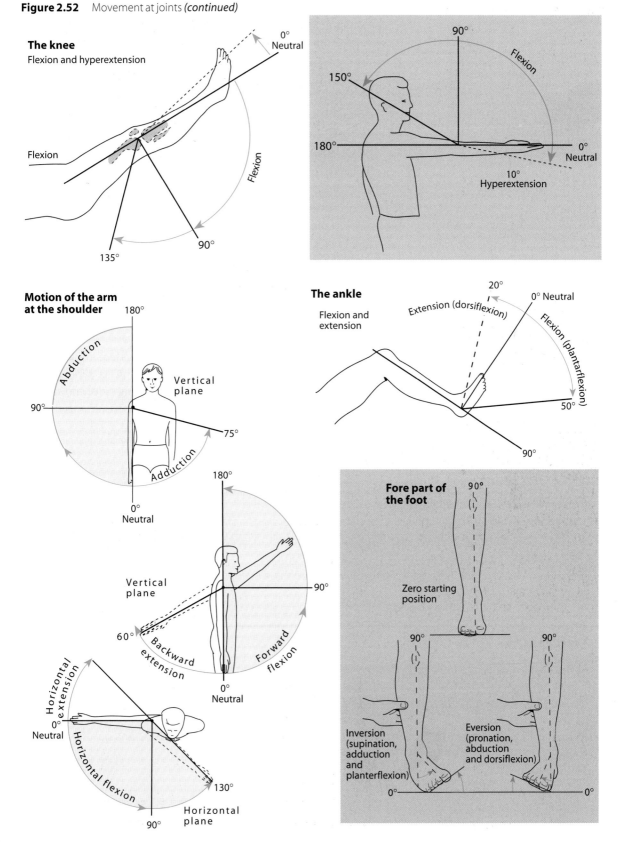

4 The hip flexors act as agonists (the extensors relax and lengthen as antagonists). Depending on how much activity occurs in the knee flexors, the hamstrings act as agonists to initiate knee flexion, but as much of the movement is produced by gravity, the knee extensors, acting as antagonists will probably lengthen to allow knee flexion to occur.

The ankle dorsiflexors act as agonists.

5 The hip flexors contract isotonically, and concentrically to flex the hip.

The knee flexors contract isotonically, and concentrically to initiate knee flexion, then the knee extensors contract isotonically and eccentrically to control knee flexion.

The dorsiflexors contract isometrically to keep the foot at right angles to the leg.

6 The hip flexors are working in outer to middle range. The knee flexors are working in outer range (to initiate knee flexion).

The knee extensors are working in inner to middle range to control knee flexion.

The ankle dorsiflexors are working in middle range to hold the ankle at right angles to the foot.

Obviously, many other muscles are working during this simple activity. The hip abductors of the standing leg are acting as synergists to prevent excessive dropping of the hip on the lifting side, and the hip flexors and extensors of the standing leg and the trunk muscles are working as fixators to stabilise the pelvis.

Questions

1 Describe the sliding filament theory of muscle contraction.
2 What are the different types of muscle contraction? Give examples of each type.
3 Explain what happens when the patella tendon is tapped with a reflex hammer.
4 What is meant by the 'group action of muscles'? Give examples.
5 Analyse what is happening in the lower limbs when you stand up from and sit down on a stool.

SUMMARY

- Voluntary muscle functions to produce movement and stability at joints. Involuntary muscle controls the functioning of internal organs and structures.
- The basic unit of muscle is the muscle fibre. It contains filaments, which consist of contractile proteins (actin and myosin).
- During muscle contraction, myosin crossbridges attach to sites on the actin filaments, and pull the actin filaments towards the centre of the myosin filaments.
- Calcium ions and energy are necessary for muscle contraction.
- The force of muscle contraction depends on the number, type and size of motor units activated.
- Peripheral modifiers of muscle force are the muscle spindles and the golgi tendon organs.

Part 2   Control and maintenance systems

Objectives

To understand

- the structure and function of the heart, lungs and vascular system
- the structure and function of blood
- control of heart and respiratory rates during rest and exercise
- the regulatory role of the endocrine system

The previous section dealt with the locomotor system, considering the basic musculo-skeletal framework and how it moves. This section will consider those systems which deliver essential nutrients for normal function, remove waste products, and control the body's response to internal and external stimuli. The main emphasis of the chapter will be on the cardiovascular and respiratory systems, but the endocrine system will also be examined briefly.

The cardiovascular system

The cardiovascular system consists of the heart, the blood vessels and the circulating blood. The heart may be regarded as the pump or engine of the system, the blood vessels as a series of conducting tubes, and the blood as a means of transporting nutrients and the products of metabolism to and from the various organs of the body. The prefix 'cardio' refers to the heart, and 'vascular' refers to the blood vessels.

The heart – cardiac anatomy

The heart is a hollow, cone-shaped structure, approximately 12 cm long, 9 cm wide at its broadest point, and 6 cm thick. The pointed end of the heart (the apex) is found down and to the left. Opposite to the apex, the base of the heart is broad and flat, and forms the upper and posterior margin. It consists of four chambers, two atria and two ventricles, and is positioned slightly to the left of the midline of the body, resting on the diaphragm. It is near the middle of the thoracic cavity, in a space called the mediastinum, which extends from the vertebral column behind to the sternum in front, between the lungs (figure 2.52). The heart is surrounded by the pericardium, a triple layered sac which maintains the heart in its position in the mediastinum, but provides enough space for the heart to contract and relax during heartbeat. The outer layer is called the fibrous pericardium, and is tough and inelastic; the middle layer (the parietal layer) and the inner layer (the visceral layer) are continuous, and form a double layer around the heart, separated by a thin film of serous fluid which

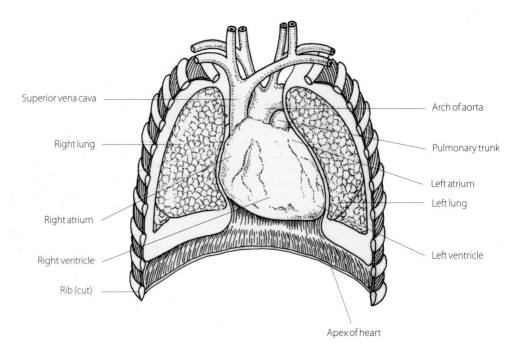

Superior vena cava

Arch of aorta

Right lung

Pulmonary trunk

Left atrium

Left lung

Right atrium

Right ventricle

Left ventricle

Rib (cut)

Apex of heart

Figure 2.53   Location of the heart

reduces friction between the layers. The visceral layer of the pericardium adheres firmly to the muscle of the heart, and is also known as the epicardium (figure 2.54).

The heart wall

The heart wall also consists of three layers, the epicardium (external layer), the myocardium (middle layer) and the endocardium (inner layer). The epicardium (also known as the visceral layer of the pericardium) consists of a thin layer of delicate connective tissue which provides a smooth slippery surface to the heart. The middle layer, the myocardium, comprises the bulk of the heart wall, and is made up of cardiac muscle fibres. This layer is responsible for the pumping action of the heart. The cardiac muscle fibres are involuntary (meaning that they are not under your control), striated (striped) and branched. They swirl diagonally around the heart in two distinct networks, one atrial and one ventricular.

Figure 2.54   Pericardium and heart wall

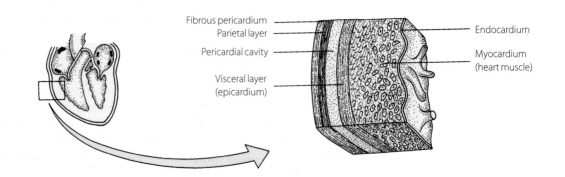

Fibrous pericardium

Parietal layer

Endocardium

Pericardial cavity

Myocardium (heart muscle)

Visceral layer (epicardium)

Figure 2.55 Cardiac muscle

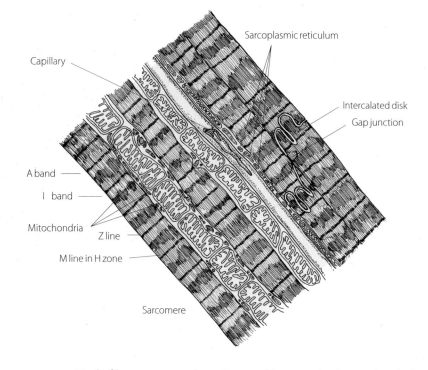

Each fibre contacts the adjacent fibres at the intercalated discs (figure 2.55), which are thickenings of the sarcolemma. Within the sarcolemma there are gap junctions (electrical synapses) which allow muscle action potentials to spread from one fibre to another. The mechanism of cardiac muscle contraction will be explained later. As a result of this arrangement, the entire atrial network contracts as one unit. Similarly, the ventricular network contracts as one unit.

The innermost layer of the wall of the heart (endocardium) consists of a thin layer of endothelial cells on a thin connective tissue base. It provides a smooth friction-free lining for the inside of the heart, and covers the valves of the heart. It is continuous with the endothelial lining of the large blood vessels associated with the heart.

Chambers of the heart

The heart is divided into four compartments, or chambers which receive the circulating blood. The two superior chambers are called the right atrium and the left atrium, each of which has an appendage called an auricle, which increases the volume of the atrium. The two inferior chambers are called the right ventricle and the left ventricle.

There is no direct communication between the right and left sides of the heart; the inter atrial septum separates the right and left atria, and the interventricular septum separates the two ventricles. This effectively separates the oxygenated blood in the left side of the heart from deoxygenated blood in the right side of the heart. Occasionally, children are born with a hole in this dividing septum (a ventricular or atrial septal defect) which requires repair to avoid mixing the two types of blood.

There are openings in the dividing septa between the atria and the ventricles, and these are guarded by valves. The valves function to permit a one-way flow of blood. They are also present at the openings of the major vessels which carry blood away from the heart, where they prevent it from re-entering the heart. The valves are named by their location and their shape, and can be seen in figure 2.57.

- the **tricuspid valve** – between the right atrium and the right ventricle; it has three cusps or flaps.
- the **bicuspid (mitral) valve** – between the left atrium and the left ventricle; it has two cusps, and is thought to look like a bishop's mitre.
- the **pulmonary semilunar valve** – at the opening of the pulmonary artery, which carries blood to the lungs
- the **aortic semilunar valve** – at the opening of the aorta, the main artery which carries blood from the heart to the rest of the body.

Blood vessels attached to the heart

There are four major blood vessels (or groups of vessels) which are attached to the heart:

- The venae cavae carry blood from all parts of the body to the right atrium. The superior vena cava carries blood from the head and upper limbs, while the inferior vena cava carries blood from the trunk and lower limbs. The blood which enters the heart through the venae cavae is deoxygenated, that is, it has given up oxygen to cells in different organs in the body.

Figure 2.56 Exterior of the heart showing chambers and major blood vessels

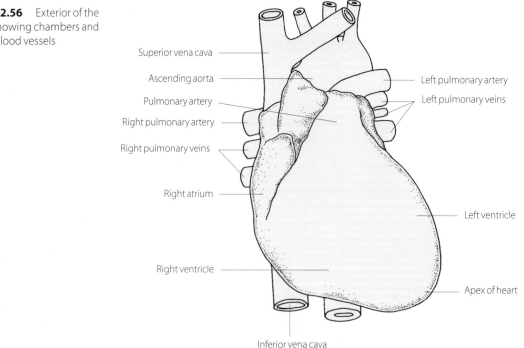

Superior vena cava

Ascending aorta

Pulmonary artery

Right pulmonary artery

Right pulmonary veins

Right atrium

Right ventricle

Left pulmonary artery

Left pulmonary veins

Left ventricle

Apex of heart

Inferior vena cava

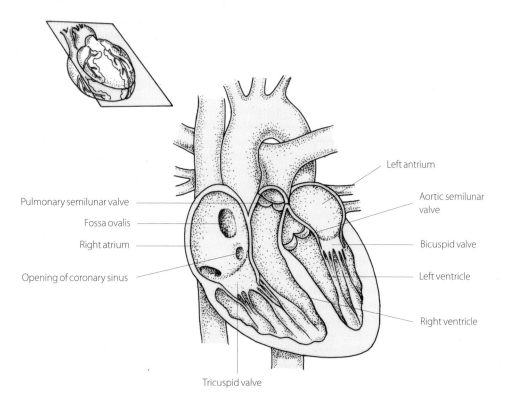

Left antrium

Aortic semilunar valve

Pulmonary semilunar valve

Fossa ovalis

Right atrium

Bicuspid valve

Opening of coronary sinus

Left ventricle

Right ventricle

Tricuspid valve

Figure 2.57   The valves of the heart

- The **pulmonary trunk**, which divides into the right pulmonary artery and left pulmonary artery, carries blood from the right ventricle to the lungs. This blood is deoxygenated.

- The **right pulmonary veins** and the left pulmonary veins carry blood from the lungs to the left atrium. This blood is oxygenated, that is, it carries oxygen which it can give up to the cells.

- The **aorta** carries blood from the left ventricle to distribute it throughout the body through its branches. This blood is oxygenated.

The major vessels can be seen in figure 2.56.

Blood supply to the heart

The heart itself also requires a blood supply. This is provided by the coronary circulation, which consists of a network of blood vessels encircling the heart. There are two major coronary arteries, the right and left coronary arteries, which branch from the base of the aorta, and supply blood to the corresponding sides of the heart. The branches of these two arteries form a very extensive and overlapping network to supply the heart muscle with many connecting branches (anastamoses). This arrangement helps to ensure adequate blood supply to the heart even when some of the blood vessels become blocked.

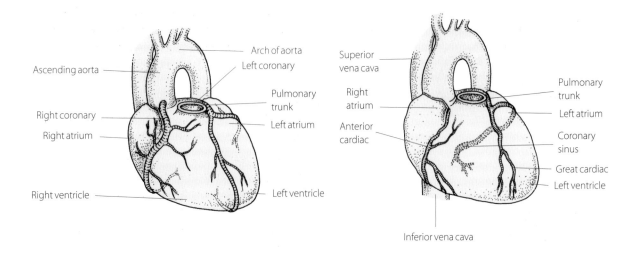

Figure 2.58 Blood supply to the heart

Deoxygenated blood, having given up oxygen to the heart muscle, returns to the heart via the great cardiac vein and the middle cardiac vein. These cardiac veins drain into the coronary sinus which in turn empties into the right atrium. The arrangement of the blood vessels supplying the heart is shown in figure 2.58.

Blood flow through the heart

The heart functions as a pair of linked muscle pumps, formed by the two sides of the heart, which maintain a continuous flow of blood around the body. The right side of the heart receives and pumps deoxygenated blood, while the left side of the heart receives and pumps oxygenated blood. Although the two sides of the heart are separated internally by the septum, the arrangement of the muscle fibres is such that the two atria contract as a single unit, and the two ventricles also contract as a single unit. The atrial and ventricular muscle masses are separated by connective tissue, with the result that the contraction of the ventricles and the atria occur independently of each other.

The action of the heart (cardiac cycle) takes place in three phases:

1   During atrial and ventricular relaxation (diastole) deoxygenated blood enters the right atrium through the superior and inferior venae cavae, and oxygenated blood enters the left atrium through the pulmonary veins. Both atrio-ventricular valves are closed, and the semilunar valves at the arterial openings are also closed.

2   As the atria fill, the atrio-ventricular valves open, and blood flows into the ventricles. The semilunar valves remain closed. Blood continues to flow into atria and the ventricles until both are full. The atria then contract (atrial systole) to force more blood into the ventricles, which become stretched.

3   The ventricles then contract (ventricular systole), the atrio-ventricular valves close, and the increased intra-ventricular pressure forces the blood into the arteries, through the now open

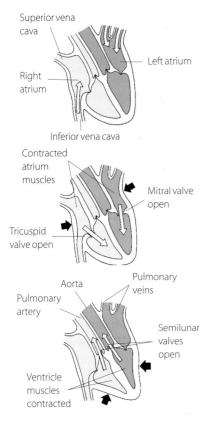

Figure 2.59   The action of the heart

semilunar valves. Deoxygenated blood passes into the pulmonary trunk, from where it passes to the lungs, and oxygenated blood passes into the aorta and subsequently around the body.

The events of the cardiac cycle are shown in figure 2.59.

If we consider a single unit of blood, its circulation through the heart would be as follows:

1   Having passed around the body, and given up oxygen to the cells, it enters the right atrium through the vena cava.

2   It passes through the tricuspid valve into the right ventricle.

3   It passes through the pulmonary semilunar valve into the pulmonary trunk, and then via one of the pulmonary arteries to the lung, where it becomes oxygenated.

4   It travels back to the heart via one of the pulmonary veins, and enters the left atrium.

5   It passes through the mitral valve to the left ventricle.

6   It passes through the aortic semilunar valve into the aorta and begins its journey around the body again.

The conduction system of the heart

Cardiac muscle has been described as involuntary, meaning that it is not under voluntary control. Certain cardiac muscle cells repeatedly fire spontaneous impulses which cause the heart muscle to contract. This means that the heart, unlike skeletal (voluntary) muscle continues to contract even when its nerve supply has been removed, although the beats are slow and irregular. Consequently, the heart needs a mechanism which will maintain a regular beat at the required rate to deliver an adequate blood supply to the organs of the body.

Figure 2.60 shows the conducting system of the heart, which consists of a number of specialised cardiac muscle fibres. These have become differentiated into auto-rhythmic cells, capable of repeatedly and rhythmically generating impulses. These cells act as a pacemaker, setting the contraction rhythm for the whole heart, ensuring that the cardiac chambers contract in a co-ordinated manner.

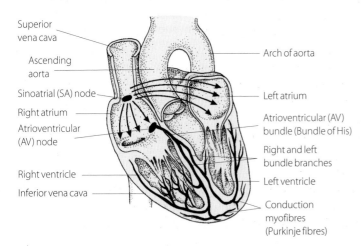

Figure 2.60   Conducting system of the heart

The autorhythmic cells are organised into two nodes and three groups of fibres. These are:

● the **sinoatrial (SA) node** found in the right atrium close to the opening of the superior vena cava.

● the **atrioventricular (AV) node** found in the lower part of the septum between the two atria.

- the **atrioventricular (AV) bundle of His**, which passes between the atria and ventricles.
- the **right** and **left bundle branches**, which pass within the atrio-ventricular septum towards the apex of the heart.
- the conducting **Purkinje fibres** which permeate the ventricular muscle tissue.

Cardiac excitation starts in the SA node. It passes through the atrial muscle via the gap junctions in the intercalated discs, causing the atria to contract. The impulse is then picked up by the AV node, and passes into the ventricles via the bundle of His. Subsequently, it passes through the interventricular septum via the right and left bundle branches to the Purkinje fibres. These then conduct the impulse to the ventricular muscle mass, causing it to contract.

The SA node generates impulses at a rate of 60 to 100 times per minute, and acts as the pacemaker of the heart. The impulse passes throughout the atrial muscle in approximately 50 milliseconds, but slows considerably at the AV node, because the fibres have smaller diameters. This causes a delay of 100 ms in the transmission of the impulse between the atria and the ventricles. The delay gives time for the atria to complete their contraction and add to the volume of blood in the ventricles before the ventricles start their contraction. After the impulse enters the AV bundle of His, conduction again is rapid, and contraction of the ventricles occurs within 150 to 200 ms. The entire cardiac cycle takes approximately 800 ms (0.8 sec).

If the SA node is damaged, the heartbeat may be maintained by AV node, at a slower rate of 40 to 50 beats per minute. If both nodes are damaged, the autorhythmic fibres in the ventricles can maintain heartbeat, but at a much slower rate of 20 to 40 beats per minute. This is too slow to maintain adequate blood flow to the brain. When this occurs, normal heart rhythm may be restored and maintained by implanting an artificial pacemaker, which generates impulses at the required rate.

Systolic and diastolic phases

The term systole refers to the phase of contraction of the cardiac muscle, while diastole refers to the period of relaxation of the cardiac muscle. As the cardiac cycle is a rhythmic event, the timings of the phases can be calculated for both atria and ventricles. The resting heart rate (HR) is about 75 beats per minute, resulting in a cardiac cycle of approximately 0.8 sec duration. The relative timings of the systolic and diastolic phases associated with the resting HR of 75 are as follows:

0.0 sec — 0.4 sec	atrial diastole ventricular diastole
0.4 sec — 0.5 sec	atrial systole ventricular diastole
0.5 sec — 0.8 sec	atrial diastole ventricular systole

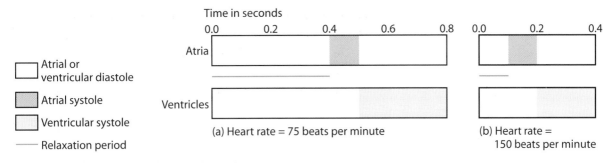

Time in seconds

Atrial or ventricular diastole		
Atrial systole		
Ventricular systole		
Relaxation period		

(a) Heart rate = 75 beats per minute

(b) Heart rate = 150 beats per minute

Figure 2.61 Temporal relationships of systole and diastole

As the the heart rate increases, the systolic phase duration for both atria and ventricles remains fairly constant, but the diastolic (relaxation) phase becomes shorter (figure 2.61). This obviously imposes a greater load on the heart.

Heart sounds

When a stethoscope is placed over the heart, the heart beat can be heard. The sound of the heart beat (the heart sounds) is caused by turbulence of the blood produced by the closing of the heart valves, and less audibly, by the movement of blood through the heart. There are four heart sounds in total, but only the first two are loud enough to be heard through a stethoscope.

The first sound (S1), is usually described as a lubb sound. It is caused by the blood turbulence associated with the closure of the AV valves soon after ventricular systole begins, and is louder and longer than the second sound.

The second sound (S2), is shorter than the first and is described as a dupp sound. It is produced by blood turbulence associated with the closure of the semilunar valves at the beginning of ventricular diastole.

The locations at which these sounds are best heard are illustrated in figure 2.62.

The third sound (S3) is associated with rapid ventricular filling. The fourth sound (S4) is caused by atrial contraction. The third and fourth sounds are not normally loud enough to be heard. Abnormalities in the heart sounds usually indicate that the valves are not functioning normally, either by not opening sufficiently (stenosis), or by not closing completely (incompetence).

Cardiac output

Cardiac output (CO) is the amount of blood ejected by the heart from the left ventricle (into the aorta) and the right ventricle (into the pulmonary trunk) each minute. Cardiac output is determined by the volume of blood ejected by the ventricles per beat (stroke volume SV) and the number of heart beats per minute (heart rate HR).

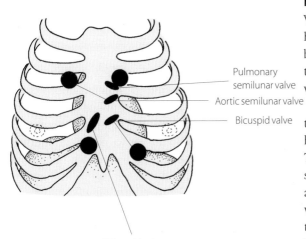

Pulmonary semilunar valve

Aortic semilunar valve

Bicuspid valve

Tricuspid valve

Figure 2.62 Location of heart sounds

In the healthy resting adult, with a stroke volume of approximately 70 millilitres per beat, and a heart rate of 75 beats per minute, cardiac output is 5.25 litres per minute (SV (70ml)) x (HR (75)) = 5250 ml (5.25 l). As the normal total blood volume, that is all the circulating blood in the body, in an adult male is about five litres, this means that the entire blood supply flows through the pulmonary (lungs) and systemic (body) circulations every minute!

Three important factors regulate the stroke volume in different circumstances, and ensure that the left and right ventricles pump equal volumes of blood:

- **preload** – the stretch on the heart before it contracts.
- **contractility** – the forcefulness of contraction of the individual ventricular muscle fibres.
- **afterload** – the pressure that must be exceeded before ejection of blood from the ventricles can begin.

When the demands of the body for oxygen increase or decrease, cardiac output changes to meet the demand. Thus, during mild exercise cardiac output might rise to 11 litres per minute, with a heart rate of 100 and a stroke volume of 110 ml/beat. During intense, but not maximal exercise, cardiac output may reach 21 litres per minute (HR = 150 and SV = 140). As the heart rate can be measured by the pulse rate, this is why you can feel your pulse rate going up during and following exercise.

Regulation of heart rate

Cardiac output depends on heart rate and stroke volume. In some pathological conditions, stroke volume may be much reduced due to poor cardiac muscle function, which reduces the ability of the heart to contract forcefully. In these circumstances, the heart rate increases to compensate for the reduced stroke volume to maintain adequate cardiac output for the demands of the body. It has already been noted that in normal circumstances the SA (sinoatrial) node initiates contraction, and maintains a steady heart rate. However, different circumstances demand different responses from the heart, and other regulatory mechanisms come into play. The most important of these are the autonomic nervous system (sympathetic and parasympathetic divisions), and chemical factors.

Autonomic control of heart rate

The cardiovascular centre is situated in the medulla, in the inferior posterior part of the brain. It receives input from a number of sources to control the cardiovascular system. For example, consider what happens in an exercise situation. Even before exercise commences, there is an anticipatory rise in heart rate. This is due to signals passing from the limbic system (which influences emotional aspects of behaviour) situated in the brain stem, to the cardiovascular centre. Then when exercise begins, proprioceptors, which monitor the position of joints and muscles, send increased input to the cardiovascular centre, resulting in a rapid rise in heart rate (figure 2.63).

The heart is supplied by nerves from both the sympathetic and parasympathetic divisions of the nervous system. The sympathetic cardiac accelerator nerves secrete norepinephrine (noradrenaline) and epinephrine (adrenaline) at their endings on the heart to make the heart speed up. The parasympathetic (vagus) nerve endings secrete acetylcholine which slows the rhythm of the heart. Heart rate

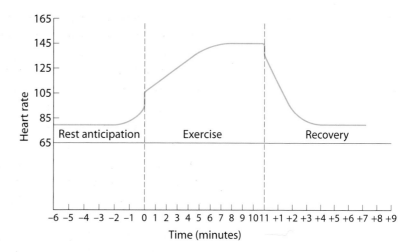

Figure 2.63 Heart rate response before, during and after moderate exercise

is normally controlled by a balance between the activity of the two divisions, although at rest it is more powerfully influenced by the vagal (decelerator) nerves. In situations such as emotional excitement, changes in muscle chemistry, blood pressure and arterial pH cause an increase in activity of one division with a parallel decrease in the other division. This results in either a rise or fall in heart rate. It is thought that most of the increase in heart rate during exercise is due to inhibition of vagal activity.

Hormonal control of heart rate

Hormones circulating in the blood can directly affect heart rate. Epinephrine and norepinephrine secreted from the adrenal gland are the most powerful of these, and increase heart rate. Hormones from the thyroid gland also increase heart rate.

Intrinsic control of heart rate

Several factors concerned with the heart tissue itself can influence heart rate:

- Warming the heart muscle increases heart rate, cooling decreases heart rate.
- Increased filling of the heart with blood causes stretch on the sinoatrial node (pacemaker) and increases heart rate.
- Changes in electrolyte balance (sodium and potassium) in the heart muscle can result in changes in heart rate.

Cardiac function and exercise

The normal response of the heart to exercise is to increase heart rate and stroke volume.

Heart rate

- The anticipatory rise in heart rate is due to emotion or anxiety causing increased activity of the limbic system (resulting in increased firing of the cardiac accelerator nerves) and of the adrenal glands (resulting in increased epinephrine and norepinephrine in the circulating blood)

- During exercise, impulses from the cardiovascular centre in the medulla excite the cardiac accelerator nerves and inhibit the vagus nerves, resulting in an increase in heart rate.
- Chemicals released by contracting muscles (potassium, lactic acid) stimulate nerve endings which transmit messages to the cardiovascular centre to increase heart rate.
- Nerve endings in the aorta and the carotid arteries register changes in oxygen and carbon dioxide content of the blood, and blood pH. Although their role in exercise is unclear, they may have an effect on heart rate.
- During high intensity exercise (HR > 150), for at least 20 minutes, increased levels of circulating epinephrine and norepinephrine cause an increase in heart rate.
- Stretch of cardiac muscle and the sinoatrial node due to increased venous rate, and a rise in temperature of heart muscle cause an increase in heart rate.

Stroke volume

Stroke volume can increase up to twice the value at rest during strenuous exercise in the upright posture.

- Circulating epinephrine and norepinephrine cause both increase in heart rate and force of contraction of the heart, thus ejecting more blood during each contraction.
- Increased filling of the heart causes stretch of the cardiac muscle, more effective cross bridge formation between the actin and myosin filaments, and a more forceful contraction of the cardiac muscle.

In the horizontal position, stroke volume is near maximal, even at rest. Consequently, increased cardiac output in this position during exercise (for example, swimming) is due almost entirely to increased heart rate. Exercise in the upright position increases stroke volume to the level achieved at rest in the horizontal position.

Cardiac output is the primary indicator of the functional capacity of the circulatory system to meet the demands of physical activity. It is an indicator of both the rate and force of cardiac contraction.

Cardiac output at rest is widely variable, but on average the entire volume of five litres of blood is pumped from the left ventricle each minute. This value is similar for trained and untrained subjects, but the means by which it is achieved is different.

For the average untrained individual, the five-litre cardiac output is sustained by a heart rate of about 70 beats per minute, which produces a stroke volume of 71 ml per beat. Stroke volumes for females usually average 25% below values for males (50 – 70 ml at rest), and this is due to smaller body size.

Aerobic training, that is, training which utilises energy produced by oxidative means, causes the sinoatrial node of the heart to come under greater influence of acetylcholine. This is the parasympathetic hormone (with a reduction of resting sympathetic activity) which slows heart rate. Maximum heart rate is not significantly affected by endurance training, and may in fact be slightly reduced, but resting heart rate is considerably reduced. Thus, the resting heart rate of many male and female endurance athletes generally average 50 beats per minute at rest, although resting heart rates below 40 beats per minute have been recorded. Obviously, to maintain a resting cardiac output of five litres, stroke volume must increase to compensate for the reduced heart rate. Figure 2.64 summarises trained and sedentary cardiac function at rest.

Figure 2.64 Cardiac output, heart rate and stroke volume at rest for sedentary and trained individuals

	Cardiac output	Heart rate	Stroke volume
Sedentary	5000 ml	70 per min	71 ml
Trained	5000 ml	50 per min	100 ml

The training response may be twofold. Firstly, the vagal tone which reduces heart rate is increased, and secondly, the heart muscle is strengthened through training, and is capable of more forceful contraction.

During exercise, blood flow increases in proportion to the intensity of exercise. In progressing from rest to steady state exercise, cardiac output increases rapidly initially. It then rises more gradually to reach a plateau, when presumably, blood flow is sufficient to meet the demand of the exercise.

Heart rate response for three people of high (A), medium (B) and low (C) levels of fitness during a stepping test is shown in figure 2.65. Heart rate rises rapidly during the early part of the exercise, to reach a plateau, which is maintained throughout the exercise. The person with a high level of fitness can cope with the exercise demand with a lower exercise heart rate than the person with a medium level of fitness. This person in turn has a lower exercise heart rate than a sedentary person with a low level of fitness. When exercise ceases, during the recovery period, heart rate decreases rapidly during the first minute for the three people tested. Thereafter it decreases more slowly to regain pre-exercise levels. Note that the fit person (A) returns to resting heart rate more quickly than the other two people.

In relatively sedentary young males (20 – 25 years) cardiac output during strenuous exercise increases to about four times the resting level to an average maximum of 22 litres per minute. Maximum heart rate for these young adults is about 195 beats per minute, resulting in a stroke volume of 103 – 113 ml per beat during maximal exercise.

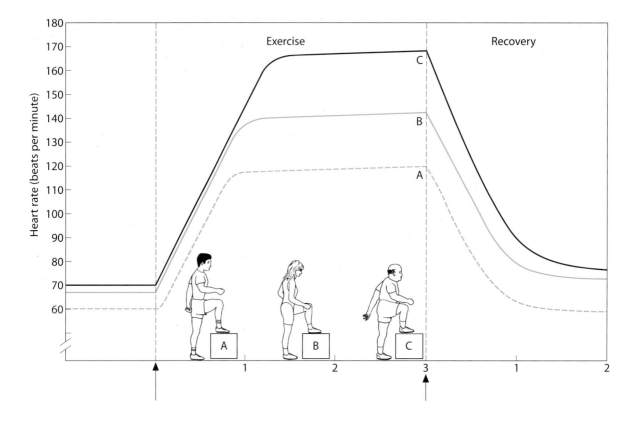

Figure 2.65 Heart rate response of three people during a stepping exercise and in recovery

In contrast, world class endurance athletes may have cardiac outputs of 35 – 40 litres per minute, which is accounted for by a greatly increased stroke volume. For example, the cardiac output of an Olympic medal winner in cross country skiing increased almost eight times that at rest to 40 litres per minute in maximal work, with a stroke volume of 210 ml per beat.

The principal limiting factor for most types of exercise which last for more than three to four minutes is the capacity of the heart, lungs and circulation to deliver oxygen to the working muscles. This maximal functional capacity of the circulorespiratory system during sport and exercise is best evaluated by testing the body's capacity to consume oxygen at a maximal rate. This is usually measured in a maximal oxygen uptake (VO_2 max) test.

Maximal oxygen uptake is determined by heart function, the ability to circulate blood to the active tissues, and the ability of the tissues to extract and utilise oxygen. In sub-maximal activity, heart rate has often been used to predict VO_2 max. Figure 2.66 shows the approximate relationship between heart rate and exercise load expressed as a percentage of maximal oxygen uptake. Figure 2.67 shows maximal oxygen uptake in a variety of activities for male and female, trained and sedentary individuals.

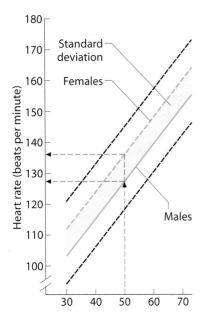

Figure 2.66 Approximate relationship between heart rate and exercise load for healthy, fit young adults

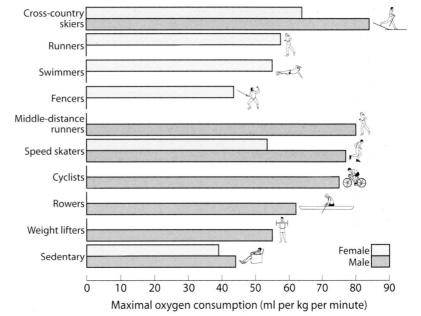

Figure 2.67 Maximal oxygen consumption of male and female olympic calibre athletes and healthy sedentary subjects

Measuring heart rate

Heart rate is a useful and simple measure which can be used to a limited extent to indicate levels of aerobic fitness. This is because in normal active individuals, the points at which maximal aerobic power and maximal attainable heart rate are reached, are very close. If you are training, measurement of heart rate is even more useful to let you know if you are exercising at a sufficiently high intensity to obtain a training effect.

Figure 2.66 shows the relationship between aerobic power and heart rate. To obtain a training effect, you should exercise at between 60% and 80% of your maximal aerobic power. This equates to 70% to 85% of your maximal attainable heart rate, and is known as the heart rate zone. Because you are able to count your own heart rate, but cannot easily determine your aerobic power, the heart rate zone provides a means of regulating your performance.

It may not be possible, or desirable, to measure maximal heart rate. However, you can estimate your maximum heart rate by subtracting your age in years from 220 to give a rough value of maximal heart rate. For example, a 20-year old man will have a maximal heart rate of approximately 200 (220 – 20), and to achieve a training effect, should exercise at an intensity which produces a heart rate of between 140 (70%) and 170 (85%). If you look at figure 2.69, you can see how maximal attainable heart rate declines with age, so that at the age of 65, the maximal heart rate is 153 (cf 220 — 65 = 155 (approx)). From

Figure 2.68 Relationship between aerobic power and heart rate

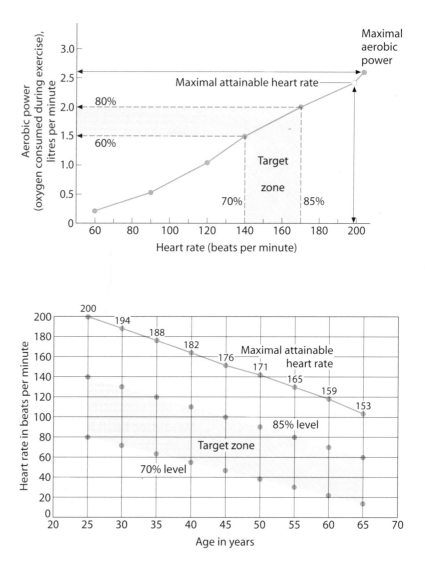

Figure 2.69 Maximal attainable heart rate and target zone

the indication of the target heart rate zone, a 65-year old man would need to exercise at an intensity which produces a heart rate of between 107 (70% of maximal HR) and 130 (85% of maximal HR). Although the 65-year old is exercising at a lower heart rate than the 20-year old, they are both at the same percentage of their maximum capacity, and consequently working at the same relative level.

To gain an understanding of exercising within your 'target heart rate zone', you could try a number of types and intensities of exercise to determine which will raise your heart rate to the target zone. You could try running, swimming or stepping. Usually, exercising for 20 to 30 minutes in the target zone will provide a significant conditioning effect on the cardiovascular system. The target period should be preceded by a five- to ten-minute warm-up period, and followed by a similar duration of cool-down. This is summarised in figure 2.69.

Figure 2.70 The exercise training pattern

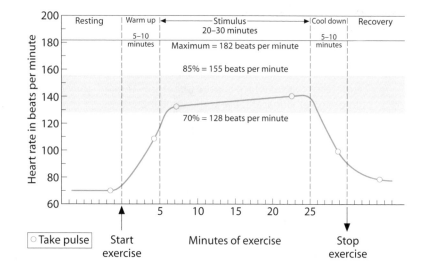

How to count your pulse

Pulse rate can be palpated (that is, felt) anywhere that a major artery is relatively close to the surface of the skin. The most common, and easily palpated, places are on the front of the forearm, just above the wrist on the thumb side, and on the side of the neck, just below the angle of the jaw. The first time you try this, it is best to sit in a comfortable position, and place the tips of the index and middle finger lightly over the pulse to be counted. Once you have located the pulse you will feel a gentle, regular beat under your fingers. When you are sure you can feel this regular beat, try a practice count over the duration of one minute. The resting count will be somewhere in the region of 70, so this will be a useful check on your accuracy.

When counting pulse rate following exercise, it is important to count immediately following the cessation of exercise, as the heart rate falls rapidly when vigorous exercise stops. This can be seen clearly in figure 2.70 as the steep downward slope in the cool down period.

Obviously, the ideal time to count exercise heart or pulse rate is actually during exercise, but this is impossible without special equipment. Pulse meters are available to count and record pulse rate during activity, but many of these are limited to recording within a confined space. Consequently, they can cope only with activities like step-ups, sit-ups, treadmill running, which do not involve the person moving any substantial distance from the recording apparatus. A variety of mobile heart rate monitors are now available, which enable heart rate to be monitored and recorded during exercise. These consist of a compact recorder which is strapped to the chest, usually approximately over the apex beat, and a wrist display monitor. The more sophisticated heart rate monitors can store heart rate over considerable periods of time, display maximum, minimum and mean values, and can be downloaded on to a computer to allow further analysis of the data.

The most common approach to counting post-exercise pulse is to find the pulse within the first second following cessation of exercise, and to count the number of beats in 10 seconds; this should then be multiplied by six to give the exercise pulse or heart rate. Do not count for the whole minute, or even for 15 seconds, as the fall off rate is too fast. An alternative approach is to locate the pulse immediately following exercise, ignore the first beat, and then time the next ten beats. To do this you obviously require a very accurate stop watch, so it is less commonly used.

103

SUMMARY

- The heart is a hollow cone-shaped structure, which is divided into four chambers – two atria and two ventricles.
- There are four valves which control blood flow through the heart – the tricuspid, the bicuspid, the pulmonary semilunar and the aortic semilunar valves.
- There are four blood vessels or groups of blood vessels attached to the heart – the venae cavae, the pulmonary trunk, the pulmonary veins and the aorta.
- The cardiac cycle takes place in three phases and lasts approximately 0.8 seconds.
- The cells which control the heart rate are organised into two nodes (sinoatrial and atrioventricular) and three groups of fibres (atrioventricular bundle of His, the right and left bundle branches and the Purkinje fibres).
- The normal response of the heart to exercise is to increase heart rate and stroke volume.
- To achieve a training effect you should exercise at 70% – 85% of your maximal heart rate, which is calculated at 220 minus your age.
- Heart rate is a simple measure which can be used to a limited extent to indicate levels of aerobic fitness.

Questions

1 Describe the structure of the heart.
2 How does blood flow through the heart?
3 How do the valves control blood flow through the heart?
4 How does the conducting system work to maintain heart rate?
5 What are the mechanisms which increase heart rate and stroke volume during exercise?

The vascular system

The vascular system consists of a closed network of blood vessels which transports the blood from the heart, carrying oxygen and nutrients to the various organs and tissues of the body, and returns it, carrying carbon dioxide.

Anatomy of blood vessels

There are two major types of blood vessels, namely arteries and veins. Where the smallest arteries (arterioles) and veins (venules) meet, the connecting vessels are called capillaries. The structure of these blood vessels is illustrated in figure 2.75.

Arteries

Arteries are vessels which carry blood from the heart to the tissues of the body. The wall of the artery consists of three layers, the inner, middle and outer layers. The inner layer (tunica intima) consists of a smooth lining of flat endothelial cells, which provides a smooth friction-free lining for the passage of blood. The inner layer also has a basement membrane and a thin layer of elastic tissue (internal elastic lamina).

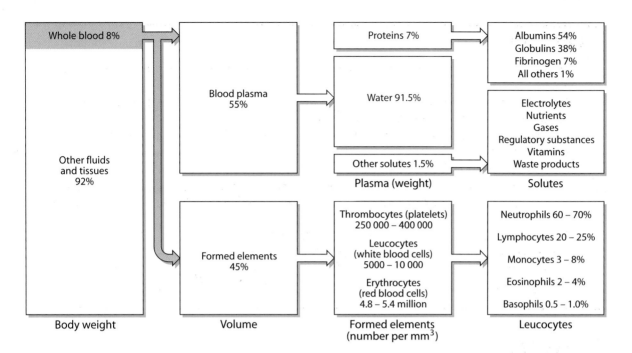

Body weight	Volume	Formed elements (number per mm³)	Leucocytes
Whole blood 8%	Blood plasma 55%	Proteins 7%	Albumins 54% / Globulins 38% / Fibrinogen 7% / All others 1%
		Water 91.5%	Electrolytes / Nutrients / Gases / Regulatory substances / Vitamins / Waste products
Other fluids and tissues 92%		Other solutes 1.5%	
		Plasma (weight)	Solutes
	Formed elements 45%	Thrombocytes (platelets) 250 000 – 400 000	Neutrophils 60 – 70%
		Leucocytes (white blood cells) 5000 – 10 000	Lymphocytes 20 – 25%
			Monocytes 3 – 8%
		Erythrocytes (red blood cells) 4.8 – 5.4 million	Eosinophils 2 – 4%
			Basophils 0.5 – 1.0%

Figure 2.71 Components of blood in a normal adult

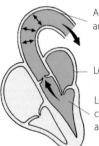

Aorta and elastic arteries

Left atrium

Left ventricle contracts (systole) and ejects blood

Elastic aorta and arteries stretch

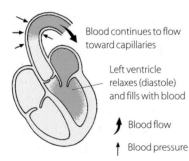

Blood continues to flow toward capillaries

Left ventricle relaxes (diastole) and fills with blood

Blood flow

Blood pressure

Elastic aorta and arteries recoil

Figure 2.72 Elastic arteries

The middle layer of the arterial wall (the tunica media) is usually the thickest layer. It consists of smooth muscle tissue and elastic tissue, the proportion of which depends on the site and function of the artery. Closest to the heart, the arteries are large, and have a large proportion of elastic tissue in the tunica media. These are known as elastic arteries, and they are capable of stretching and recoiling in response to the pumping of blood from the heart. The medium-sized arteries are further from the heart, have a higher proportion of smooth muscle fibres in the tunica media, and are known as muscular or distributing arteries. The smooth muscle in the wall of these arteries allow the arterial wall to contract, narrowing the size of the internal channel (the lumen), and consequently reducing the blood flow within the vessel. This narrowing of the lumen of the blood vessel is called vasoconstriction. The opposite situation, when the smooth muscle in the wall of the blood vessel relaxes to allow widening of the lumen and increased blood flow, is called vasodilation.

This alteration of blood vessels diameter and consequently blood flow to the tissues, allows shunting of blood from areas of low metabolic demand to areas of high metabolic demand. For example, during exercise, the blood vessels supplying the working muscles dilate to increase the blood flow to provide nutrients and remove waste products. At the same time, blood flow is reduced to areas, such as the gastro-intestinal tract, which do not require a large blood flow at that time. In the reverse situation, during and immediately following a meal, blood flow to the gastro-intestinal tract is increased, perhaps at the expense of blood flow to the muscles. This is why it is inadvisable to exercise immediately following a substantial meal.

The outer layer of the artery (tunica adventitia) is composed primarily of collagen and elastic fibres, and provides a supporting outer coat to the vessel.

Arterioles

Arterioles are small diameter arteries which deliver blood to the capillaries. Where they are close to their junction with the muscular arteries, the structure of their walls resembles that of the muscular artery. As they mover further away from the muscular artery, they become smaller in diameter. They also lose much of the outer and muscular layers, more closely resembling the structure of capillaries.

The muscular arterioles play a key role in regulating blood flow from the arteries into the capillaries through vasoconstriction and vasodilation as described above. They also influence blood pressure, as extensive vasoconstriction of the arterioles will result in increased blood pressure due to increased resistance to blood flow. Conversely, extensive vasodilation will result in decreased blood pressure.

Capillaries

Capillaries are microscopic vessels which usually connect arterioles and venules (small veins). As the primary function of capillaries is to deliver nutrients to and remove waste products from the tissue cells, they form extensive networks throughout all tissues of the body. They are particularly extensive in areas of high metabolic activity such as the muscles, liver, kidneys, lungs and nervous system. The walls of the capillaries are very thin, consisting only of a single layer of epithelial cells on a basement membrane. This permits the exchange of nutrients and waste products with the adjoining tissue cells.

Figure 2.73 Capillary network with metarterioles

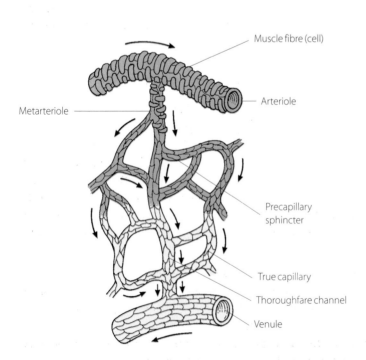

Muscle fibre (cell)

Metarteriole

Arteriole

Precapillary sphincter

True capillary

Thoroughfare channel

Venule

The flow of blood through the capillary network is controlled by a specialised arteriole which passes through the capillary network to connect with a venule. This specialised arteriole is called a metarteriole. It forms junctions with capillaries as it passes through the capillary bed (figure 2.73). The part furthest from the artery has no smooth muscle fibres in its wall, allowing unresisted flow of blood, and is known as a thoroughfare channel.

There is a ring of muscle fibres around the capillaries close to the point at which they emerge from the arterioles or metarterioles (the precapillary sphincter) which controls the the flow of blood entering the capillary. Intermittant contraction and relaxation of the precapillary sphincters creates a sporadic rather than a continuous flow through the capillaries.

Venules

Venules are formed where several capillaries unite. They collect blood from the capillaries to eventually drain into the veins. At the capillary end, the walls of the venules consist only of an inner layer of endothelial cells, and an outer layer of connective tissue. As they approach the veins, they also contain a middle layer with some elastic and smooth muscle fibres, but this layer is thin in comparison to the equivalent layer in arterioles.

Veins

The walls of veins consist of the same three layers as in arteries, but the relative thickness of the layers is different. The outer layer is thicker, and the middle layer is thinner, although still consisting of both elastic and smooth muscle tissue. The inner layer has specialised valves, consisting of a folding of the endothelial cell lining. These function to prevent a backflow of blood, and assist in the flow of blood back to the heart.

Constituents of blood

Although blood appears to be a red coloured liquid, it is actually composed of two portions; 55% is blood plasma, a watery liquid containing dissolved substances, and 45% is solid elements (known as formed elements), which are cells and fragments of cells (figure 2.71).

Blood plasma

When the formed elements are removed from blood, a pale yellow liquid (plasma) is left. Plasma is 91.5% water, and 8.5% dissolved substances, of which about 7% are proteins (plasma proteins). The plasma proteins include albumins, globulins and fibrinogens, and are important in the regulation of body fluid balance, by maintaining the correct blood osmotic pressure.

Formed elements

There are three major types of formed elements:

Erythrocytes (red blood cells) (RBC)

These form more than 99% of the formed elements. They contain haemoglobin, which is responsible for the red colour of the blood. In appearance, they are biconcave discs, about 8 m in diameter,(that is 8 x 10^{-6} m) and having no nucleus. Their main function is to transport oxygen and carbon dioxide, which is assisted by their structure which enables them to pass through the narrow capillaries which form networks within the issues of the body. Their life span is about 120 days (figure 2.74).

Leucocytes (white blood cells) (WBC)

There are two main types of white blood cells, both of which contain a nucleus and have no haemoglobin. Their life span is from a few hours to a few days.

Granular leucocytes have lobed nucleii, and have conspicuous granules in their cytoplasm. There are three types:

8µm

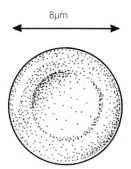

Surface view

Sectioned view

Figure 2.74 The shape of the red blood cells

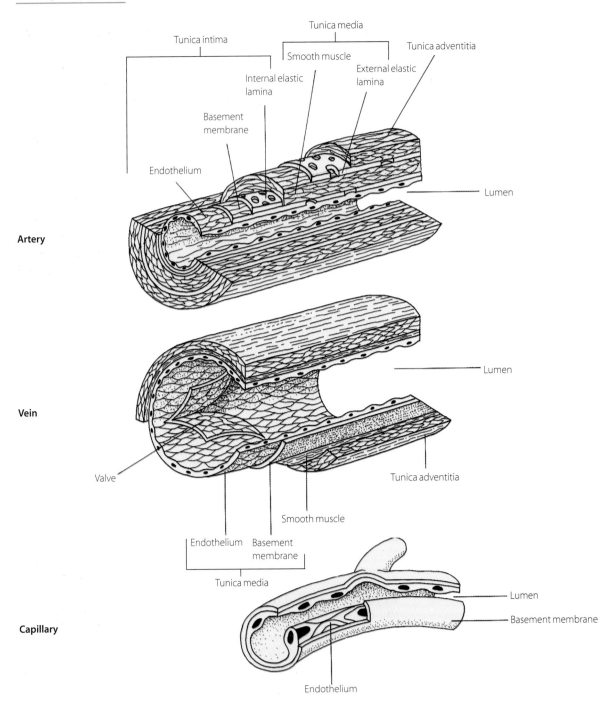

Figure 2.75 The comparative structure of blood vessels

- **Neutrophils** constitute about 65% of the total white blood cells (WBC) and function to destroy bacteria (phagocytosis).
- **Eosinophils** (2 – 4%), control allergic reactions by limiting the effect of histamine.
- **Basophils** (0.5 – 1%) intensify the inflammatory response by liberating heparine, histamine and serotonin.

Agranular leucocytes do not have granules in their cytoplasm. There are two types:

- **Lymphocytes** (20 – 25% of total) mediate immune responses by promoting the production of antibodies, and by attacking invading mechanisms such as viruses, cancer cells, transplanted tissue cells.
- **Monocytes** (3 – 8%) act as wandering phagocytes, which destroy bacteria.

Thrombocytes (platelets)

These are formed from fragments which break off from blood producing cells (haemocytoblasts) in the bone marrow, and become enclosed in a cell membrane. They function to repair slightly damaged blood vessels, and release chemicals which promote clotting of blood. This is of obvious importance in limiting bleeding, both internally and externally. Their life span is five to nine days.

Functions of the blood

The functions of the blood may be summarised as follows:

- Transport of oxygen and carbon dioxide (RBC).
- Transport of dissolved nutrients and waste products (plasma).
- Combatting bacterial infection (WBC – neutrophils).
- Controlling allergic reactions (WBC – eosinophils).
- Promoting inflammatory response (WBC – basophils).
- Mediating immune responses (WBC – lymphocytes).
- Mobile phagocytosis (WBC – monocytes).
- Clotting mechanism (thrombocytes).
- Regulation of fluid balance (plasma proteins)

Circulatory anatomy

The blood vessels are arranged into two major systems, which transport the blood through the tissues of the body. These systems are called the pulmonary (the lungs) circulatory system, and the systemic (the remaining tissues and organs of the body) circulatory system.

The pulmonary circulation

The pulmonary circulation carries deoxygenated blood (collected by the veins) from the right ventricle to the air sacs of the lungs. Here the blood gives off carbon dioxide, and takes up oxygen. This oxygenated blood is returned to the left atrium (figure 2.76). Deoxygenated blood is delivered to the heart (right atrium) via the superior and inferior vena cava, and then passes into the right ventricle. The pulmonary trunk emerges from the right ventricle, and divides into the right and left pulmonary arteries, which carry the deoxygenated blood to the right and left lungs. These are the only arteries which carry deoxygenated blood. In the lungs the pulmonary arteries divide and subdivide until they form capillaries which surround the air sacs

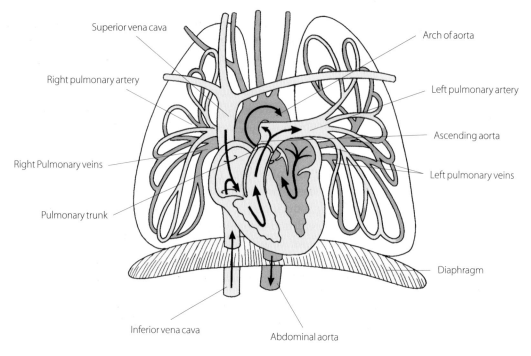

Superior vena cava

Right pulmonary artery

Right Pulmonary veins

Pulmonary trunk

Arch of aorta

Left pulmonary artery

Ascending aorta

Left pulmonary veins

Diaphragm

Inferior vena cava

Abdominal aorta

Figure 2.76   Pulmonary circulation

(alveoli) of the lungs. There is an exchange of oxygen and carbon dioxide through the capillary walls. These capillaries join up to form venules and finally the left and right pulmonary veins, which return the oxygenated blood to the left atrium. These veins are the only ones to carry oxygenated blood. The oxygenated blood then moves into the left ventricle, and finally into the systemic circulation via the aorta.

The systemic circulation

The systemic circulation carries oxygen and nutrients to the body tissues, and removes carbon dioxide, heat and the waste products of metabolism. All arteries supplying the systemic system arise from the aorta, and the system is organised in parallel routes, so that it can deliver a proportion of the cardiac output directly to each tissue (figure 2.76).

After leaving the heart from the left ventricle, the aorta passes upward (the ascending aorta), and then arches to the left (the arch of the aorta). The descending aorta begins at this point, and passes downward close to the vertebral bodies to the level of the fourth lumbar vertebra, where it divides into the two common iliac arteries which carry blood to the lower limbs. The section of the aorta between the arch and the diaphragm is called the thoracic aorta, and the section between the diaphragm and the iliac branches is the abdominal aorta.

Blood returns to the heart through the systemic veins. All the veins of the systemic circulation drain into the superior vena cava (from the upper body, the inferior vena cava (from the lower body), and the coronary sinus, which ultimately drain into the right atrium.

The main circulatory routes are shown in figure 2.77, and the arterial and venous distributions are demonstrated in figure 2.78. A summary of the major paired arteries and veins is given in 2.78.

Figure 2.77 General plan of the circulation

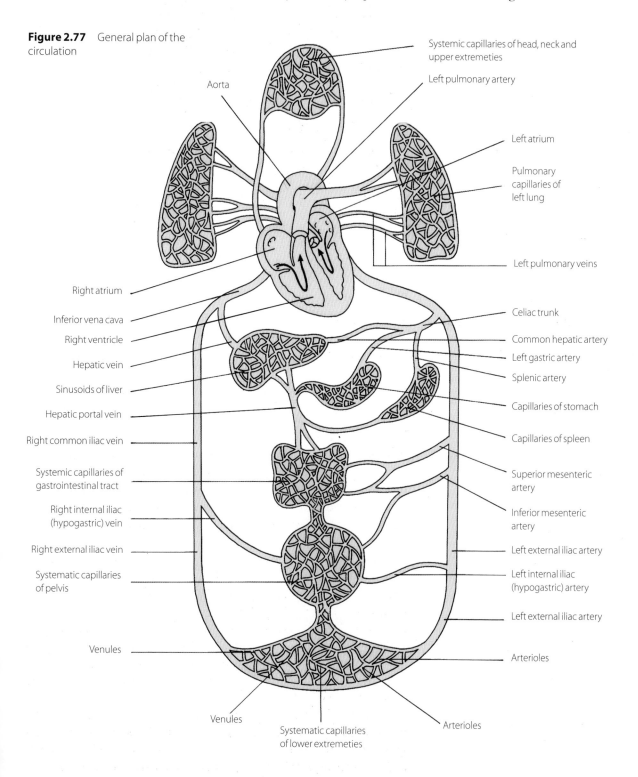

- Systemic capillaries of head, neck and upper extremeties
- Left pulmonary artery
- Aorta
- Left atrium
- Pulmonary capillaries of left lung
- Left pulmonary veins
- Right atrium
- Celiac trunk
- Inferior vena cava
- Common hepatic artery
- Right ventricle
- Left gastric artery
- Hepatic vein
- Splenic artery
- Sinusoids of liver
- Capillaries of stomach
- Hepatic portal vein
- Capillaries of spleen
- Right common iliac vein
- Systemic capillaries of gastrointestinal tract
- Superior mesenteric artery
- Right internal iliac (hypogastric) vein
- Inferior mesenteric artery
- Right external iliac vein
- Left external iliac artery
- Systematic capillaries of pelvis
- Left internal iliac (hypogastric) artery
- Left external iliac artery
- Venules
- Arterioles
- Venules
- Arterioles
- Systematic capillaries of lower extremeties

Figure 2.78 Arterial and venous distributions

Region	Arterial supply	Venous drainage
Head/neck	Right and left common carotid arteries Right and left vertebral arteries	Right and left internal jugular veins Right and left external jugular veins
Upper limb	Right and left subclavian arteries	Right and left subclavian veins
Liver	Common hepatic artery	Hepatic portal vein
Spleen	Splenic artery	Splenic vein
Stomach	Right and left gastric arteries	Right and left gastric veins
Kidneys	Right and left renal arteries	Right and left renal veins
Intestinal tract	Superior and inferior mesenteric arteries	Superior and inferior mesenteric veins
Reproductive system	Right and left gonadal arteries (ovarian/testicular arteries)	Right and left gonadal veins (ovarian/testicular veins)
Urinary system	Internal iliac artery	Internal iliac vein
Lower limbs	External iliac artery	External iliac vein

Circulatory dynamics

Blood flow

The volume of blood which flows through any tissue in a given period of time (measured in millilitres per second) is called the blood flow. The velocity of blood flow is inversely related to the cross section area of the vessels through which it is flowing. For example, the cross section area of the aorta ($3 - 5$ cm^2) is considerably smaller than the total cross section area of the capillaries ($4500 - 6000$ cm^2), so the blood flow in the aorta is faster (40 cm/sec) than in the capillaries (<0.1 cm/sec). Similarly, the velocity of blood flow in the capillaries is slower than in the veins through which the blood returns to the heart. Velocity in the venae cavae is $5 - 20$ cm/sec. The slow velocity of flow in the capillaries allows time for the exchange of oxygen/carbon dioxide, nutrients/waste products between the capillaries and the surrounding tissues.

Blood pressure

Blood pressure (BP) is the pressure exerted by the blood on the wall of the blood vessel. Blood pressure is generated by the contraction of the ventricles. In the aorta of a resting young adult, BP rises to about 120 mm Hg during systole (during contraction – systolic blood pressure) and falls to about 80 mm Hg during diastole (relaxation of the ventricles – diastolic blood pressure).

If the total volume of circulating blood (about 5.25 litres in an adult) decreases, for example, due to haemorrhage, the amount of blood flowing through the arteries decreases, and blood pressure drops. Anything which increases blood volume, for example, water retention in the body, will result in a rise in blood pressure. There is a gradual drop in blood pressure as blood flows through the systemic circulation, with the greatest pressures in the aorta and the large and

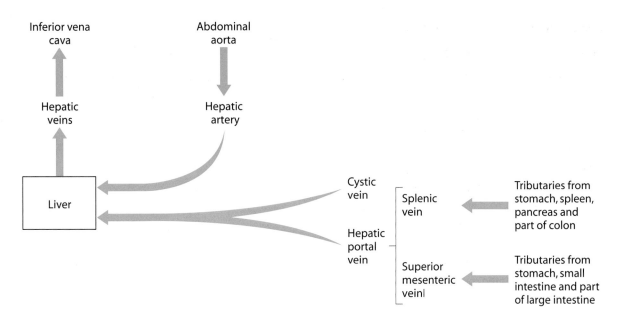

Figure 2.79 Hepatic portal circulation system

small arteries, which are close to the pumping action of the heart. The pressure continues to decrease through the arterioles, capillaries, venules, large and small veins, until it has reached zero at the right atrium (figure 2.80).

Venous return

The volume of blood flowing back to the heart from the systemic veins is called venous return. A satisfactory rate of return depends on the pressure difference between the venules (about 16 mm Hg) and the right atrium (0 mm Hg). Although the pressure difference is small, the venous return to the right atrium normally keeps pace with the cardiac output from the left ventricle. If the pressure in the right atrium increases, as occurs in some heart diseases, venous return will decrease, and cause a build-up of venous blood in the periphery (most commonly the lower limbs).

Two other mechanisms act as pumps to boost venous return.

- Skeletal muscle pump – as skeletal muscles contract, they exert pressure ('squeeze') on the veins which lie between them, forcing the blood to flow along the veins. As the veins contain valves which only allow blood flow in one direction (towards the heart), and prevents back-flow of blood when the muscles relax, this muscle action assists venous blood flow back to the heart.
- Respiratory pump – as you breath in (inspiration), the diaphragm (a large sheet of muscle which separates the thorax from the abdomen) moves downwards. This causes a decrease of pressure in the thoracic (chest) cavity, and an increase in pressure in the abdominal cavity. As a result, blood moves from the compressed, high pressure abdominal cavity to the low pressure thoracic veins. When the position reverses during expiration (breathing out), the valves in the veins prevent back-flow of blood into the abdomen.

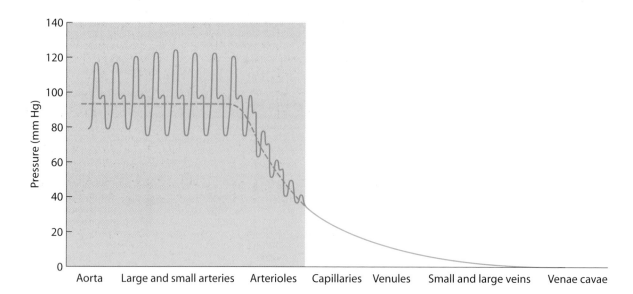

Figure 2.80 Blood pressure in systematic blood vessel

Control of blood pressure and blood flow

A number of inter-connecting factors control blood pressure by altering heart rate, stroke volume, systemic vascular resistance and blood volume. These may act to cope with sudden changes, or more slowly to provide long term control of blood pressure. Additionally, it may be necessary to change the distribution of blood flow, and this is done by changing the diameter of the arterioles. For example, in strenuous exercise, blood flow to the skeletal muscles may increase ten to fifteen times its resting value, and blood flow to the heart and skin may increase threefold. To compensate, blood flow to the digestive tract and kidneys may reduce to half the normal resting value. Blood flow to the brain remains fairly constant, irrespective of the activity of the body.

The cardiovascular centre

The cardiovascular centre is a group of nerve cells found in the medulla of the brain. It controls heart rate, force of contraction of the ventricles and the diameter of the blood vessels. It receives information from a number of sources.

- **Centres in the brain** – even before you start to exercise, your heart rate will increase due to impulses from other parts of the brain to the cardiovascular centre.
- **Sensory receptors** – baroreceptors in the aortic arch and the carotid sinus register the amount of stretch in the walls of the blood vessels. Chemoreceptors found close to the baroreceptors are sensitive to the oxygen and carbon dioxide levels, and to hydrogen ion concentration in the blood. For example, when there is an increase in tension in the blood vessel walls, the baroreceptors send impulses to the cardiovascular centre. This centre responds by sending impulses to the heart to slow down the rate of contraction, and to the blood vessels to cause vasodila-

tion. If blood pressure falls, the heart rate will increase, and vasoconstriction will occur. Similarly, if blood oxygen levels decrease, and hydrogen ion and carbon dioxide levels increase, the cardiovascular centre will respond by causing vasoconstriction. This results in an increase in blood pressure.

Additionally, other factors may operate to control blood pressure and blood flow.

- **Hormones** – epinephrine and norepinephrine (produced by the adrenal medulla) increase the rate and force of cardiac contraction, and bring about vasoconstriction of the abdominal and skin arterioles, and vasodilation of cardiac and skeletal muscle arterioles.
- **Local control** – physical changes and chemical mediators may cause changes in blood flow to meet local needs.

Vasomotor tone

The cardiovascular centre controls the diameter of the blood vessels through the sympathetic nervous system, via the vasomotor nerves. The vasomotor nerves supply the blood vessels in the viscera (organs of the body) and peripheral tissues (skin). Through these nerves, the vasomotor centre (a specialised part of the cardiovascular centre) continually sends impulses to the arterioles. This results in a degree of vasoconstriction called vasomotor tone. Increased activity of the vasomotor centre will produce increased vasomotor tone (vasoconstriction), whereas decreased vasomotor activity will produce decreased vasomotor tone (vasodilation).

This system has the ability to be selective, that is, to produce vasoconstriction in some tissues, and vasodilation in others. The tissues in which vasodilation occurs will receive the greater part of the cardiac output. Sympathetic stimulation of most veins results in constriction which moves blood from the venous reservoirs towards the heart, and increases blood pressure.

Blood flow, blood pressure and exercise

It has already been noted that during exercise blood flow in muscle may increase ten to fifteen times its resting value. This flow is not constant, but falls sharply when muscles contract, and rises when they relax. This pattern of flow is caused by the rhythmical muscle contraction and relaxation, which alternately compresses the blood vessels to reduce blood flow, and then allows dilation of those vessels to increase flow. This variation of flow can be seen in figure 2.81.

During exercise, blood pressure is increased. This is due primarily to increased cardiac output, and the fact that there is a tendency for arterioles to constrict in tissues other than skeletal muscle. Blood vessels in the liver, the kidney, the digestive organs are relatively constricted during exercise. This increases resistance to blood flow in those tissues, thus raising the blood pressure. It also diverts blood into the dilated arterioles of the working muscles.

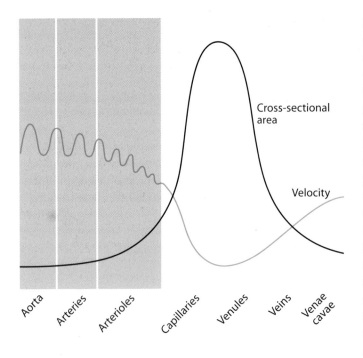

Cross-sectional area

Velocity

Aorta Arteries Arterioles Capillaries Venules Veins Venae cavae

Figure 2.81 Velocity of blood flow

During static (isometric) exercise, the constant contraction of the muscle causes constant compression on the blood vessels. This is unlike the rhythmic contraction and relaxation which occurs during rhythmic isotonic exercise. This compression causes an additional resistance to blood flow in the working muscles, and will result in a greater increase in blood pressure than in isotonic exercise. For this reason, people with high blood pressure should avoid strong isometric exercise.

In addition to an anticipatory rise in heart rate prior to exercise, heart rate increases almost instantaneously when exercise starts. It is thought that this is due to a nerve reflex originating in receptors in the muscles and joints, rather than the metabolic demands of the exercise. As the muscles begin to contract and joints begin moving through a range of motion, impulses are generated in the muscle and joint receptors. These impulses pass to the cardiovascular centre in the medulla, which results in an increase in heart rate.

SUMMARY

- The vascular system consists of a closed network of blood vessels which carries blood (carrying oxygen and nutrients) from the heart to the organs and tissues, and returns it (carrying carbon dioxide) to the heart.
- The vascular system consists of arteries, arterioles, capillaries, venules and veins.
- Blood consists of plasma (55%) and formed elements (45%), which include erythrocytes, leucocytes and thrombocytes.
- There are two circulatory paths – the pulmonary circulation and the systemic circulation.
- Blood pressure is the pressure exerted by the blood on the walls of a blood vessel, and is generated by the contraction of the ventricles.
- The cardiovascular centre controls heart rate, force of contraction of the ventricles and the diameter of the blood vessels.

Questions

1 Describe the structure of arteries, arterioles, capillaries, venules and veins.
2 What is the composition of blood?
3 What are the functions of blood?
4 How does blood circulate through the pulmonary and systemic systems?
5 How does the cardiovascular system control heart rate, and the diameter of the blood vessels?
6 How does exercise influence blood flow and blood pressure?

The respiratory system

The respiratory system consists of the nasal passages, pharynx (throat), larynx (voice box), trachea, (wind pipe), bronchi (air ways) and lungs. The structure and function of these features (omitting the larynx and pharynx) will be described.

The nasal passages

The external part of the nose consists of a supporting framework of bone and hyaline cartilage, covered with skin and muscle and lined with mucous membrane. The internal part of the nose consists of a large cavity in the skull, that lies below the cranium and above the mouth. The nasal cavity is divided into right and left sides by the nasal septum. Ducts (passages) from a number of sinuses open into the internal part of the nasal cavity. Sinuses are cavities in the skull which are lined with mucous membrane.

The nose has three functions.

- To warm, moisten and filter the incoming air. Air entering the nose is filtered by the hairs which line the external part of the nose, and mucous secreted by the goblet cells moistens it. An arrangement of shelf-like projections in the upper nasal cavity

Figure 2.82 The respiratory system (Rib-cage Removed)

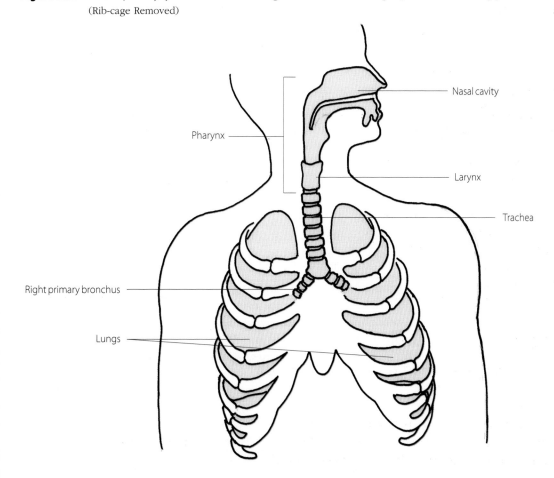

causes the air to be distributed over a wide area, where it is warmed by the blood in the capillaries.

- To receive olfactory (smell) stimuli. The olfactory receptors are found in the lining membrane in the upper part of the nasal cavity.
- To provide large, hollow resonating chambers which modify speech sounds - note how your voice becomes dull and thick when you have a heavy head cold!

Trachea

The trachea is a hollow tube, about 12 cm in length, and 2.5 cm in diameter, which extends from the lower part of the larynx (throat) to the level of the fifth thoracic vertebra. Here it divides into a right and left bronchus (figure 2.83). The wall of the trachea consists of connective tissue with C-shaped incomplete rings of hyaline cartilage, which prevent the tube from collapsing. The open part of the C-shaped cartilage is in contact with the oesophagus (food pipe) behind. Internally, the trachea is lined with a mucosa, which contains ciliated columnar cells (cells with hair-like projections which protrude into the centre of the trachea), and goblet cells which secrete mucous.

The trachea acts as a semi-rigid tube to carry air to the bronchi and lungs. The mucous lining helps to moisten the air, and the cilia (hair-like projections) move excessive mucous upwards so that it can be removed from the respiratory system by expectoration (spitting). During infections and in some diseases (bronchitis), the goblet cells secrete excessive mucous. At the lower end of the trachea, where it divides into the bronchi, there is an internal ridge called the carina. This is an area of highly sensitive mucous membrane, which when stimulated causes a cough – the cough reflex.

Bronchi

At the level of the fifth thoracic vertebra the trachea divides into a right main bronchus, which goes to the right lung, and a left main bronchus which goes to the left lung. The right bronchus is shorter, wider and more vertical than the left bronchus. The structure of the main bronchi is similar to that of the trachea, with C-shaped cartilages, and a mucous lining consisting of ciliated columnar cells and goblet cells.

After entering the lungs, the main bronchi divide – the left bronchus into two lobar bronchi, and the right bronchus into three lobar bronchi – one for each lobe of the lungs. In the lobes, the bronchi continue to divide, first into tertiary bronchi, then into bronchioles, and finally into fine tubes called terminal bronchioles. This branching arrangement of the bronchi and bronchioles is called the bronchial tree (figure 2.83).

Lungs

The lungs are a pair of cone-shaped structures, of a spongey consistency, which lie in the thoracic cavity. They are separated from each other by the heart and other structures in the central portion of the thoracic cavity known as the mediastinum. They have a two-layered

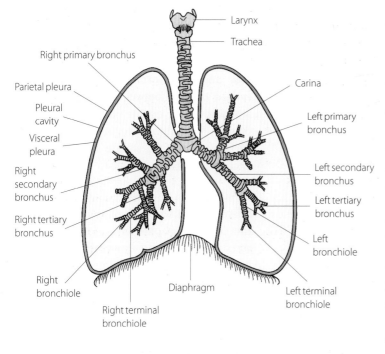

Larynx

Trachea

Right primary bronchus

Parietal pleura

Pleural cavity

Visceral pleura

Right secondary bronchus

Right tertiary bronchus

Right bronchiole

Right terminal bronchiole

Diaphragm

Carina

Left primary bronchus

Left secondary bronchus

Left tertiary bronchus

Left bronchiole

Left terminal bronchiole

covering called the pleural membrane. The outer layer is in contact with the inner surface of the thoracic cavity, and is called the parietal pleura. The inner layer is in contact with the outer surface of the lung, and is called the visceral pleura. Between the two layers of the pleural membrane is a thin layer of lubricating fluid secreted by the membranes, and because the two layers are continuous, there is a slight negative pressure between them. This means that if one layer moves, the other layer moves with it.

Each lung is divided into lobes – the right lung into three lobes and the left lung into two lobes by one or more fissures.

The gross structure of the lungs can be seen in figure 2.84.

Figure 2.83 The trachea and bronchial tree

Right lung	three lobes	superior lobe
		middle lobe
		inferior lobe
	two fissures	horizontal fissure
		oblique fissure
Left lung	two lobes	superior lobe
		inferior lobe
	one fissure	oblique fissure

Each lung is further divided into segments, each of which is supplied by a tertiary bronchus, and which are discrete, that is, separate from each other. This means that if a disease process affects one segment, it can be surgically removed as a separate structure, and need not affect adjoining segments.

The finest divisions of the respiratory system are the alveoli. These are cup-shaped pouches formed from the terminal branches of the bronchial tree. The terminal bronchioles eventually divide into respiratory bronchioles, which finally divide into alveolar ducts. Each duct expands into an alveolar sac, which contain several alveoli (figure 2.85), each consisting of a thin elastic membrane with an epithelial lining.

The alveolar cells secrete a fluid which contains an element (surfactant) which lowers the surface tension of the alveolar fluid. This prevents collapse of the alveoli. Closely associated with each alveolus, is a capillary. The alveolar membrane (elastic basement

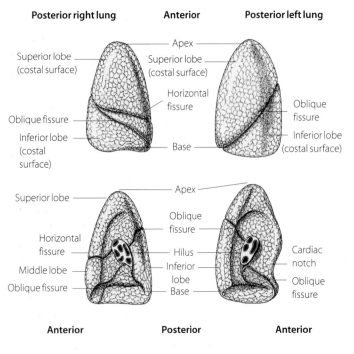

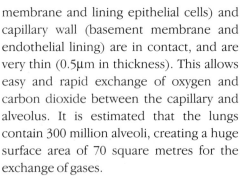

Figure 2.84 Gross structure of the lungs

membrane and lining epithelial cells) and capillary wall (basement membrane and endothelial lining) are in contact, and are very thin (0.5μm in thickness). This allows easy and rapid exchange of oxygen and carbon dioxide between the capillary and alveolus. It is estimated that the lungs contain 300 million alveoli, creating a huge surface area of 70 square metres for the exchange of gases.

Mechanics of respiration

Respiration is the flow of air in and out of the lungs (inspiration and expiration) associated with the movement of the rib cage, and with the lowering and raising of the diaphragm.

Within the rib cage are the right and left pleural cavities. In normal circumstances, there is no air space between the two layers of the pleura (visceral and parietal), and this creates a slight negative pressure (intra-pleural pressure) between the two layers.

In order that air may be drawn into the lungs, the volume of the thorax and the lungs must increase. This increase in volume is caused by contraction of the diaphragm at the base of the thorax, and the external intercostal muscles (small muscles attached between the ribs). The diaphragm is dome-shaped when it is relaxed, so that when it contracts the dome flattens and moves downwards. This increases the vertical dimension of the thorax. As the diaphragm moves downwards, it eventually comes to rest on the abdominal contents, and cannot move down any further. At this stage, the central part of the dome remains fixed, so when it continues to contract, it moves the lower ribs upward and outward, which increases the lateral dimension of the thorax. Finally, the external intercostals contract, and pull the ribs upward, and the sternum is pushed forward. This increases the antero-posterior dimension of the thorax.

As the size of the thorax increases, the lungs also increase in volume due to the negative intrapleural pressure which pulls the walls of the lungs outwards. The increase in volume of the lungs causes a decrease in pressure inside the lungs (intrapulmonary pressure), to a level which is below atmospheric pressure. The intrapulmonary pressure drops from 760 to 758 mm Hg (figure 2.87). Air rushes from the atmosphere into the lungs in an attempt to equalise the pressure inside and outside the lungs. This is inspiration.

Expiration (breathing out) reverses this procedure, and is caused by the relaxation of the muscles of inspiration (diaphragm and external intercostals) and the elastic recoil of the lungs. As these

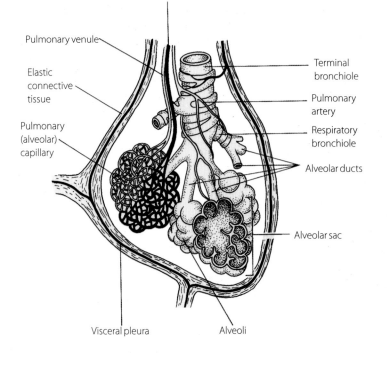

Pulmonary venule
Elastic connective tissue
Pulmonary (alveolar) capillary
Terminal bronchiole
Pulmonary artery
Respiratory bronchiole
Alveolar ducts
Alveolar sac
Visceral pleura
Alveoli

Figure 2.85   Terminal divisions of the lungs

Figure 2.86   Mechanics of respiration

muscles relax, the diaphragm moves upward and the rib cage collapses downwards and inwards. This causes a decrease in all dimensions of the thorax, a decrease in volume of the thorax and the lungs, and consequently an increase in pressure (from 760 to 762 mm Hg). Air then flows from the higher pressure in the lungs to the lower pressure outside the lungs, until they are equal.

This activity happens in normal, quiet respiration, when you are at rest, or performing undemanding tasks. When the level of activity increases, the demand for oxygen increases, as does the need to remove carbon dioxide from the system. The body responds by an increase in the rate and depth of respiration. Extra muscles, known as the accessory muscles of respiration, (the scalenes and sternomastoid)

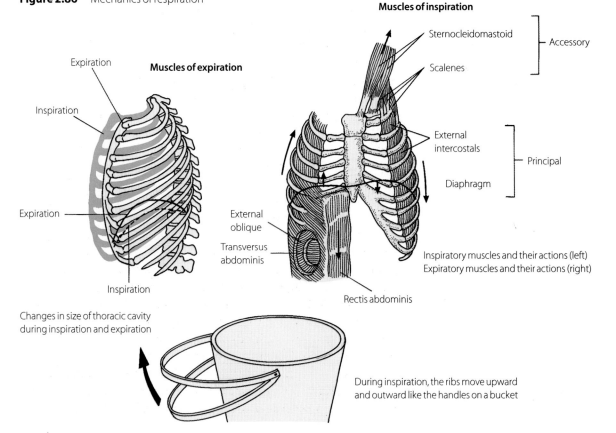

Muscles of inspiration

Sternocleidomastoid — Accessory
Scalenes

External intercostals
Diaphragm — Principal

Inspiratory muscles and their actions (left)
Expiratory muscles and their actions (right)

Muscles of expiration

Expiration
Inspiration
Expiration
External oblique
Transversus abdominis
Inspiration
Rectis abdominis

Changes in size of thoracic cavity during inspiration and expiration

During inspiration, the ribs move upward and outward like the handles on a bucket

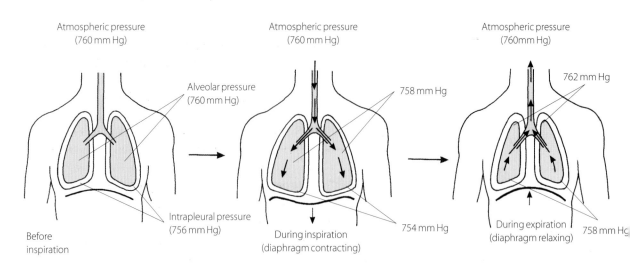

Atmospheric pressure
(760 mm Hg)

Atmospheric pressure
(760 mm Hg)

Atmospheric pressure
(760mm Hg)

762 mm Hg

Alveolar pressure
(760 mm Hg)

758 mm Hg

Intrapleural pressure
(756 mm Hg)

754 mm Hg

During expiration
(diaphragm relaxing)

758 mm Hg

Before
inspiration

During inspiration
(diaphragm contracting)

Figure 2.87 Pressure changes during respiration

come into action to assist in the elevation of the rib cage, and increasing further the volume of the thorax. This extra movement of the thorax is obvious when you watch someone who has just been involved in strenuous exercise. Expiration can also be assisted by active muscle contraction of the muscles of expiration, which are the abdominals and the internal intercostals. These muscles assist in pulling the ribcage downwards and inwards, and in forcing the diaphragm upwards (figure 2.86).

The activity during inspiration and expiration is summarised in figure 2.88.

Figure 2.88 Summary of inspiration and expiration

Inspiration
During normal quiet inspiration, diaphragm and external intercostal muscles contract and during laboured inspiration, sternocleidomastoid, scalenes and pectoralis minor also contract

Alveolar pressure increases to 762 mm Hg

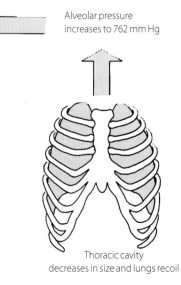

Thoracic cavity
increases and lungs expand

Thoracic cavity
decreases in size and lungs recoil

Alveolar pressure decreases
to 758 mm Hg

Expiration
During normal quiet expiration, diaphragm and external intercostal muscles relax and during laboured inspiration, abdominal and internal intercostal muscles contract

Control of respiration

The basic rate and depth of respiration is controlled from the respiratory centre in the brain, which is found in the brain stem. This centre is divided into three areas:

- The medullary rhythmicity area dictates the basic rate of respiration, in which inspiration lasts for about two seconds, and expiration lasts for about three seconds. There are two types of neurons (inspiratory and expiratory) which carry impulses from this area to the muscles involved in respiration.

  The inspiratory neurons actively convey impulses from the inspiratory centre to the muscles of inspiration as inspiration occurs, and then they become inactive.

  During quiet respiration, both the inspiratory and expiratory neurons (in the expiratory centre) are inactive during expiration, as this occurs passively, due to relaxation of the muscles of inspiration and the elastic recoil of the lungs. However, during forced expiration (as in blowing), the expiratory neurons carry impulses to the muscles of expiration.

- The pneumotaxic area has an inhibitory influence on inspiration. As the lungs fill with air, the pneumotaxic centre transmits inhibitory impulses to the inspiratory centre, to stop its activity. This then stops the impulses passing to the muscles of inspiration, which relax and allow expiration to occur.

- The apneustic area sends stimulatory messages to the inspiratory centre to prolong inspiration.

Other factors can modify the basic rhythm set by the respiratory centre:

- The cerebral cortex can exert voluntary control over respiration. This is important because it means we can voluntarily stop breathing to prevent water or irritating gases entering the lungs.

- Stretch receptors in the walls of the bronchi and bronchioles are stimulated when the lungs become over-inflated. Impulses are then sent to the inspiratory centre which inhibit its activity and cause expiration to occur. This reflex is called the Hering-Breuer reflex.

- Chemoreceptors which are sensitive to the concentration of hydrogen ions (H^+), carbon dioxide and oxygen in the blood are situated in the carotid arteries (carotid bodies) and the aortic arch (aortic bodies). Any increase in carbon dioxide (hypercapnia) will cause an increase in H^+, which will stimulate the chemoreceptors to send impulses to the respiratory centre to increase the rate and depth of respiration. This will remove more carbon dioxide until the levels are back to normal, in which the partial pressure of carbon dioxide (pCO_2) is 40 mm Hg. Low levels of carbon dioxide (hypocapnia) (below 40 mm Hg) will decrease respiratory stimulation and may result in a slow rate of respiration. The moreceptors are also sensitive to decreases in the partial pressure of oxygen (pO_2), but only to considerably large changes. The normal pO_2 value is 105 mm Hg, and only when this decreases to about 50 mm Hg are the chemoreceptors stimulated.

- Proprioceptors in the muscles and joints are thought to stimulate the respiratory centre to increase the rate and depth of breathing immediately upon commencing exercise, even before carbon dioxide and oxygen levels have changed.

Gaseous exchange

In the lungs there is an exchange of oxygen and carbon dioxide between the alveoli of the lungs and the pulmonary blood capillaries. This exchange of gases relies on differences in the partial pressure of these gases in the alveolar air and the pulmonary capillaries.

During inspiration, the pO2 of the alveolar air is 105 mm Hg, and the pO2 of the deoxygenated blood in the pumonary capillaries is only 40 mm Hg. Due to the difference in partial pressure, oxygen diffuses from the area of higher pressure (the alveoli) to the area of lower pressure, until the partial pressure of the pulmonary capillary blood reaches 105 mm Hg. This newly oxygenated blood is gathered into the pulmonary veins, and transported to the heart, and eventually into the circulation via the aorta.

At the same time that oxygen is diffusing from the alveoli to the pulmonary capillaries, the opposite is happening to carbon dioxide. The partial pressure of carbon dioxide (pCO_2) in the pulmonary capillaries is 45 mm Hg, whereas the pCO_2 of the alveolar air is 40 mm Hg. The carbon dioxide diffuses from the pulmonary capillaries to the alveoli, and finally is eliminated during expiration.

Oxygenation of haemoglobin

As oxygen does not dissolve easily in water, little is carried in the blood plasma (1.5%), and the vast majority is carried in the haemoglobin of the red blood cells (98.5%). Haemoglobin consists of a protein called globin and an iron-containing pigment called haeme. Each haemoglobin molecule has four haeme groups, and each group can combine with one molecule of oxygen. Oxygen and haemoglobin combine in a reversible reaction to form oxyhaemoglobin.

Hb (de-oxyhaemoglobin) + O_2
$\rightleftharpoons$ HbO_2 (oxyhaemoglobin)

The reversible nature of the reaction means that haemoglobin can both take up oxygen, and give it away. As the oxygen is held in the haemoglobin of the red blood cells, it can only combine or be released when the partial pressure of oxygen in the tissues is at an appropriate level.

When the pO_2 is high, oxygen combines readily with haemoglobin, until the haemoglobin becomes saturated with oxygen. When the pO_2 is low, haemoglobin releases oxygen to the tissues. Haemoglobin combines readily with oxygen at partial pressures of oxygen between 100 and 60 mm Hg. This means that even when the pO_2 is as low as 60 mm Hg (as in exercising at high altitude, or in some heart or lung diseases), the oxygen saturation of haemoglobin is 90%. At the other end of the range, there is a rapid reduction in the oxygen saturation of haemoglobin at partial pressures of oxygen between 40 and 10 mm Hg. This means that large amounts of oxygen are released from the haemoglobin in response to relatively small reductions in pO_2. For example, the pO_2 in working muscles is approximately 40 mm Hg and the oxygen saturation of haemoglobin is 75%. At this level, large amounts of oxygen are released from the haemoglobin to be used by the muscles (figure 2.87). This demonstrates efficiency in both the uptake of oxygen and in its release in response to changes in partial pressures of oxygen.

Lung volumes and capacities

During quiet respiration, about 500 ml of air moves in to and out of the lungs with each breath. This is called the tidal volume. Of this, about

Figure 2.89 Transport of oxygen and carbon dioxide in the blood

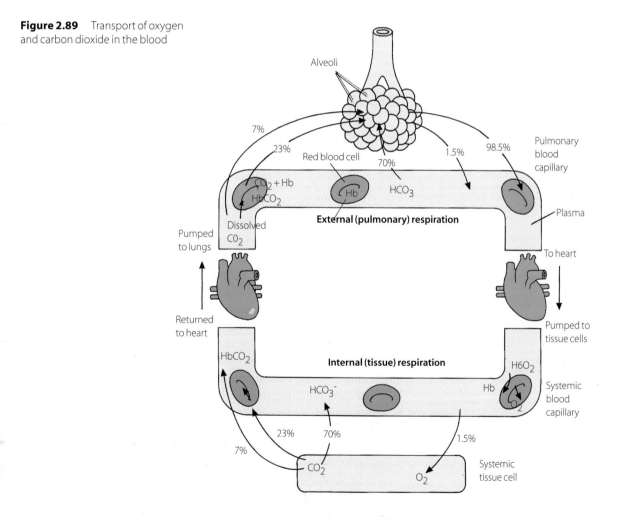

350 ml actually reaches the pulmonary alveoli, the remaining 150 ml remaining in the nasal cavity and airways. These are collectively known as the anatomic dead space. The amount of air breathed in a minute can be calculated by multiplying the tidal volume by the number of breaths taken in a minute, usually about 12. This volume of air is called the minute respiratory volume.

If you take a deep breath, the normal tidal volume is increased. The extra air taken in (above the normal tidal volume) is called the inspiratory reserve volume, and can reach over 3000 ml air. This gives a total inspiratory capacity of over 3500 ml.

During quiet respiration, a considerable amount of air remains in the lungs following expiration. If you breath out as hard as you can, about 1200 ml of air can be pushed out in addition to the 500 ml of normal expiration. This extra air is known as the expiratory reserve volume. Even after you have blown out as hard as you can, a considerable amount of air remains in the lungs to maintain a degree of inflation of the alveoli. This air remaining after the expiratory reserve volume is called the residual capacity of the lungs, and amounts to approximately 1200 ml.

Pulmonary function testing is used to provide information on lung capacities and on the efficiency of the respiratory tissues.

Lung volumes and capacities are summarised in figure 2.90.

Figure 2.90 Lung volumes and capacities

Lung capacities are made up of combinations of the various lung volumes:

Inspiratory capacity = tidal volume + inspiratory reserve volume (3600 ml)

Functional residual capacity = residual volume + expiratory reserve volume (2400 ml)

Vital capacity = inspiratory capacity + expiratory reserve volume (4800 ml)

Total lung capacity = vital capacity + residual volume (6000 ml)

Simple investigations of lung function

Spirometry measures the breathing capacity of the lungs, and this can be carried out by spirometers such as the vitalograph, which produces a digital read-out or a graph. The person blows into the measuring device as hard as s/he can, for as long as s/he can ('Blow the living daylights out of the machine, and keep blowing until your lungs are empty!'). A simple device to measure this is the water spirometer which consists of a drum inverted in a tank of water. The drum is suspended by a pulley and counterbalanced by a weight. As the person breathes through the mouthpiece, the drum moves up and down, and a recording is made on a chart on a rotating drum.

Most measures of lung function are measures of expiration. Figure 2.91 shows a trace from a vitalograph, which shows that in a forced expiration, most of the air is expelled in the first second. This is known as FEV1 (forced expiratory volume in one second), and it should be more than 70% of the forced vital capacity (FVC). Changes in either of these volumes may indicate lung disease. However, the water spirometer can provide a measurement of both inspiratory and expiratory volumes, under all conditions of rest or exercise.

Respiratory muscle strength can be assessed by measurement of maximal inspiratory (P_{Imax}) and maximal expiratory (P_{Emax}) mouth pressures, which are measured following maximal expiration and maximal inspiration respectively. A pressure guage or transducer is attached to a mouthpiece, and the best value from three efforts is recorded.

Effects of exercise on ventilation volumes

At rest, the lungs are ventilated at approximately six litres per minute. During prolonged 'steady state' endurance exercise, maximal ventilation is about 80 – 100 litres per minute in young adult males, and 45 – 80 litres per minute in young adult females (who have smaller lungs than males). With brief maximal exercise, such as an 800-metre run, ventilation rates in excess of 120 – 140 litres per minute may be recorded. During exercise, both the frequency of respiration and depth of respiration increases. The frequency can increase from 12 per minute at rest to 45 per minute during strenuous exercise. The depth of respiration can increase from 0.5 litres per breath at rest to 2.5 litres per breath during strenuous exercise.

In normal people, little or no change in pulmonary function at rest is observed as a result of training. If subjects specifically improve the strength of their breathing musculature (for example swimmers, who have to breathe against the resistance of the water), they may experience some increase in their vital capacity and in maximal breathing capacity. Otherwise, only slight decreases in respiratory rate and slight

Figure 2.91   Vitalograph traces

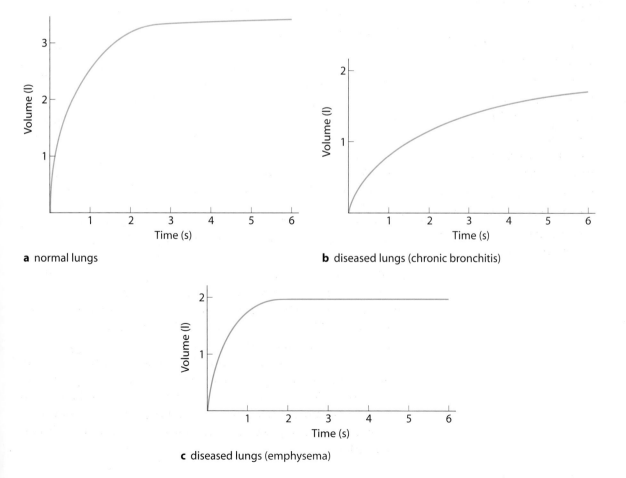

a normal lungs

b diseased lungs (chronic bronchitis)

c diseased lungs (emphysema)

increases in tidal volume may occur. Studies of marathon runners have indicated that there was essentially no difference in the actual lung function measures (FVC, FEV1, total lung capacity [TLC], the volume of air breathed each minute [MV], breathing rate) when compared with sedentary subjects of similar body size.

SUMMARY

- The respiratory system functions to deliver oxygen to the lungs, and remove carbon dioxide.
- The system consists of the nose, trachea, bronchial tree and lungs.
- Inspiration occurs when air is drawn into the lungs by the reduction in interpleural pressure caused by the increase in all dimensions of the thorax.
- Expiration occurs when the interpleural pressure increases as the dimensions of the thorax decrease, and air is forced out into the atmosphere.
- During normal breathing, inspiration is produced by the activity of the diaphragm and the intercostal muscles. Expiration occurs when these muscles relax.
- During exercise, both the rate and depth of breathing increase. This is brought about by accessory muscle activity.
- Control of respiration is by the respiratory centre in the medulla of the brain. Additionally, voluntary effort, changes in the chemical composition of the blood and sensory receptors in the lungs, muscles and joints can exert control over the rate and depth of respiration.
- Total lung capacity is the sum of tidal volume, inspiratory reserve volume, expiratory reserve volume and residual volume (6000ml).

Questions

1 Describe the components of the bronchial tree.
2 Describe the structure of the lungs.
3 What happens in the rib cage and lungs during normal inspiration and respiration?
4 What factors control the rate and depth of respiration?
5 What are the normal lung capacities and ventilation volumes? How do these change during exercise?

The endocrine or hormone system

The endocrine system functions to develop and regulate body functions. Throughout the chapters on anatomy and physiology, reference has been made to neurological, chemical and hormonal control of body functions. This section will briefly summarise the role and nature of hormone effects on the various systems and functions of the body.

The body contains basically two types of glands:

- The **exocrine glands** secrete their products directly to the exterior of the body, into body cavities or into body organs.

● The **endocrine glands** secrete their products, called hormones, into the extracellular space, which eventually pass into the blood stream, and are distributed in the circulation.

The endocrine system, through its potential to deliver hormones to almost all cells of the body, plays an important role in homeostasis. This is the attempt to maintain the body systems in a state of equilibrium. In this role, the endocrine system works along with the nervous system in a co-ordinated fashion. It is important that the two systems work together, as they regulate each other's activity. For example, some elements of the nervous system stimulate the release of hormones, and some inhibit their release; some hormones stimulate nervous activity, and some inhibit this activity. Consequently, under normal circumstances, the body systems operate under a balance between the two systems, but when something disturbs the equilibrium of the body, the systems will co-ordinate their activity to produce the appropriate response to restore homeostasis.

Generally speaking, the nervous response to a disturbance in equilibrium occurs rapidly, and often is of short duration. On the other hand, the hormone response may be either rapid or slow, and its duration may be short or prolonged.

Some examples of hormones and their function are listed below. It can be seen that the endocrine system has the potential to control all aspects of human growth, development and function. It affects every aspect of everyday activity, and its co-ordinated activity with the nervous system is crucial for the control and regulation of all body systems.

Figure 2.92   Hormones and their function

Human Growth Hormone	Stimulates general body growth and regulates metabolism
Thyroid Stimulating Hormone	Controls metabolism, growth and development, activity of the nervous system.
Gonadotrophic Hormone	Stimulates sperm production and secretion of testosterone (males) and ova production and secretion of eostregen and progesterone (females)
Adrenocorticotrophic hormone	Stimulates production of glucocorticoids which promote normal metabolism by ensuring adequate supply of ATP, provide resistance to stress and have an anti-inflammatory function.
Antidiuretic Hormone	Controls (limits) urine output; can increase blood pressure.
Glucagon	Raises blood glucose levels.
Insulin	Lowers blood glucose levels.
Epinephrine/Norepinephrine	Promote 'fight or flight response' to stress increase heart rate and blood pressure, increase rate of respiration, increase efficiency of muscle contractions, increase blood sugar levels, stimulate cellular metabolism.

SUMMARY

- The endocrine system functions to develop and regulate body functions.
- The endocrine system is based upon endocrine glands which secrete hormones into the extracellular space and eventually into the blood stream.
- The endocrine system plays an important role in homeostasis, working in conjunction with the nervous system.

Questions

1 Explain the balance between the activity of the nervous system and the endocrine system.
2 How does the response to disturbances in equilibrium differ between the nervous and endocrine systems?
3 Describe the function of five hormones.

References

Guyton A C *Human Physiology and Mechanisms of Disease* (3rd Edition), W. B. Saunders Co. (1982)

Lamb D R *Physiology of Exercise — Responses and Adaptations* (2nd Ed), Macmillan (1984)

Lamb J F, Ingram C G, Johnson I A, Pitman R M *Essentials of Physiology*, Blackwell Scientific Co. (1991)

Lumley J S P, Craven J L, Aitken J T *Essential Anatomy,* Churchill Livingstone (1975)

Noble B J *Physiology of Exercise and Sport,* Times Mirror/Mosby College Pub (1985)

Rasch P J *Kinesilogy and Applied Anatomy* (7th ed), Lea & Febiger (1989)

Wirhed R *Athletic Ability and the Anatomy of Motion*, Wolfe Medical Publications (1984)

3 ENERGY SYSTEMS

Objectives

To understand

- energy sources in the human body
- the different roles played by the metabolic energy systems during rest and exercise
- how the energy systems respond during the recovery process
- the application of energy concepts to sport and exercise

Energy and its effects are all around us. All our activities rely on the continuous provision of energy. It is generally accepted that the most relevant concept related to exercise and sport science is energy production by the human body. The importance of this concept becomes obvious when we think how versatile the human body is, with respect to the kinds of movements and sport activities it is capable of performing. The range extends from those activities which require large bursts of energy over short periods of time, for example, the shot putt, to those activities which need small but sustained energy production, such as distance running. Even within the same activities, the energy requirements change from one moment to the next. One of the purposes of this chapter is to show how the understanding of energy concepts can be applied to sport and physical education. Another, is to develop the concept of human energy production as it relates to these applications.

Energy, work and power

Energy

The building processes of the body such as the construction of bones, the growth of hair and the replacement of injured cells, require energy. Our bodies require energy to enable us to run, swim or jump. The body extracts this energy from the food we eat and transfers it to the muscles. The breakdown of the food we eat occurs through decomposition. When foods decompose, they release energy which can be used by the body for its building processes. Some of the energy stored in the food is converted within the body into mechanical energy by the muscles. All energy transformation ultimately results in the

A **joule** is the energy used when 1 kg is moved 1 metre by a force of 1 Newton. It is equivalent to 4186 calories.

A **calorie** is the heat required to raise 1 g of water by 1° C but, since the calorie is a very small quantity, the kilocalorie is more frequently used.

production of heat. This is why the most commonly used unit of energy is the calorie. A newer system for measuring energy uses units called joules (J), and kilojoules (kJ). It is simple to make an approximate conversion from kcal to kJ: 1 kcal = 4.2 kJ.

In scientific terms, energy can be defined as the ability to perform work. When you run longer or faster, you do more work and you produce and utilise more energy in your muscles.

Work

In physics, work is defined with a limited meaning. For example, the physicist defines work as the application of force through a distance. When you move a load that weighs 500 g, vertically ten metres, the work you performed would have been 50 g/metre.

Work = Force x Distance

Work units may be expressed in different terms such as kilogram per metre (kg/m) or foot per pound (ft/lb).

Power

Power is defined as the work performed over a unit of time. In the previous example, if the load was moved ten metres in one second, power would be expressed as 50 g/metre per second. Power may be expressed as kilogram-metre per minute (kg-m/min), kcal/min, kJ/min, or watt (W).

Power is usually expressed as follows:

$$Power = \frac{Work}{Time}$$

$$Power = \frac{Force \times Distance}{Time}$$

1 Watt = 6.118 kg-m/min.

It is important for us to understand what energy, work and power mean and that energy can be converted from one form to another. During physical activity the amount of energy we expend depends on how much work is accomplished in a given period of time. The term activity has little scientific meaning because it cannot be quantified; therefore we must find some other means to quantify physical activity. There are several commonly available devices with which to study the energy production during physical activity such as the motor-driven treadmill, the arm-crank ergometer, the stationary cycle, the rowing ergometer, and the swing ergometer. Some of these devices can be connected with and monitored by a computer sensor.

$$Power = \frac{Force \times Distance}{Time} = Force \times Speed$$

Forms of energy

Energy can be classified into six different forms: chemical, mechanical, heat, light, electric, and nuclear. Energy can be converted from one form to another. Human living cells transform the potential chemical energy available within food into other forms of energy for normal body functions, such as the mechanical energy for movement, the thermal energy for keeping warm and the electrical energy for the conduction of a signal along nerves. Energy is involved whenever bonds between atoms in molecules are formed or broken down during the chemical reactions that take place in the body. When a chemical bond is formed, energy is required (endothermic). When a bond is broken, energy is released (exothermic).

Measuring chemical energy

Energy metabolism ultimately depends on the complete combustion of foodstuffs within the cell, in the presence of oxygen, in order to liberate the potential energy stored within the food. The quantity of energy generated by the body during rest and during muscular effort can be determined accurately by several different methods. These methods are broadly classified as **direct** and **indirect calorimetry**. In order to measure the energy content of a given food, a technique called **bomb calorimetry** is commonly used. All the organic material is combusted completely and the heat liberated is measured. The use of this bomb calorimeter is referred to as the direct method. For example, if we were to determine the amount of energy contained in yoghurt, coca cola or a small-sized pizza, we would simply burn the item in the calorimeter. The increase in temperature of the circulating water would be equivalent to the energy or calorie value of the food.

On the other hand, when we measure the oxygen consumption required in metabolising food, we are using an indirect method in determining energy. In our body, the situation is different from the laboratory, due to the fact that not all the energy within food is completely absorbed or combusted. In the process of oxidising the molecules of carbohydrate, fat and protein within the cell, oxygen is used and carbon dioxide is given off in relative amounts, depending on the molecule of fuel being combusted. This measurement of oxygen consumption is an indirect measure of energy.

The efficiency of the human machine

We generally think of efficiency as 'getting the most with the least effort'. The concept of efficiency can be seen as the relationship between input and resulting output, or the ratio of work done to the amount of energy used. In terms of human movement, the basic concern is the quantity of energy required to perform the actual work. To evaluate the relationship between input (metabolic energy expenditure) and resulting mechanical output in exercise, we need to calculate the actual mechanical efficiency of human movement. This provides an indication of the per cent of total energy expended that can produce external work.

Per cent efficiency is defined as the ratio of work output over work input (energy expenditure) times 100, or

$$\% \text{ Efficiency} = \frac{\text{useful work output}}{\text{energy expenditure}} \times 100$$

As with all machines, the efficiency of the human body for producing mechanical work is significantly less than 100%. The biggest factor that affects efficiency is the energy required to overcome internal and external friction. The per cent efficiency is usually within the range of 12% to 25% for human activities. This means for every movement made, only 25% of the energy consumed contributes directly to the actual movement and the other 75% is converted into heat energy. In general, the efficiency of human locomotion in walking, running, and cycling range between 20% to 25%. Activities in which there is considerable air or water resistance, per cent efficiency is lower than 20%. If the intensity of exercise is sufficiently low so that the amount of oxygen supplied is adequate for performing the physical task, the efficiency of this work is higher than when work depends on anaerobic contractions. In order to measure the work of muscles of the body while the individual remains in one place, either a treadmill or a cycle ergometer can be used.

Applying energy concepts

There are five different applications of energy concepts to sport and exercise:

Warming up and the construction of training programmes

It is a common practice for athletes and others who take part in regular physical exercise to warm up and cool down, that is, perform light or mild exercise immediately before and following training and competition sessions. The physiological reasons for performing warm-up exercises in relation to energy are increased body and muscle temperature which in turn promote other changes; firstly, an increase in enzyme activity and in the metabolic reactions associated with the energy system, and secondly, increases in blood supply and the amount of oxygen transported to the skeletal muscle.

Training programmes must be designed to develop the energy supply system required to perform a specific sports activity. For example, when you sprint you use an energy supply system which is different from that which your body requires when you run a marathon. You should not assume that a training programme designed to improve the energy supply system during long distance running will improve the energy supply system used during sprinting.

Prevention, delay and recovery from fatigue

Essentially, energy for body activities depends on chemical changes produced by combining oxygen and food substances. Food may be considered the 'fuel' and oxygen the flame which ignites it. Since the body can store food, but not oxygen, the amount of work it can perform depends mainly on its ability to supply oxygen to meet the demands of the working muscles. When the oxygen supply is adequate to keep up with the energy demands of the body, the end-products of the energy-making process are carbon dioxide and water. These are carried off by the blood and removed through the lungs and other organs. This process of energy production is referred to as the aerobic process (with oxygen). When the oxygen supply is insufficient to meet the demands of the activity, the energy-making process ends at an intermediate stage in which lactic acid is the end-product. Energy produced in this manner is referred to as anaerobic process (without oxygen or with an inadequate supply of oxygen). Understanding how energy is produced within the body will provide us with some insight into what fatigue is, how it can be delayed or in some instances, even be avoided during performance. Fatigue is linked with the way energy is produced and can be delayed through proper training programmes.

Nutrition and performance

One of the most important nutritional aspects concerning athletes, recognised since the sports competitions in ancient Greece, is the increased need for energy. Athletes involved in heavy physical activity need more food than more sedentary individuals, or less active people. Physical activity during training or competition increases the daily energy expenditure by 500 kcal to more than 1000 kcal per hour, depending on physical fitness, intensity, duration and type of sport. For this reason, athletes must adapt their energy intake by increasing food consumption, according to the level of daily energy expenditure, in order to meet their energy needs.

Control of body weight

The quantity of energy required by an individual above that which is necessary for body maintenance and growth, depends on the amount of physical activity that she or he experiences. For body weight to remain constant, food intake must equal energy needs.

Energy input < energy output ⇨ decrease in body mass (negative energy balance)

Energy input = energy output ⇨ stable body mass (energy balance)

Energy input > energy output ⇨ increase in body mass (positive balance)

To prevent an increase in body mass and fat because of a calorie disequilibrium, an effective programme of weight control must establish a balance between energy input and energy output.

Maintenance of body temperature

Some energy is liberated as heat from within our bodies. In order to maintain a constant body temperature this heat must be dissipated. If it is not removed, it will be stored within our bodies, causing the whole body temperature to rise.

Heat gain ⇨ Heat storage ⇨ Heat loss

As we sit or otherwise use little energy, our body temperatures remain at 37°C (98.6°F). In other words, the energy we expend in performing light activity is constantly being liberated by the body to the environment so that we maintain heat balance; as a result, our body temperatures remain constant. The body gains or loses heat through convection, conduction, radiation, and evaporation.

SUMMARY

- Energy, work, and power are functionally related. Energy is defined as the capacity to perform work, whereas work (W) is the application of a force (F) through a distance (D), or W = F x D. Power (P) is the time (t) rate of performing work, or P = W/t = (F x D)/t.
- The unit of measurement of energy is the calorie, which is the amount of heat required to raise the temperature of one gram of water by one degree centigrade.
- The direct quantification of energy in the body involves the measurement of the heat production, whereas the indirect method involves the measurement of oxygen consumption.
- Per cent efficiency is the ratio of work output over work input (energy expenditure) times 100. The per cent efficiency is usually within the range 12 % to 25 % for the human body.

- Some examples of how energy concepts apply to sports are:
  - Construction of physical training programmes.
  - Prevention and delay of fatigue.
  - Nutrition and performance.
  - Control of body weight.
  - Maintenance of body temperature.

Questions

1 Define, in words, energy, work, and power. Express work and power by formulae.
2 What fundamental measurements are needed when indirectly measuring the energy expenditure of a given exercise?
3 Explain efficiency and indicate how the efficiency of a human movement is measured.
4 What is the value of warming up in physiological terms?

Energy metabolism

ATP

The energy in the food is not transferred directly to the cells for mechanical work. Rather, it is used to manufacture another chemical compound called adenosine triphosphate (ATP) which is stored in all muscle cells. The potential energy within the ATP molecule is then utilised for all the energy requiring processes of the cells. Figure 3.1 shows the ATP molecule formed from one adenosine molecule linked to three phosphate molecules. The bonds that link the two outermost phosphates are termed high-energy bonds because they represent a considerable quantity of potential energy within the ATP molecule. When one of these phosphates' bonds is broken, that is, removed from rest of the molecule, 7 – 12 kcal of energy is liberated and adenosine diphosphate (ADP) plus inorganic phosphate (Pi) are formed.

The total quantity of ATP within the muscles is very small and it is only enough to provide energy for maximal contraction for a few seconds. Fortunately, the body has the ability to replenish ATP almost as quickly as it is broken down. There are three common energy-yielding processes for the production of ATP:

- In the ATP-PC or phosphagen system, the energy for resynthesis of ATP comes from only one compound, creatine phosphate (CP).

Figure 3.1   The structure of ATP

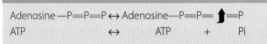

- Anaerobic glycolysis, also called the lactic acid system, provides ATP from the partial decomposition of glucose or glycogen.
- The oxygen system (aerobic) involves the complete oxidation of carbohydrate and fatty acids.

Any physical or chemical process that results in a release of energy to its surroundings is termed exergonic. Exergonic reactions can be viewed as 'downhill' processes, since they result in a decline in free energy, that is, energy useful to work. Processes that store or absorb energy are termed endergenic; these reactions represent 'uphill' processes and proceed with an increase in free energy. The energy liberated from the breakdown of foodstuffs and the energy released when CP is broken down are used to put the ATP molecule back together again. The functional coupling of energy from one series of reactions to another is referred to as coupled reactions (figure 3.2) and is the fundamental principle in the metabolic production of ATP.

Figure 3.2 The principle of coupled reactions

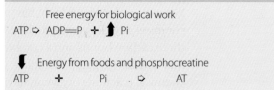

The phosphagen energy yield system (alactacid anaerobic system)

The first fuel reserve to be called upon when ATP is being used up is a molecule called creatine phosphate (or phosphocreatine), which is stored in the muscle fibres. Because both ATP and CP contain phosphate groups, they are collectively referred to as phosphagens (hence the name phosphagen system). The concentration of CP is about three to five times greater than that of ATP. For this reason, CP is considered the high energy phosphate reservoir. The CP molecule is similar to the ATP molecule in that a large amount of free energy is released when the bond between creatine and phosphate molecule splits. This reaction is catalysed by the enzyme creatine kinase (figure 3.3). The enzyme must be present for the reaction to occur, although it takes no other part in the reaction.

The breakdown of CP does not require the presence of oxygen,

Figure 3.3 The structure of creatine phosphate (CP)

Useful energy
CREATINE==P ↔ CREATINE ⬆ P
        CREATINE
        KINASE
  CP   ↔   C + Pi

therefore it is said to be an anaerobic process. Also, because no lactic acid is formed, this system is called the alactacid anaerobic system. This resynthesis or rebuilding of ATP at the expense of CP is especially important when extremely heavy exercise is sustained for less than 30 seconds. Examples would include a sprinter coming off the starting blocks, a shot putter in action, or pedalling a cycle ergometer rapidly against heavy resistance.

The lactic acid energy yield system

The other anaerobic system in which ATP is resynthesised within the muscle is anaerobic glycolysis. It involves an incomplete breakdown of one of the foodstuffs, that is, carbohydrates to lactic acid (hence the name lactic acid system). In the body, all carbohydrates are converted to the simple sugar glucose, which can either be used immediately in that form or stored in the liver and muscle as glycogen for use later. Like the ATP-PC system, glycogen stores are high in power but low in capacity because not much glycogen is stored in muscle. Anaerobic glycolysis consists of breaking down the six carbon bonds in the glucose molecule (which has a great deal of energy stored in its chemical bonds) into two lactic acid molecules. Each of these has three carbon bonds and a combined total of chemical energy less than that found in more complex glucose molecule (figure 3.4). The chemical reactions of glycolysis occur entirely in the sarcoplasm of the cell and not in the mitochondria because all the enzymes that catalyse the reactions of glycolysis are located in the sarcoplasm. On the other hand, enzymes for aerobic ATP production are all located in the mitochondria.

When lactic acid accumulates in the muscle and blood and reaches a very high level, fatigue occurs. This is because the resultant low pH within the cell inhibits the enzyme actions in the cell's mitochondria. The lactic acid system is extremely important to us, because it too provides for a rapid supply of ATP energy. For instance, exercises that are performed at maximum rates for between one and three minutes such as racing over 400 or 800 metres, depend heavily upon the lactic acid system for ATP energy. After exercise has stopped, extra oxygen is taken in to remove the lactic acid by changing it back into pyruvic acid.

Aerobic energy yield system

The aerobic system relies on the presence of oxygen for the complete breakdown of carbohydrate and fat. In the presence of oxygen, the complete breakdown of 180 grams of glycogen to carbon dioxide (CO_2) and water (H_2O) yields enough energy to generate 36 to 38 moles of ATP. When oxygen supply is plentiful and the muscles are not working strenuously, the breakdown of glycogen or glucose starts in the same way as anaerobic glycolysis. Under aerobic conditions, the pyruvic acid molecules are not converted to lactic acid but pass instead from the sarcoplasm into the mitochondria where a series of

Figure 3.4 The lactic acid system

	Muscle Cell		
Blood	Sarcoplasm Glycogen		Mitochondria
Glucose →	Glucose 6 phosphate		
Blood Lactic acid ←	← Lactic acid ← Pyruvic acid →		→ if O_2 available

reactions break down three carbon pyruvic acid molecules into three molecules of carbon dioxide (CO_2) and three water (H_2O) molecules.

The two molecules of pyruvic acid are irreversibly converted to a form of acetic acid, acetyl Co-A. This intermediate compound enters the second stage of carbohydrate breakdown known as the citric acid cycle (Kreb's cycle). The main function of the Kreb's cycle is to reduce the acetyl Co-A to carbon dioxide and hydrogen atoms. This process occurs in the mitochondria, slipper-shaped cell bodies containing the enzymes of the citric acid cycle. Figure 3.5 shows the microscopic detail of the mitochondrion. The hydrogen atoms produced are oxidised in a process involving electron transport. As electrons and hydrogen ions are transferred from one compound to the next, in the Electron Transport System chemical energy is given up at several stages to provide energy for the formation of ATP from ADP and phosphate groups. The net ATP yield from the complete breakdown of the glucose molecule in skeletal muscle is 36 molecules of ATP (figure 3.6).

Figure 3.5 A schematic illustration of a mitochondrion

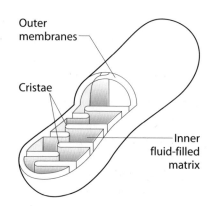

Outer membranes

Cristae

Inner fluid-filled matrix

Figure 3.6 ATP yield from energy transfer during the complete oxidation of glucose

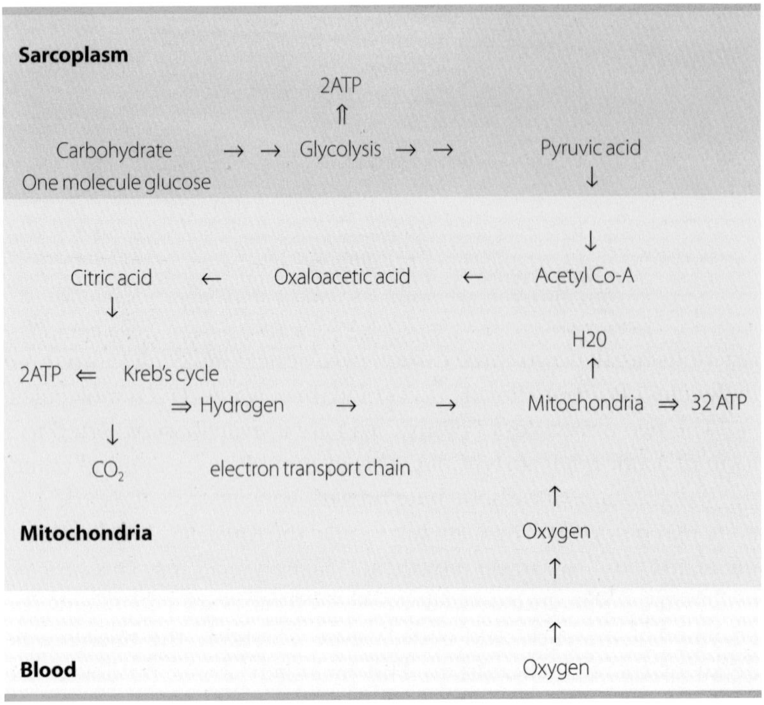

Sarcoplasm

2ATP
⇑

Carbohydrate → → Glycolysis → → Pyruvic acid
One molecule glucose
↓

↓

Citric acid ← Oxaloacetic acid ← Acetyl Co-A
↓

H_2O
↑
2ATP ⇐ Kreb's cycle

⇒ Hydrogen → → Mitochondria ⇒ 32 ATP
↓

CO_2 electron transport chain
↑
Mitochondria Oxygen
↑

↑
Blood Oxygen

It should be noted that the production of energy (ATP) for exercise is much more efficient when glucose is used aerobically rather than anaerobically. The aerobic breakdown of glucose results in 18 or 19 times more ATP production per glucose molecule than does anaerobic glycolysis (36 or 38 moles of ATP compared to two moles ATP).

Another feature of the aerobic system that should be noted is the type of foodstuff used for energy production. Not only glycogen and fat, but also protein can be broken-down aerobically to carbon dioxide and water, with energy released for ATP synthesis. With respect to sports, it is easy to see that the aerobic system is particularly suited for manufacturing ATP during prolonged, endurance type activities, for example, during marathon running and cross country skiing.

SUMMARY

● In the human body, energy in food is used to furnish adenosine triphosphate ATP – the chemical compound that, when broken down, supplies energy for muscular contraction and other biological processes. The coupling of energy release and energy usage (called coupled reactions) is a fundamental principle involved in the metabolic production of ATP.

● The production of ATP involves both anaerobic (without oxygen) and aerobic (with oxygen) metabolism (chemical reactions). There are two anaerobic systems: the phosphagen or ATP-PC system, and anaerobic glycolysis, or lactic acid system.

● The ATP-PC system is used predominantly during the performance of high power, short duration activities, such as sprinting 100 metres that involve high power output.

● The lactic acid system is used predominantly during activities that require between 30 seconds and three minutes to perform, such as sprinting 400 and 800 metres. Accumulation of lactic acid causes muscular fatigue

● The aerobic system releases energy from carbohydrates and fats, and sometimes protein. This system is used predominantly during low-intensity, long duration exercise, such as the marathon.

Questions

1 Briefly explain the main process by which ATP is produced during a 60-metre indoor sprint.
2 During high intensity exercise, lactic acid builds up within the working muscle.
What is lactic acid and how is it formed?
3 What are two major fuels for generating ATP during aerobic exercise?
In which structure of the cell is the bulk of ATP produced under aerobic conditions? Outline the process by which ATP is produced aerobically in muscle cells.
4 Why does glycolysis become less important during prolonged exercise ?

General characteristics of the energy system

Oxygen consumption / Oxygen uptake

Knowledge of the energy system used in various physical activities is considered very important for the precise prescription of exercise intensity and duration. It is possible, but difficult and costly, to measure accurately the energy used by a subject who exercises inside a closed chamber which has walls specifically designed to absorb and measure the heat produced. It is much simpler to estimate that energy indirectly by means of the amount of oxygen consumed by the subject. The oxygen required for the breakdown of carbohydrate and fats comes from the air we breathe. For example, 192 grams of oxygen are needed in order to oxidise 180 grams of glycogen. In terms of volume, this works out to be 134.4 litres of oxygen per 180 grams of glycogen. With a typical fat such as palmitic acid, 515.2 litres of oxygen are required for oxidation of 256 grams of the fat.

The oxygen consumption is expressed as VO_2. At rest we consume oxygen at a rate of approximately 0.3 to 0.4 litres per minute. However, during maximal exercise, the rate increases to 3 to 6 litres per minute. The term maximum oxygen uptake (referred to as the maximal volume of oxygen consumed per minute during strenuous exercise) is the same as the terms maximum oxygen consumption and maximum aerobic power. It represents the greatest difference between the rate at which inspired oxygen enters the lung, and the rate that expired oxygen leaves the lungs.

The rate of maximum oxygen uptake is abbreviated to VO_2 max where the VO_2 represents the volume of oxygen consumed, usually in litres or millilitres, and the dot over the V is a notation that tell us that this volume is to be expressed per unit of time, usually per minute. Thus the expression VO_2 max = 3.5 l/min means that a person can consume oxygen maximally at a rate 3.5 litres per minute. For young adult women VO_2max is about 2.4 litres per minute, whereas men can consume about 3.4 litres per minute. There is a fairly broad range of values for VO_2 max, depending on factors such as body mass as well as physical fitness and genetic endowment, and it is therefore sometimes expressed in millilitres per kilogram of body mass per minute (ml/kg/min).

Oxygen consumption (oxygen uptake) is the difference between the volume of oxygen inspired and that expired. It represents the oxygen used in the electron transport system of the mitochondria.

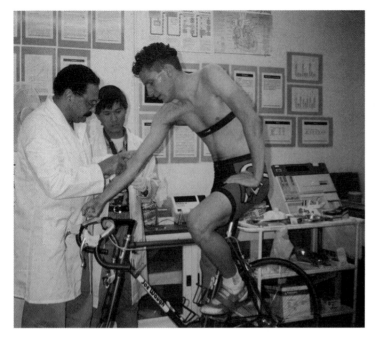

Figure 3.7 The measurement of VO₂ max using the computer technology

The newest approach to indirect calorimetry is to use computer technology and micro electronic instrumentation for the collection, measurement, and computation of respiratory and metabolic data. The computer as shown in figure 3.7 is pre-programmed to perform all of the necessary computations for oxygen consumption, carbon dioxide production and energy expenditure.

Heat (energy) production

When energy is used by the human body in performing work, heat is produced by the working muscles. Hence, the metabolism of foodstuffs (caloric value) should be equivalent to the amount of heat the body liberates. The expenditure of a fixed amount of energy will always result in the production of the same amount of heat. In order to express the amount of oxygen consumed in heat equivalents (that is, kilocalories), it becomes necessary to know what type of food (carbohydrate, fat, or protein) is being metabolised. For example, when these kinds of food are placed in a bomb calorimeter and 1 litre of oxygen is used in breaking down the foodstuff, the heat energy equivalent will be obtained; carbohydrate 5.05 kcal; protein 4.46 kcal; and fat 4.74 kcal. For example, when 134.4 litres of oxygen oxidise 180 grams of glycogen, 686 kilocalories of heat (energy) are released. Accurate measurements of the kilocalories of heat produced as the result of oxygen utilisation show that normal subjects on a mixed diet of fat, carbohydrate, and protein use about 5 kcal of energy for each litre of oxygen they consume. In terms of kcal per gram of food metabolised, there is a slight difference in values between the results when food is metabolised inside the body compared with outside the body, such as, in a bomb calorimeter. The small losses of energy are due to digestion and some protein lost in the urine.

Energy expenditure

Energy expenditure refers to the amount of energy required to perform a given activity. It is usually measured or estimated from the amount of oxygen consumed during rest or performance of the activity. For example, we should remember that when sitting and reading a book, the amount of oxygen consumed is between 250 and 300 ml/min, or between 3.5 to 4.5 ml/kg/min (for somebody who weighs 70 kg), and heat production is between 1.2 and 1.5 kcal/min. The energy expenditure during rest is between 60 and 85 kilocalories

For example, let us assume the following:

-Your body weight is 60 kilograms,

-You ran a distance of 1500 meters

-Therefore your oxygen consumption will be:

0.2 x 60 x 1500 = 18 litres of oxygen.

-If we further assume that glycogen was the major food fuel involved.

-Then 18 litres of oxygen would represent:

18 x 5 = 90 kilocalories of energy expended during the run.

per hour for a person who weigh 70 kilograms. In physical activity such as running, the energy expenditure is approximately 0.2 ml of oxygen per kilogram body weight and per metre run.

In another example, skiing at moderate speed, the energy expenditure is approximately 10.8 to 15.9 kilocalories per minute. The energy expended in this exercise for one hour can be calculated from kilocalories expended per minute; by multiplying the 10.8 and 15.9 by 60, we arrive at an energy expenditure of 648 to 954 kcal.

Our total energy expenditure over 24 hours is the sum total of the energy required in basal and resting metabolism, thermogenic influences, together with the energy required in physical activity. Energy expenditure ranges from less than 1300 kcal for very small children to 2900 kcal for young adult males. Depending upon the type and duration of athletic practice and competition engaged in, an athlete may need 400 – 2000 kcal in addition to the average energy needs. To estimate our daily energy needs it is possible to determine the duration of various physical activities pursued during the day, then calculate the energy cost of those activities, and add this cost to the normal calorific requirements.

Sports activities and the energy continuum

The appropriate approach to exercise training is to analyse an activity in terms of the specific energy systems that are stressed. We then need to improve those systems in order to ensure optimal physiological and metabolic adaptations. Figure 3.7 illustrates the relative contribution of anaerobic and aerobic energy sources during maximal exercise of various durations. In the short term, in high intensity types of activities such as weight lifting, most of the ATP is supplied almost entirely by the phosphagens. In intense exercise, for example, in 1500-metre and mile runs, about half of the energy is supplied by the ATP-PC and lactic acid system, whereas aerobic reactions supply the remainder. Under these conditions, it is desirable to possess a high capacity for both aerobic and anaerobic metabolism. The anaerobic systems supply the major portion of ATP during the sprint at both the start and finish of the race. It can be seen from this example that during physical activities we move along an energy continuum. This is a continuum, which reflects the way in which ATP is made available and the type of physical activity being performed. Intense exercise of an intermediate duration performed for five to ten minutes, as in middle distance running and swimming, basketball, or soccer, results in a greater demand for aerobic energy. Performance of long duration such as marathon running, distance swimming, cycling, recreational jogging, or hiking requires a fairly constant supply of aerobic energy with little reliance on the mechanism of lactic acid formation. An understanding of the energy demands of various activities provides some explanation as to why a world-record-holder in the one-mile run is not necessarily a noted runner over a longer distance.

Figure 3.8   The energy continuum and various sport activities

Per cent aerobic	Events		Primary energy sources
0	weight lifting 200 metre dash	100 metre dash	
10	wrestling 100 metre swim	basket ball 400 metre dash	ATP-PC and lactic acid system
20			
	tennis		
30		soccer	
40			
	800 metre dash		
50	boxing		ATP-PC, lactic acid and oxygen systems
60	rowing (2 km)		
		1500 metre run	
70			
		800 metre swim	
80	2 mile run		
			Oxygen system
90	skating (10 km)		
		cross-country skiing	
100	jogging		

SUMMARY

- Oxygen consumption or oxygen uptake is the difference between the volume of oxygen inspired and that expired. It represents the oxygen used in the electron transport system of the mitochondria.
- Maximum oxygen uptake (maximum oxygen consumption = maximum oxygen uptake = maximum aerobic power) represents the greatest difference between the rate at which inspired oxygen enters the lungs, and the rate that expired oxygen leaves the lungs.
- The expenditure of a fixed amount of energy will result in the production of the same amount of heat.
- Energy expenditure is usually measured or estimated from the amount of oxygen consumed during rest or during the performance of the activity.
- The energy continuum concept is based on the fact that the ability of each energy system to supply ATP is related to the specific kind of activity performed.

Questions

1 Explain what is meant by maximum oxygen uptake (VO_2 max).
2 Describe the factors affecting aerobic power.
3 Give three examples of physical activities which rely predominantly on anaerobic metabolism for their energy supply.
4 Give three examples of physical activities which rely predominantly on aerobic metabolism for their energy supply.

Fuels for exercise

Athletic performance improves with wise nutrition and crumbles with a poor diet. An adequate water intake has by far the most immediate and serious effect on performance. The carbohydrate, fat and protein nutrients consumed daily provide the necessary energy to maintain body function both at rest and during various form of physical activity. Carbohydrate, fat and protein (called macronutrients) are the only sources of food energy; hence, they are called energy nutrients. Food also contains other nutrients, namely minerals and vitamins (micronutrients), but these do not provide energy.

Carbohydrates

There are three kinds of carbohydrate: monosaccharides, disaccharides and polysaccharides.

↗ **Monosaccharides**: glucose, fructose and galactose e.g fruit

Carbohydrate: → **disaccharides**: sucrose and maltose e.g. sweets

↘ **Polysaccharides**: glycogen and starch e.g. bread

Some common food sources of carbohydrate are baked beans, bread, cereals, honey, potatoes, and rice.

The most common form of monosaccharide or simple sugar is glucose (also called dextrose or blood sugar). Glucose, which is the basic usable form of carbohydrate in the body, is formed as a natural sugar in food or is produced in the body as a result of the digestion of more complicated carbohydrates. Glucose can be used directly by the cell for energy, stored as glycogen in the muscle and liver, or converted to fats as an energy store.

Blood glucose levels are regulated mainly through the glycogen stored in the liver. A constant blood glucose level, within a narrow physiological range, is important since this is the primary energy source for the nervous system. Glycogen metabolism in the liver regulates the blood glucose level. After meals, glucose is taken up by the liver with the help of a hormone called insulin, leading to a storage of liver glycogen. During the night or during fasting, liver glycogen will be broken down with the help of a hormone called glucagon by a process called glycogenolysis to maintain a normal blood glucose level. The muscle glycogen is designed to serve as a rapid energy source, which can be made available in a situation of sudden intensive muscular work.

Fats

Fats or lipid are present in the body mainly as triglycerides, phospholipids, and cholesterol. The basic structure of triglycerides is one molecule of a compound called glycerol and three molecules of free fatty acids (FFA). Stores of triglycerides are found in the adipose (fat) tissue and in the skeletal muscle. Free fatty acid, like glucose, is a usable form of fat for energy production circulating in the blood.

A free fatty acid whose carbon atoms are saturated with hydrogen atoms is referred to as a saturated fatty acid. Consumption of large amounts of saturated fats is thought to lead to high blood cholesterol levels and coronary heart disease. Saturated fat includes most animal fat, such as pork, beef, and lamb. Unsaturated fats are those fatty acids whose carbon atoms are not saturated with hydrogen atoms. These fats are in a liquid state in room temperatures. They are found in vegetable oils such as peanut oil, corn oil, and soybean oil.

As with glycogen, the synthesis of fat or its breakdown depends on the concentration of the building blocks, in this case fatty acids. This concentration is determined mainly by uptake or release of free fatty acids in and from triglycerides and their withdrawal for energy metabolism. Thus, when energy production is low, the supply of fatty acids after a meal will lead to an increase in the fatty acid concentration within the cell. In the case of increased energy requirement, fatty acids will be used in energy production. This will result in a decrease in the fatty acid concentrations, which will stimulate the breakdown of triglycerides into glycerol and free fatty acids to compensate this. Such a process is caused by a large number of interactions, in which hormonal and nervous influences play a major role. Two major fuel forms of fat available to the muscle during exercise are free fatty acids mobilised from adipose tissue and triglycerides from within the muscle cells.

Proteins

The basic structural units of proteins are amino acids. Foods that are richest in essential amino acids are animal proteins and milk. Common sources of protein are cereal, cheese, eggs, fish, lean meat, and liver. All proteins in the body are functional proteins, that is, either part of tissue structures or part of metabolic systems such as transport systems, hormones or enzymes. We do not have a protein store as is the case with carbohydrate (stored in the liver and muscles as glycogen), or fat stored in the adipose tissue in the form of triglycerides. Although the role of protein in providing energy has not been considered important for most forms of muscular activity, it is becoming increasingly clear that protein metabolism is increased during endurance exercise .

Water

Fluids are often forgotten in discussion about nutrient requirements. Humans can live for a prolonged period of time without food intake, but not without water. Water is an essential ingredient in a daily diet because it dissolves more substances than anything else. Water is very important as a heat regulator. For example, blood plasma (fluid part of the blood) takes up heat and transports it to the body surface where it can be radiated away from the body.

Water balance is regulated by hormones and the presence of electrolytes, especially sodium and chloride. Water is the largest component of the human body, representing 45 – 70 % of total body weight. Under normal conditions the body water content is kept remarkably constant. It is not possible to store water in the body as any excess water will be excreted as urine by the kidneys. On the other hand, it is possible to dehydrate (reduce body water content) by having an imbalance between fluid intake and fluid loss.

Minerals

Minerals are essential substances for the musculoskeletal system as well as for numerous biological actions, such as nervous transmission processes, muscle contraction, and enzyme activity. Minerals are required by the body in such small quantities that they are called trace elements, and although fourteen are essential only a few will be mentioned here.

Iron is widely distributed about the body, and about 60% to 70% is present in the blood. Iron is an important mineral in the diet of both male and female athletes because it is an essential constituent of haemoglobin, myoglobin, and several enzymes in the metabolic pathways. Iron deficiency can be a contributor to diminished performance, especially in endurance events. Iodine is taken up by the thyroid gland where it is used for the formation of the hormone thyroxin. Copper plays an important role in the formation of haemoglobin, while manganese has a variety of metabolic functions. Zinc is a constituent of the hormone insulin which is concerned with carbohydrate metabolism.

The mineral content differs among tissues. For example, bone has a very high calcium and phosphate content, the muscle cell has a high content of potassium and magnesium, and blood and water in the tissues are high in sodium and chloride. The concentration of minerals in circulating body fluids depends on the input (from food) and on uptake or release by tissues or losses by sweat or urine. Mineral intake largely depends on the type of food selected and quantity of food intake. Mineral replacement and/or supplementation in healthy subjects consuming well-balanced diet, will not improve performance capacity.

Vitamins

Vitamins, are essential nutrients for the human body since they are involved in almost every biological function. They serve an important role in many energy producing reactions. Vitamins are present in a wide variety of fresh unprocessed food such as vegetables, fruits, grains and other starchy foods. Vitamins are classified as water soluble or fat soluble. The water soluble ones such as vitamin C and vitamin B-complex are not stored in the body and therefore must be constantly supplied in the diet. The fat soluble ones such as vitamins A,D,E and K, are stored in the body. The excessive accumulations of these vitamins can cause toxic effects. A normal, well-balanced diet composed of a variety of foods is, therefore, believed to supply all necessary vitamins in sufficient quantities. As it is the case with minerals, extra vitamins in normal healthy subjects will not improve exercise performance capacity.

Effects of exercise on energy supply

The use of carbohydrate, fat or protein as a fuel for exercise depends primarily on exercise intensity and duration. At rest practically all the energy is derived from fat, with the exception of the central nervous system and the red blood cells, which mainly rely on blood glucose. The possible energy supply ratio in this situation may be in order of 90% fat to 10% carbohydrate. During a situation of increased activity, that is, physical work, or a moderately intensive sport activity, the body under the influence of metabolic, hormonal, and nervous mechanism, will additionally use glucose from the liver and from the muscle glycogen pool, to produce energy. At the same time the use of fatty acids will increase until a metabolic steady state has been reached. At a higher exercise intensity the body will start to use more and more carbohydrate. This means that during highly intensive sport activities such as wrestling, carbohydrate will become the most important fuel for the active muscles.

Figure 3.9 During prolonged cycling, the major supply of energy is through the oxygen, or aerobic, system

SUMMARY

- Carbohydrates, fats, and proteins, water, minerals, and vitamins are essential ingredient for the human diet.
- Carbohydrates, fats, and proteins are called the energy nutrients since they are used as food fuels during metabolism.
- Carbohydrates are found in the blood as blood glucose and are stored in the muscles and liver as glycogen.
- Fats are found in the body as triglycerides, phospholipids, and cholesterol.
- Triglycerides are stored in the skeletal muscles and in the fat cells and are made up of glycerol and free fatty acids.
- Carbohydrate and fat usage is dependent upon the intensity and duration of exercise.

Questions

1   In what form is carbohydrate stored in the body?

Where is it stored?

Explain how energy is released from carbohydrates during muscular work.

2   The digestion of fats results in the release of glycerol and free fatty acids into the blood stream.

- With reference to both the short-term and long-term provision of energy for muscular contraction, describe what can happen to these compounds once they are released into the blood stream.
- Very little fat is stored in muscle fibre, yet fat is a main energy source during aerobic exercise. Explain how the fat stores of the body become available to working muscles.
- What are the disadvantages of fat as an energy source during exercise?
- After prolonged, continuous exercise there can be a severe drop in available energy, even though the body still has considerable fat reserves. Explain why this is so.

The recovery process

Normally after exercise, bodily processes do not immediately return to resting levels. If the activity is particularly stressful, such as running a half-mile race or trying to swim 200 metres as fast as possible, the body requires a considerably longer time to return to rest. Recovery from both moderate and strenuous exercise is largely associated with the specific metabolic and physiological processes that resulted from each form of exercise. You will recall that there are two sources of energy that are reduced to various degrees during exercise: the phosphagens ATP and PC stored in the muscles cells, and the glycogen stored in large amounts in muscle as well as in the liver. During recovery from exercise, our energy demand is considerably less since we are no longer exercising. However, our oxygen consumption remains relatively high for a period of time, the length of which is dependent on the intensity of the preceding exercise. The amount of oxygen consumed above the resting oxygen consumption during recovery from exercise is called the recovery oxygen (so-called oxygen debt). The concept of recovery oxygen means that the oxygen consumed above the resting level during recovery is used to provide energy for restoring the body to its pre-exercise condition. This includes replenishing the energy stores that were reduced and removing any lactic acid that accumulated during exercise. The 'oxygen debt' is calculated as the total oxygen consumed in recovery less the total oxygen theoretically consumed at rest. Figure 3.10 shows oxygen uptake during exercise and recovery. This figure shows that the early portion of the 'oxygen debt' falls very quickly within just a minute or two, whereas the latter portion falls at a more gradual rate over a prolonged period of time. The rapid portion of the 'oxygen debt' is called the 'alactacid oxygen debt' component , or rapid recovery oxygen phase, whereas the slower portion is called 'lactacid oxygen debt' component, or slow recovery oxygen phase.

Alactacid oxygen debt component

The term alactacid was used because the oxygen consumed during the rapid portion of the 'debt' is not related to lactic acid removal. 'alactacid oxygen debt' component is attributed to the restoration of the high energy phosphate ATP and PC reduced during exercise. Therefore, this process is commonly known as the restoration of muscle phosphagen stores. The ATP energy required for phosphagen restoration is provided mainly by the aerobic breakdown of carbohydrate and fats. This is through the oxygen consumed during the 'alactacid debt' phase of the recovery. A small portion of the recovery oxygen is also used to reload the muscle myoglobin as well as the haemoglobin in the blood returning from previously active tissues. The oxygen myoglobin stores provide a very rapid source of oxygen for energy production. For example, during the initial phase of exercise, before the oxygen transport system can supply additional oxygen to meet the demand of exercise, the oxygen bound to myoglobin is consumed. This supply of oxygen helps to delay the accumulation of lactic acid in the muscles and blood. Since the oxygen taken in during recovery is also used for replenishment of myoglobin, replenishment of oxygen in myoglobin is considered part of the repayment of the 'alactacid oxygen debt'. The 'alactacid oxygen debt' is completed within two to three minutes. The greater the phosphagen depletion during exercise, the greater the oxygen required for the restoration during recovery. The maximum size of the 'alactacid debt' component is usually between 2.0 and 3.5 litres of oxygen; depending on the intensity of the exercise and the individual level of fitness.

Interval training, as the name implies, is a series of repeated

Figure 3.10 Oxygen uptake during exercise and recovery.

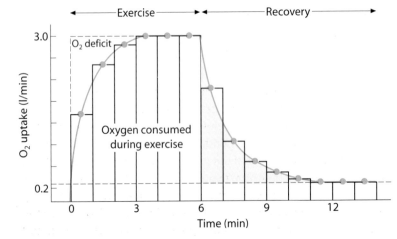

bouts of exercise alternated with periods of rest. Light or mild exercise usually constitutes this rest or recovery period. During recovery intervals, a portion of the muscular stores of ATP and PC that were reduced during the preceding work periods will be renewed via the aerobic system. In this case, during the rest intermissions, part of the rapid recovery phase is completed. In addition, a portion of the myoglobin stores will also be renewed.

Lactacid oxygen debt component

The 'lactacid oxygen debt' component was so named because at the time it was thought that the oxygen used during this phase of the debt was quantitatively related to the removal of the lactic acid that had accumulated in the muscles and blood during exercise. The increased oxygen consumption during the slow recovery phase is now known to be associated with a number of other physiological events, including elevated body temperature, the glycogen resynthesis, and the oxygen cost of the heart's activity.

It was mentioned when describing the lactic acid energy system earlier that when lactic acid, the by-product of anaerobic glycolysis, accumulates in the blood and muscles, fatigue occurs. Also, the low pH (acidity) caused by build-up of lactic acid, can stimulate pain receptors which causes muscle soreness. The normal amount of lactic acid circulating in the blood is about one to two millimoles per litre of blood (mmol/l). In medium intensity workout, such as a 30-minute run, this amount of lactic acid is increased. During high intensity exercise, such as 400-metre flat out sprint, lactic acid levels can reach up to 15 – 20 times resting values. Blood lactate concentration can be used to evaluate exercise performance and also to provide important information related to the level of fitness. Blood lactate measurement during exercise has been used to determine the onset of blood lactate accumulation (OBLA), that is, the equilibrium between lactate production and lactate removal. Blood lactate at OBLA is also referred to as the anaerobic threshold.

There are four possible fates of lactic acid during recovery

- excretion in urine and sweat
- conversion to glucose and glycogen
- conversion to protein
- oxidation/conversion to carbon dioxide and water.

The use of lactic acid as a metabolic fuel for the aerobic system accounts for the majority of the lactic acid removed (65%).

Lactic acid can be removed from blood and muscle more rapidly following heavy to maximal exercise, by performing light exercise rather than by resting throughout the recovery period. For example, several laps of jogging or walking would follow hard running, and free throw or field goal shooting might follow a hard basketball practice. This light exercise immediately following competition or training sessions is known as warm-down. A warm-down will also reduce the effect of muscle soreness by keeping blood capillaries dilated, and flushing oxygenated blood through muscles. From this information, it would be wise to advise athletes to exercise continuously throughout the recovery period. The exercise intensity that produce the fastest or optimal rate of removal of blood lactic acid during recovery has been calculated to be between 30% and 45% VO_2 max for untrained subjects, and 50% and 66% VO_2 max for trained subjects.

Muscle glycogen resynthesis

The full replacement of the muscle glycogen stores following exercise requires several days and is dependent upon the type of exercise performed that caused glycogen reduction, and the amount of dietary carbohydrate eaten during the recovery period. With continuous exercise such as swimming, running, or cycling, about twice the amount of glycogen is used compared with intermittent exercise such as wresting, badminton or tennis. The energy for resynthesis of glycogen comes in the form of ATP generated by the aerobic system. Following intermittent, exhausting exercise, 50% of muscle glycogen stores may be replenished within five hours and restoration is fully completed in 24 hours. Following continuous, exhausting exercise, restoration is 60% completed in ten hours of recovery and is fully completed within 48 hours. Thus with less overall glycogen to resynthesise, less time is needed. The amount of glycogen resynthesised in skeletal muscle during recovery from exercise can be increased to values much higher than normal (muscle glycogen supercompensation). This information has proved to be useful to the coach in so far as the training schedules are concerned. Such a procedure has been shown to improve endurance performance significantly .

SUMMARY

- The oxygen debt is the amount of oxygen used during recovery above that which would have ordinarily been used at rest in the same time.
- 'Oxygen debt' has two components, alactacid (independent of the removal of lactic acid) and lactacid..
- 'Alactacid oxygen debt' or rapid recovery oxygen phase supplies the energy for phosphagen replenishment. 'Lactacid oxygen debt' or slow recovery oxygen phase supplies energy for the removal of lactic acid from muscle and blood.
- Following exhaustive exercise, removal of lactic acid from muscle and blood is most rapid when light exercise is performed during recovery.
- During recovery, lactic acid can be converted to muscle or liver glycogen, blood glucose or protein, or oxidised and converted to carbon dioxide and water.
- Warm-down hastens recovery and reduces the effect of muscle soreness.
- Restoration of the muscle and liver glycogen stores depleted during exercise is dependent upon the type of exercise performed and the amount of dietary carbohydrate consumed during the recovery period.

Questions

1 Define recovery oxygen and its components.
2 How rapidly are the phosphagen stores (ATP-PC) replenished during recovery ?
3 How long does it take to replenish the stores of muscle glycogen ?
4 Explain the process of lactate conversion which will take place during recovery.
5 What does a warm-down do physiologically ?

References

Astrand P O, Rohdahl K *Textbook of Work Physiology*, McGraw Hill Book Company (1975)

Clarke D H *Exercise Physiology*, Prentice Hall, inc. (1975)

Fox E F *Sport Physiology*, Saunders Philadelphia (1979)

Karpovich P V, Sinning W E *Physiology of Muscular Activity*, W. B. Saunders Co (1971)

Mc Ardle, Katch F I, Katch V L *Exercise Physiology, Energy. Nutrition and Human Performance* (3rd edition), Lea and Febiger(1991)

4 TRAINING AND FITNESS

Objectives

To understand
- the four basic components of fitness
- the value of different training programmes
- the four main principles of fitness training
- the effects of training on the heart and on maximal oxygen uptake
- the principles and methods used in the evaluation of fitness
- the effects of altitude training, nutrition and drugs on performance
- the effects of exercise and training in childhood and adolescence
- the value of exercise and its effects on the body systems

There are four main types of fitness – strength, speed, stamina and flexibility. In some sports, the dominance of one type may be critical in allowing the athlete to perform at high levels. For example, in weightlifting the emphasis is on strength, in sprinting, speed, in marathon running, stamina and in gymnastics, flexibility. However, in the majority of sports, more than one type of fitness is required. Consider hockey, where the player needs speed for running, strength for tackling and stamina to cope with the length of the game. Needing all these basic fitness requirements to enable the player to participate fully and safely in the game means that considerable training and long term planning are required. Effective use of the game rules (such as 'rolling substitutions') can enable the coach to protect players who have outstanding capabilities within a particular area, such as a fast forward with limited stamina.

A number of sports require specialist positional skills and a partic-ular fitness component, in addition to the basic game requirements. For example in rugby, strength and flexibility are required for the scrummaging group, lower limb strength for the specialist kickers, and speed and agility for the back row.

Strength

Although there are many different types of strength and ways of assessing performance, we must first ensure that an accurate description of strength is given, and that it can be used to reflect the nature of the exercise.

> **Strength** is the ability to apply force and overcome a resistance.

Absolute strength

Absolute strength is the maximum strength that can be applied by a body regardless of mass or muscle size. Although this is a useful measure, it does not take into account the size of the person lifting the weight.

Relative strength

By relating the absolute strength value to an individual's body mass we can determine his or her relative strength.

In some sporting events, competitors only compete within specified weight categories. It would be possible however to compare the relative strength of all competitors by using the equation shown in the margin.

$$\text{Relative strength} = \frac{\text{load lifted}}{\text{body mass}} \times 100$$

We can also determine strength by considering the speed of a movement. This is a vital measure when you consider that most sporting activities are performed at speed. There are four categories under which we can assess strength in this way:

Static strength

Static strength is the ability to maintain an isometric contraction which holds the weight in a constant position. This reflects static force where an increase in tension within the muscle occurs with a minimal change in muscle length. To state that there is no change in muscle length is not quite true. There is a minor initial shortening to establish tension to take control of the load. Static contraction might be a more accurate description than static strength.

Dynamic strength

Dynamic strength, also known as ballistic strength, involves repeated muscular forces being applied over a period of time. This force may involve isotonic or isokinetic contractions and can be further described by looking at the direction of pull within the muscle in one of two directions:

- **Concentric contraction** involves active muscle shortening. This results in changes in muscle length producing forces which bring about a change in the body position.
- **Eccentric contraction** involves active muscle lengthening while developing tension. These contractions are important when taking body weight. For example, when sitting down from standing, the quadriceps contract eccentrically.

155

Dynamic strength can also be described in terms of the nature of the resistance. This may be looked at in two ways as an isotonic or isokinetic contraction.

- In isotonic contraction, the muscle changes in length to overcome a set resistance but the speed at which this muscular contraction occurs may vary. This is one of the most common forms of contraction which many weight training units are designed to produce. The set resistance is the load that is selected, for example, within the stack, when using multigym systems or on the bar in a free weight system.

- Isokinetic contraction is a maximal contraction where the speed is constant over a full range of movement but the resistance is accommodating. When the muscle is biomechanically weak, the force produced is less but it will still be maximal. It is the best force that the muscle can produce at that angle. As a result, the quality of work is extremely high and frequent rest periods are needed during training sessions. Modern machines use both concentric and eccentric contractions. The systems that produce these type of forces are usually expensive and generally do not involve rotational forces. Most systems involve movement in two directions – extension and flexion, abduction and adduction.

With maximal force production throughout the whole range of movement possible, it is easy to see why these systems are so effective for conditioning at speed.

Speed and power

The ability of a athlete to perform at speed is critical in sprint events as in running, cycling, rowing and swimming, for example. In terms of time-scale, this includes events that last less than 35 seconds and involves the alactacid energy system.

In most sports we generally notice the production of force at speed. Athletic field events such as the high jump, javelin and shot putt are good examples of the production of explosive force. The ability to produce high power output is limited by the energy stores in the muscle cells. Power activities quickly 'burn out' these stores and the ability to repeat quality movements diminishes until stores are replaced.

Pace is a vital element in the longer sprint events. Terms such as maximal, acceleration and endurance speed have been used to describe the different types of pace that a 'sprinter' may employ.

Speed can be defined as the production of repeated maximal muscular contractions over a short distance within a minimal period of time.

Power can be defined as the rate at which energy and is expended or work is done, is measured in watts of work per unit time. This can be represented as:

$$\text{Power} = \frac{\text{work done}}{\text{time taken}}$$

$$\text{or Power} = \frac{\text{force} \times \text{distance}}{\text{time}}$$

Stamina

Stamina has been further divided into three particular time-scales:

Short: 35 secs – 2 mins

Medium: 2 mins – 10 mins

Long: more than 10 mins

Two main energy systems are involved in this system, which relates to the pace at which the athlete is working.

- The short endurance system involves high quality endurance work commonly known as muscular endurance, and uses the lactacid energy system.
- The longer system, known as cardiovascular endurance, uses the oxidative energy system. This involves low level quality work which continues for considerable time periods and is particularly evident in distance running, swimming, walking and cycling.

Flexibility

A number of constraints limit the range of movement of a joint.

- bony and soft-tissue structures e.g. trunk in hip flexion
- neurogenic constraints (voluntary and reflex control)
- passive and active resistance properties e.g. elasticity of muscles, tendons and ligatures

The range of movement of a joint can be subdivided into three further divisions known as the outer, middle and inner ranges. The limitations of each range will therefore vary. The outer range is limited by the joint or soft-tissue structures. The inner range is limited by the body parts or by the tension in the antagonist muscle. Muscles work in pairs. As one muscle contracts (the agonist, for example, the biceps) the opposing muscle (antagonist, for example, the triceps) relaxes. This is why it is important to develop flexibility in both the agonist and antagonist group. Excessive strength development in one group of muscles can only increase the tension in the opposing group and increase injury risk.

There are three main types of stretch which can be used to increase the range of movement around a joint.

Static stretch

The joint is stretched first to the limits of its range by either the player or the coach. An additional stretch is further applied by the use of external force, such as that applied by a coach, gravity or weights. The length of time for which sports people are advised to hold such a stretch has been researched in a number of studies. It is generally advised to gradually build up the length of time for which you hold a static stretch from seven seconds to two minutes over a period of years. You should never stretch into pain and should always allow time for the muscle to recover before you increase the stretch further. A good practice is to work the agonist and then the antagonist, in this way muscles can recover and adapt in a progressive way.

Ballistic stretch

Ballistic stretch involves fast dynamic movements into the extremes of range within the joint. Considerable resistance to any form of dynamic stretching has been promoted over the last decade. This clearly causes problems when we consider that the nature of most sporting skills involves fast dynamic muscular actions around the joint. The important thing to note is that dynamic stretching around a cold muscle can cause considerable damage to the muscle fibres. The action of kicking for distance involves ballistic or fast movements around the hip joint, therefore not only should you warm up in terms of stretching but also in terms of gradually increasing the speed and/or force produced around the joint. Skills warm-up should be a structured and organised part of any warm-up.

Proprioceptive neuromuscular facilitation (PNF) stretch

These series of stretches are based upon the principle that a maximal contraction prior to a stretch promotes muscle relaxation. The theorists suggest that receptors within the muscle (that is, muscle spindles and golgi tendon organs) limit the range to which a muscle will naturally stretch. By taking the muscle to its natural limit and then contracting the muscle, you are able to overide the **alpha-gamma linkage**, which stops any further stretch. Through **reciprocal inhibition** you decrease the control of the alpha-gamma linkage and allow an increase in the range of the muscle stretch.

There are two main techniques used in this advanced form of stretch.

Contract, or hold, relax technique

First the agonist muscle is maximally contracted and then stretched to end of range of that contracted muscle. The muscle is then subjected to a further stretch by the coach.

Contract (hold) relax, agonist contract (CRAC technique)

The CRAC technique is similar to the first technique, but this time the athlete is asked to assist with the contraction of the agonist, usually by pushing against the coach's resisting force.

This is quite an aggressive and advanced form of stretching which should not be included in an athlete's programme unless it is performed regularly and with care. It has been suggested that long-term flexibility gains can be obtained with this form of stretching.

Important points to note:

1 Always warm up the cardiovascular system first (you should be just out of breath).

2 Choose a partner who is strong enough to give you the support that you need.

3 Make sure that you both fully understand the techniques that you are to use.

4 Check that your starting positions are correct and secure,

ensuring that there is no risk of additional movements taking place which could cause injury to the athlete or coach.

5 Increase the range gradually and ensure that there is sufficient time for the neuromuscular adaptations to adjust and the muscle fibres to relax.

6 Gradually build up and decrease the forces within the muscle to avoid cramp and muscle damage.

7 Gradually increase the length of time that you hold the force.

8 Most importantly, look for a long-term regular programme rather than short infrequent sessions.

9 Consider the balance of active and passive stretching.

Training to improve fitness

With all training methods it is important to develop a skills-related training programme reflecting the exact nature of the muscular contractions needed in terms of strength, co-ordination and range.

General training patterns aim to develop the energy systems by using four main principles.

Overload

Overload refers to the chronic overloading of a muscle during regular training and the ability of the muscle to adapt to the training loads . The term 'chronic' in this text refers to regular long-term use. This underlies all forms of training whether they are aiming to develop strength or endurance. By varying the resistance (load) and the number of repetitions you can vary the training effect.

Progressive resistance

This is the increase of stress on a muscle over a period of time. It is important to consider this, not only during the short term, but also over a period of years. The resistance loading should be progressive and gradual. This can be done by looking at the way an athlete's training is organised into particular phases over time. A common term used to describe a training phase is a cycle.

The use of cycles encourages a coach or athlete to plan a clear and realistic programme which relates to the needs of the athlete and the crucial competition phase. Training cycles of varying lengths can break up an athlete's training programme into distinct phases which can enable the coach or athlete to plan both short- and long-term goals.

By varying the intensity at which an athlete works, the training load can be adjusted. This can be done by a variety of ways but the major methods used involve increasing or decreasing the following:

- load or resistance
- recovery
- speed
- duration of effort
- repetitions
- sets
- range of movement
- frequency of the sessions

megacycle – four-year block where the long term-goal is a major championship such as the Olympic Games.

macrocycle – one- or two-year block which may include an intermediate major championship such as the European Championships.

mesocycle – monthly or phasic blocks within a season, that is pre-, mid-, or post-season.

microcycle – weekly blocks, where individual training phases can be planned and minor adjustments made to other cycles if they are insufficient or over ambitious.

There are many different types of training methods. The use of body resistance exercises such as those used in circuit work (press ups, pull ups, etc.) and hill or stair work (running with and against gravity) provide a basic, yet valuable form of training. Varying the work to rest period ratio, produces overload and enables the athlete to train at a high level for a considerable time. This form of training is known as interval training. As the athlete improves in fitness, the rest period is decreased or the work period increased. In this way the training volume (that is, load times the intensity) is increased in a controlled manner.

Plyometric training encourages the use of explosive bounding and hopping type actions where the muscle (e.g. quadriceps) is stretched rapidly in response to a landing force (gravity assisted weight). This type of action produces an elastic effect within the muscle as if it is passively stretched. The returning force promotes the development of powerful and strong contractions within the muscle. Athletes who use this form of training aim to produce powerful forces quickly. Many sprinters and long jumpers use this as their main method of training.

A wide range of equipment can be used to assist in producing overload, in addition to skills-based exercises which encourage the production of high-quality work. The types of equipment used can be broadly grouped under the following categories:

- free weights
- isokinetic units
- multi-station units
- pulleys and springs
- isometric units
- harness and tractor work

There has been considerable research conducted into the area of training and the effects on skeletal muscle. In this section we shall consider the effects, both general and specific, and the need for specificity when training. We shall also look at the factors that cause muscle fatigue and the reversibility of training effects.

The effects of training on skeletal muscle

Regular training which results in the chronic stimulation of skeletal muscle brings about a number of physiological adaptations. These adaptations vary according to the fibre type and exercise intensity that is used. The speed at which a nerve-to-muscle fibre stimulation occurs enables us to classify muscle fibres. Muscle fibre type can be classified under two main categories: slow- (type I) and fast-twitch (type II). Fast-twitch fibres can be further sub-divided (into type IIA and type IIB) according to their energy source.

Changes that occur within the muscle as a result of training can be classified under two main headings — myogenic and neurogenic.

Myogenic changes refer to changes within the muscle structure.

Neurogenic changes refer to modifications in the connection between muscle and nerve.

Figure 4.1 The effects of training on skeletal fibres

Fibre Type		Colour	Description	(Abbreviation)
Fast	IIB	White	Fast Glycotic	FG
Fast	IIA	White	Fast Oxidative Glycotic	FOG
Slow	I	Red	Slow Oxidative	SO

Myogenic changes

Hypertrophy

Muscle hypertrophy increases the cross-sectional size of existing fibres by increasing:

- number of myofibrils
- sarcoplasmic volume
- protein
- supporting connective tissue (ligaments and tendons).

In some cases this can also result in the increase in the number of fibres (hyperplasia) by stimulating dormant stem cells.

Strength training programmes also increase the intramuscular stores such as adenosine triphosphate (ATP), creatinine phosphate (CP) and glycogen. In women, the potential for hypertrophy is not as great as men due mainly to the lower levels of testosterone in women.

Endurance training has produced changes in the conversion of type IIB to type IIA muscle fibres. Over extensive training periods, it has been noted that type II fibres have changed to type I. However, as soon as the training volume decreases, the fibres quickly revert back to their original type.

Capillarisation and increase in mitochondria

Endurance training programmes cause biochemical changes that occur within muscle and serve to increase the oxidative capacity of the muscle. To summarise, the endurance training affects:

- increase in the number and size of the mitochondria
- increase in the capillarisation of the muscle
- increase in the energy substrates – ATP and CP
- increase in the glycogen, triglyceride and myoglobin stores
- increase in enzymes that are involved with energy production.

In strength training programmes these changes vary slightly according to the nature of the sessions involved. To summarise, the strength training affects:

- increase in ATP, CP and glycogen concentration
- decrease in oxidative enzyme activity
- decrease in mitocarbohydratendrial density.

Specificity of training

There is a clear link between training intensity and training effect. This indicates that muscle fibres have an activation threshold within which

Figure 4.2 Specifity of training

Type	Training Intensity (expressed as a % of aerobic capacity)
I (slow)	up to 80%
IIB (FG)	above 80%
IIA (FOG)	up to 80%

To overtrain is just as bad as to undertrain

they respond to training levels and volume. The general guidelines on training vary according to the fibre type that is to be stimulated.

The recruitment of fibres follows a pattern that relates to the speed of movement. As the pace increases, we move from the recruitment of type I to IIA and to IIB. Intensities of 80% to 85% maximum involve the recruitment of all fibres.

Neurogenic changes

In addition to structural and biochemical changes, it is also important to note the various neurogenic adaptations that occur. By repeatedly stimulating muscle, you increase the rate of response of the central nervous system. The recruitment patterns become more refined and as a result, gross movement patterns become more efficient and effective. The importance of training muscles within the range and direction of movement that relate to your sport therefore becomes vital. If you do not consider functional training patterns in your training programmes, then you may not be obtaining maximum benefit and possibly be limiting performance. For example, the swimmer who builds up shoulder bulk too much may not obtain a streamlined position of the arms in relation to the trunk while in the water.

The key factor in any training programme is to outline clearly the training effects that you wish to bring about. By stating long- and short-term goals you can then look at the balance of training intensity and duration not only within the month but throughout the year.

Overtraining

Overtraining has been linked with a number of problems such as injury and illness. This is particularly important in children who, while growing rapidly, continue to exercise at high levels. Continually overloading the muscle systems can cause muscle damage and, in the case of long-term chronic training, can also affect the immune response.

By breaking down the training cycles into clear blocks you can ensure that training is progressive and safe. This means that not only do you train to develop fitness, but at some phases, you simply maintain fitness levels.

Reversibility of training effects

Once the athlete ceases training, a detraining effect takes place. The loss of muscle oxidative enzymes occurs faster than the decrease in muscle capillarisation. Considerable training effects following an extensive programme can be lost within four to six weeks of detraining. Researchers are trying to understand the processes by which the muscle reverts back to its original structural composition following short, rapid, high-quality strength gains.

Athletes who have trained for long periods, detrain at a much slower rate. In addition, optimal development in the early period of life has been linked with the avoidance of premature ageing. It has been known for a long time that the more unfit you are, the greater the initial fitness gains. As you become fitter, however, higher fitness levels become increasingly difficult to achieve.

Factors which cause muscle fatigue

Considerable research has been conducted into the cause and site of muscle fatigue. This research has also looked at muscle soreness and stiffness following intense exercise. Major invetigations have looked at the organisation and transmission of the stimulus at central and peripheral levels and at the neuromuscular junction (motor en plate) to find out if the timulus 'strength' is the cause for diminished muscular work. Also the levels of fuel, waste products and tissue damage have been thoroughly investigated. In summary, the possible sites and causes are:

- Central nervous system
- Peripheral nervous system
- Neuromuscular transmission
- Muscle fibre damage
- Muscle sheath damage
- Depletion of short- and long term fuels.
- Build-up of waste products

SUMMARY

- Basic fitness can be classified in four main categories – strength, speed, stamina and flexibility.
- Different sports will require an emphasis on different aspects of fitness for training purposes.
- Training principles enable us to train to improve our fitness through high levels of work.
- The four basic training principles are overload, progressive resistance, specificity and reversibility.
- Athletes cannot continue to train at high levels all the time or they will risk illness and injury.
- It is important to train in cycles or phases which may increase or decrease your training at certain times of the year.
- Different levels of training intensity affect different fibre types. Long-term changes include both neurogenic and myogenic changes. There is a clear link between training intensity and training effect.

Questions

1 What are the four main components of fitness? Give a brief definition for each of these components.
2 What is the difference between absolute and relative strength? Why is relative strength a useful measure in competition?
3 Which two main energy systems relate directly to endurance?
4 Identify the three main types of stretch. Why is it so important to warm up muscles before stretching?
5 Why should you not include an intense stretching programme when working with young children?
6 What are the four principles of fitness training?
7 Select a particular type of training, for example, weights, running, or swimming. Outline how you might alter the training to obtain different training effects.
8 What are the two main headings under which muscular changes are classified? Give examples of the type of changes that can occur.

The effects of training on the heart

Causes of bradycardia in the trained athlete

Bradycardia can be defined as a lowering in the heart rate. It is common to find that endurance-trained athletes have lower resting heart rates than untrained individuals. For example, resting heart rates below 60 beats per min (b.min[-1]) are quite common, while international long distance runners have been reported to have resting heart rates as low as 35 to 40 b.min[-1]. Also, during exercise at any given workload, endurance-trained persons will be able to perform the exercise at a lower heart rate than an untrained person. This lower heart rate and increased capacity to perform work results from a number of changes. These are an increased efficiency in heart function, a change in the structure of the heart, a change in the composition and capacity of the blood and a change in the efficiency of working muscles.

Since the seventeenth century, scientists have suggested that physical training results in cardiac hypertrophy, that is, an increase in the size of an athlete's heart. However, it has taken much longer to define what changes actually take place in response to specific training programmes. Individuals who take part in endurance conditioning, such as distance running and swimming, demonstrate an increase in the chamber size of the left ventricle. Those who are involved in shorter anaerobic activity, such as weight lifting and throwing, increase the size of the ventricle wall. Therefore, the changes that take place are very much activity dependent.

The changes that are made by the heart as a response to exercise load, depend upon the amount of exercise and the intensity of that exercise.

Moderate intensity training

If training is dynamic, and of a moderate amount and intensity (50 to 70% VO_2 max, 30 to 40 minutes duration), there is little or no noticeable increase in the size of the heart. The changes that take place are mostly in the functional ability of the heart, and are brought about by an increased use of the organ's potential functional properties.

For example, lower-end diastolic and systolic ventricle volumes have been observed. This means that at the end of each contraction of both the atria and ventricle, more blood is pushed out. As Starling's law states, the more the heart is filled during the diastolic stage, the greater the force of contraction in the systolic phase. It is thought that these changes are brought about due to a greater venous return of blood. Also, the heart experiences less resistance while beating. A direct result of lower arterial blood pressure. In the same way, the stroke volume of the heart (the volume of blood expelled per beat) is increased. This means that at a given intensity of work, for example 160 b.min[-1], more blood is supplied to the working muscles and therefore, more oxygen. Thus the heart is working more efficiently as a result of exercise training.

Intensive exercise training

When the type of training moves beyond what can be termed 'moderate' to intensive (75 % plus VO_2 max), the changes that take place are more marked. The increased efficiency described under moderate exercise, is insufficient to allow the body to perform the required intensity of work.

So, when an individual trains for this type of exercise, alterations in the size of the heart can be observed. As a general rule, the more intense the exercise work load, the larger the increase in heart size. The average adult has a total heart volume of about 700 to 770 ml. In high-level male middle-distance runners this can increase to 1000 ml, while in an extreme case of a male international cyclist a heart volume of 1700 ml has been reported. Women athletes also demonstrate increases in heart volume, although the increases are not as extreme as in men. The largest reported sizes being about 1000 to 1100 ml in volume.

It has been suggested that those athletes who demonstrate the largest heart sizes, also have the largest recorded maximal oxygen intake levels, when expressed in litres.min^{-1}. This is not altogether surprising when it is considered that VO_2 max is partly a measure of the body's circulatory system.

Heart wall thickness

It is often suggested that athletes who are involved in heavy anaerobic work develop the size of the muscular wall of the heart, while endurance athletes increase the chamber volume. As a response to the exercise stimulus, an endurance-trained heart pumps more blood by using more of its capacity, while the heart of an anaerobically trained individual beats faster to provide more blood.

In absolute terms, this is probably true, but when expressed in terms of body weight the comparisons are much different. Weight lifters and weight throwers have a heart mass that is equivalent to between 2.5 and 2.9 g.kg^{-1} of body weight. This is a figure very similar to that of untrained subjects. In contrast, endurance trained athletes have a relatively larger heart mass in relation to body weight (3.0 g.kg^{-1} of body weight).

Effects of age

In terms of age, it would appear that increases in heart volume can be experienced by almost everyone. Reports suggest that young adolescents can exhibit changes in heart volume that are similar to those seen in adult athletes. However when subjects reach middle-age, the changes that take place are much smaller.

Maximal oxygen consumption

The measurement of maximal oxygen uptake (VO_2 max) is a combined measure. It assesses an individual's ability to extract oxygen from the atmosphere, through the respiratory system, supply it to the working muscles via the circulatory system, and the ability of the

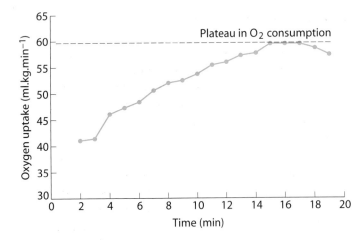

Figure 4.3 Plateau in oxygen consumption during maximal work

muscles to utlise oxygen. To measure VO_2 max, a person is required to perform muscular endurance exercise until he or she reaches exhaustion.

It is possible to measure VO_2 max using a variety of exercise types, for example, walking or cycling. The principles involved are that the exercise must involve large muscle groups, and therefore must be progressive, that is to say, it must be of gradually increasing intensity. In practice, however, the largest values are produced when the exercise is uphill running. To be certain that the person exercising has actually reached VO_2 max, their oxygen consumption must be seen to plateau (see figure 4.3). It is accepted that this means an increase in oxygen consumption of less than 2 ml.kg^{-1}.min^{-1}, or 150 ml.min^{-1}, for an increase in work load.

The effects of training on VO_2 max

The effects of training on maximal oxygen uptake can sometimes be a little confusing to interpret. There is little doubt that VO_2 max responds to training and shows an improvement. However, the difficulty comes in deciding which changes are due to modifications in the body's ability to use greater amounts of oxygen, and which come about as a result of changes in other factors, for example, a decrease in body weight and body fat.

With regular training an individual can expect an increase from between 5% and 15% in the volume of oxygen that is consumed at maximal exercise (l.min^{-1}). Also, because of decreases in body fat content, when VO_2 max is expressed in relation to body weight (ml.kg^{-1}.min^{-1}) the increase in VO_2 max may appear relatively larger.

The changes that training can produce in VO_2 max are dependent upon a number of factors. Many people disagree as to how intensive training has to be to produce an increase in maximal oxygen consumption. In previously sedentary people who are unaccustomed to exercise, it is possible to observe a 5% to 10% increase in some individuals with a training intensity as low as 50% of maximum, for 30 minutes, three times per week. However, as individuals become more highly trained it is necessary to exercise at a higher intensity, in order to bring about changes in VO_2 max. Therefore, when an athlete is training it may be necessary to increase the intensity to 70% to 75% of maximum.

The length of the training period can also influence the amount of change that takes place. Low intensity exercise that is sustained for long periods of time can produce an increase in VO_2 max. For example, brisk walking may only produce a heart rate of around 120 b.min^{-1}. However, if work of this intensity is maintained for a sufficiently long period, for example, 60 to 90 minutes, it too can produce increases in VO_2 max.

Physiologically speaking, changes in VO_2 max as a result of training occur as a result of two factors: firstly, an increase in cardiac output; secondly, muscular tissue is able to use a greater number of units of oxygen. At maximal or near maximal levels, the heart is able to deliver more blood for each beat.

It is important to note that change takes place at two levels, at a central level and at a peripheral level. Central changes involve adaptations of the heart and lungs, such as an increase in cardiac output. Peripheral changes are the adaptations that take place in localised areas in the working muscles. These changes include increased capilliary density in the musculature and increased enzymatic activity within the mitochondria of the muscle cells. In highly trained people, the peripheral changes are much more important.

SUMMARY

- Endurance trained athletes usually have lower resting heart rates than untrained individuals. Also, they have lower heart rates for a given work intensity, therefore their capacity to work at higher exercise levels is greater.
- Changes in heart rate response to an exercise load depend upon the amount of exercise and the intensity of that exercise.
- Maximal oxygen uptake is a combined measure. It assesses the individual's ability to extract oxygen from the atmosphere, through the respiratory system, and supply it to the working muscles via the circulatory system.
- Changes in maximal oxygen uptake as a result of training are difficult to isolate. This value relates not only to oxygen uptake but also to body weight.
- Changes on VO_2 max through training occur as a result of two factors – an increase in cardiac output and an ability of muscular tissue to use greater amounts of oxygen.

Questions

1 What is bradycardia?
2 How will training volume and intensity affect heart rate response?
3 What are the effects of age on the heart?
4 What does the term maximal oxygen uptake mean?
5 What are the effects of training on maximal oxygen uptake?

The principles and methods used in the evaluation of fitness

Measurement of maximal oxygen uptake and its prediction from heart rate

The assessment of cardiorespiratory endurance has one objective, that is, the measurement of maximal oxygen consumption, or VO_2 max. A test of this type measures the ability of the body to use oxygen for fuel while carrying out work for extended periods of time. When it is performed, the expired air of the subject is measured for both volume and composition. From this, the actual VO_2 is calculated and the plateau at maximal work capacity is plotted (see figure 4.4).

To carry out a test of this type, the subject must perform work involving large muscle groups. This work must also be incremental and progressive. A variety of exercise modes have been used, for example, running, cycling, rowing, stepping and swimming. It seems to be the case that running uphill produces the largest values for this type of test. When swimming, it can be as much as 20% lower than running, and in the case of cycle ergometry, the smaller VO_2 max values have been attributed to a smaller cardiac output.

An example of a VO_2 max test plan (called a protocol) is shown in figure 4.5. This type of protocol is carried out with the subject running on a treadmill. It is continuous, and it increases the work load periodically by increasing both the running speed and the grade of slope of the treadmill. It is possible to make work incremental using either increasing running speed, or increasing the slope. The British Association of Sport and Exercise Sciences protocol, succeeds in making the subject work progressively harder mostly by altering the angle of the running slope. With the distinction made between endurance athletes and games players, it has the advantage of being more sports specific. This is an important consideration, as certain test protocols work well with certain subject populations. For example, the Bruce protocol was designed for testing adults. There are also examples of protocols that are specifically designed for testing cardiac patients, and other specific groups.

This protocol allows the format to alter depending upon the type of sportsperson being tested. It should however result in exhaustion in nine to 15 minutes. It has already been stated that to get a true measure of VO_2 max there needs to be a plateau in oxygen consumption. However, the actual test can be terminated for a number of reasons. Often subjects complain, and stop the test as a result of intense fatigue in local musculature. This can happen if the subjects are asked to perform exercise types with which they are unfamiliar.

Figure 4.4 The linear relationship between submaximal heart rate and oxygen consumption to predict VO_2 max

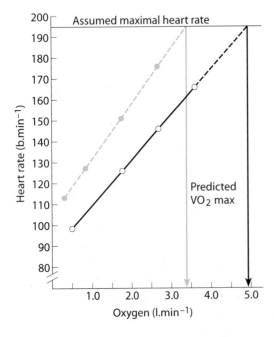

Figure 4.5 Bruce incremental treadmill protocol

Stage	Km.hr^{-1}	Grade	Time (min)
I	2.74	10%	2 3
II	4.02	12%	4 5 6
III	5.47	14%	7 8 9
IV	6.76	16%	10 11 12
V	8.05	18%	13 14 15

Figure 4.6 British Association of Sport and Exercise Sciences (BASES) protocol

	Warm-up speed Km.hr^{-1}	Test speed Km.hr^{-1}	Initial grade (%)	Grade increment (%)
Endurance atheletes				
Male	11.3	16.1	0	2.5
Female	9.6	14.5	0	2.5
Games players				
Male	11.3	12.9	0	2.5
Female	9.6	11.3	0	2.5

Whatever type of exercise is used in this test, it is clear that for a subjects to take themselves to maximum, they need to be very highly motivated. This is true if the test is being carried out on an athlete, or as a stress test for a medical examination.

Motivation is one reason why tests of maximal oxygen uptake are carried out relatively infrequently. VO_2 max testing is also very costly as it requires a great deal of equipment. During a standard test the following measurements are taken: heart rate, ventilation volume (the volume of expired air), percentage of oxygen in the expired air and the percentage of carbon dioxide of the expired air. This requires substantial investment in a number of pieces of equipment. Time is another factor. It has already been suggested that a modified bases can produce a maximal test in about nine to 15 minutes. However, there is the additional time for calibrating the equipment beforehand and preparing the subject prior to the test.

For the reasons outlined above, tests that measure VO_2 max directly are quite often impractical to carry out. You cannot, for example, perform them outside a laboratory, or with large numbers of people such as sports teams. So, other indirect tests have been devised to 'estimate' or 'predict' VO_2 max. Like VO_2 max procedures, these tests are many and varied. Many of them use heart rate response to submaximal work using the following premise – VO_2 and heart rate share a linear relationship for various intensities of light to moderately heavy exercise (see graph in figure 4.**??**). The slope of the line, which represents the rate of heart rate increase, demonstrates the fitness of an individual. If this line is extended to an assumed maximal heart rate, for example 220 minus the individual's age, then VO_2 max can be estimated.

Another method of estimating VO_2 max comes from endurance runs. Runs of various duration have been used, for example 600 metres, 1.5 miles, 12 minutes. Such tests are based on the notion that distance run in a specified time, or the distance covered in a set time, is determined by the ability to maintain high-intensity aerobic work.

It is necessary to point out the difference between direct and indirect methods of testing. Direct methods consist of the measurement of expired air. Indirect methods, on the other hand, attempt to estimate and predict using another measurement, for example, heart rate. Direct measurements have the advantage of being more precise, they measure what actually happens. Indirect methods have the advantage of being easier to use on larger numbers. However, because they estimate and predict, they are not going to be as accurate as direct measurement.

Step tests

A step test consists of an individual performing a given amount of work in a set period of time. Fitness is then estimated by monitoring the individual's recovery by taking their heart rate. Tests of this type have been used for a long time, with the Harvard step test dating back to the 1940s.

Because they are relatively simple to set up, and they require very little equipment, step tests are widely used. They have been used extensively to assess fitness for the assignment of work tasks. There are a number of versions still used to assess fitness in gymnasium and fitness classes, such as the YMCA protocol.

In spite of their simple application, there are a few problems associated with their use. Stepping up and down on a bench can create intense local fatigue in the muscles of the upper leg. For this reason, there are some protocols which incorporate a hand rail to assist the subject while exercising, for example, the Canadian Home Fitness Test.

A simpler version of a step test can be conducted as follows: the subject is asked to step up and down on a 42 cm high bench for a period of three minutes, at a stepping rate of 22 steps per minute for women and 24 steps per minute for men.

At the completion of the exercise period the subject remains standing and their heart rate is taken for 15 seconds. It is essential that the heart rate is taken from five to 20 seconds into the recovery. This figure is then multiplied by four to give a heart rate in b.min^{-1}. VO_2 max (ml.kg^{-1}.min^{-1}) can then be calculated using the following equations:

Men

VO_2 max = 111.33 — (0.42 x HR b.min^{-1})

Women

VO_2 max = 65.81 — (0.1847 x HR b.min^{-1})

Bicycle ergometry

The real benefit of bicycle ergometry is the fact that the saddle supports the subject's weight. This means that it opens fitness testing to a great many more subjects, because it produces less strain on the joints while exercising. One of the other benefits is the ability to measure workload accurately. This is because it is set by the tester prior to the beginning of the test.

Bicycle ergometer tests are founded on the principle of extrapolating heart rate to maximum as described above. Perhaps the most widely used of these is the Astrand-Rhyming test. This requires the subject to cycle for six minutes at a known work load. The work load can initially be set according to the conditioning and the sex of the subject as shown in figure 4.7.

Figure 4.7 Work load selection for Astrand-Rhyming bicycle ergometer test

	Power output (Watts)
Unconditioned	
Males	50 or 100
Females	50 or 75
Conditioned	
Males	100 or 150
Females	75 or 110

The protocol requires that the subject exercises at the set work intensity for six minutes, during which time he or she must cycle at a constant 50 rev.min^{-1}. Heart rate is taken for the last ten seconds in each of the two final minutes of exercise. This figure is then averaged. Using this figure and the workload, VO$_2$ max can be estimated. It is then necessary to correct the VO$_2$ max score for the subject's age.

Because it is so easy to administer, the Astrand-Rhyming test and other bicycle ergometer tests are very widely used. A test takes six minutes and there is very little preparation of the subject. It is, therefore, possible to test quite large numbers of people in a very short space of time. Also, as the subject's upper body is for the most part very stable during the test, there are very few problems when attaching a heart rate monitor.

One problem with this type of test is the assumption of a similar maximum heart rate for all subjects. If a subject has a lower maximum heart rate than their age predicted maximum, the test will over estimate the VO$_2$ max. In contrast, if a subject has a maximum heart rate that is larger than their age predicted maximum, the test will tend to under estimate.

Treadmill tests

When equipment for the analysis of expired air is not available, it is possible to estimate VO_2 max from the running speed obtained during treadmill exercise. When trying to estimate maximal oxygen consumption in this way, it is important to observe the test protocol as closely as possible.

An example of this is the Bruce protocol, the format of which is seen in figure 4.5. It is possible to estimate VO_2 max by applying the following equation:

$$VO_2 \, max = (1.444 \times time) + 14.99$$

Time is the total time of the test, expressed in minutes and fractions of minutes.

Tests to estimate VO_2 max from treadmill running have the advantage of being cheaper than full-scale VO_2 max tests, as there is less equipment involved. They are most frequently used in clinics where the object is to assess cardiac risk factors during exercise.

They do, however, require expensive equipment such as the treadmill. Also, they can only test one person at a time, so they are not ideally suited to mass testing. It should also be noted that, since the work involved in the test is exactly the same as that asked of a subject during a full VO_2 max test, this has both its advantages and disadvantages.

When performing a maximal oxygen consumption test of this type, some subjects cannot reach and demonstrate a plateau in VO_2. However, with a prediction equation this does not matter. The test demands that the subjects do the same work as in a full VO_2 max test, therefore the numbers that can be tested accurately will be reduced because everyone can achieve max. These tests make far more demands upon the subject than say an Astrand-Rhyming test. Those being tested have to work at far higher heart rates, and this will automatically limit the numbers of subjects who are willing to carry out the test.

Sport specific tests

A major criticism of fitness testing is that it does not accommodate sport specific movements. One may suggest that to measure athletes on a treadmill running test is sport specific, but can this be related to a hockey or rugby player who spends a considerable time running sideways and backwards?

Most fitness tests are used to assess basic fitness levels under the categories of strength, speed, stamina and suppleness. They serve only as an indication of an aspect of fitness. The challenge for the tester is to design tests that can be standardised and relate directly to a skill or series of skills performed under pressure.

A good example of this has been the test used by the England U21 Rugby Football Squad which was designed by Tony Lanaway, the coach at that time. A circuit (see figure 4.8) has been designed which uses tackle bags and requires the players to make a number of tackles from a

One test that is widely available and considered to be very relevant to team games is the 20-metre multistage Shuttle Run Test (20-MST), which predicts VO2 max. This test requires participants to run 20 metre shuttles continuously. The speed they must run at is dictated by an audio cassette. Every minute the participants are required to run a little faster (0.5km increase per minute), The overall objective is to keep running as long as possible, in time with the audio cassette. When a person cannot keep up, or drops out voluntarily, the number of shuttles they have completed is used to predict VO2 max. This is done from a table supplied with the sudio cassette. Unlikeother tests to predict VO2 max, this test is 'maximal' and as the speed gets faster, determination is required to keep going

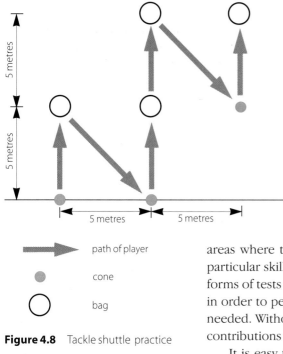

5 metres

5 metres

5 metres

5 metres

→ path of player

● cone

○ bag

Figure 4.8 Tackle shuttle practice

variety of directions. Players have clear objectives, they have to drive the tackle bag to a five-metre distance and then move onto the next designated bag. The circuit is repeated three times with no rest, additional players are used to replace the bags onto a set position for the next tackle. The time is started on a whistle and completed once the player has returned to the starting position.

By using this form of test it is able to look at skills and fitness as a combined element. While a player may be 'fit' to run in straight lines his lack of footwork and technique may mean that he is 'unfit' to play the game to his fullest potential. A good coach will be able to highlight and assess areas where the player may need to work harder and to advise on particular skills-based sessions that will help. For many players these forms of tests have more relevance, but they need to understand that in order to perform to their highest potential, a baseline of fitness is needed. Without this fitness a player will be unable to make repeated contributions throughout the whole game.

It is easy to see that such tests can be designed not only by the coach, but by the player, and can be used as a part of a skills training programme. They can be enjoyable and rewarding, as a player sees his or her time to complete the test gradually decrease and confidence increases correspondingly.

Preparation for fitness testing

A number of factors that relate directly to the value of fitness testing have already been highlighted throughout this section . Considerable emphasis has been placed on regular testing and monitoring (national and regional levels). The task of the British Association of Sport and Exercise Sciences has been to standardise testing and accredit centres and staff who will perform those tests and interpret results.

Before it is possible to put together a battery of tests, a number of issues need to be considered. These include:

● The aims and objectives of the programme need to be clearly stated. This will involve the long- and short-term needs of both the coach and the athlete.

● The nature of the sport, the skills, rules, regulations relating to the prediction of performance requirements need to be researched by the tester if he or she is new to the sport. From this research key skills and areas of fitness can be isolated.

● A battery of tests may then be proposed and discussion with the coach and athlete needs to take place. It is necessary for the athlete to fully understand the programme. To test athletes without their understanding and trust in the programme may cause resentment and mistrust of the results.

- The battery of tests must be reliable and standardised. Where possible the environmental conditions and surface should be consistent. Obviously a field test conducted on dry ground will produce different results from one undertaken in muddy conditions.

- Standardisation of the test procedures not only within tests but between tests must be considered. If there are a number of tests to complete what should be the order and how long should a player rest before the next begins? For example, testing players the day after a hard match may only assess their recovery.

- The interpretation of any results from raw data in order to advise and adjust the overall training programme, is not an easy task. The ability to collect data and perform tests relies largely on practice. The interpretation of such results relies on the tester's awareness of the overall profile of the player and his or her particular needs relating to fitness and performance.

- The ultimate goal of fitness testing would be to produce an individual programme for each player. This is fairly easy to do in individual sports such as cycling, running, swimming, but to do this for team sports is both expensive and time consuming. Without the finance to dedicate staff to a particular project many team sports have to make do with a group programme. However, to mass produce a programme that does not consider individual variations is naive and generally not appropriate for the majority of sporting activities. The ability to inject individual programmes within the overall team programme is the real challenge for the testers.

- The importance of regular monitoring and the assessment of individual players is vital. The achievement of long-term goals relies often upon the successful completion and adjustment of short term goals.

Lean body mass and percentage fat from subcutaneous measurements

The relevance and accuracy of procedures used to assess body fat and lean body mass has caused considerable debate amongst sport scientists.

It is a useful measure in the overall assessment of endurance athletes. Low body fat has been linked to injury as the shock absorbing capacity of fat pads around the joints reaches critically low levels.

The term lean body mass is used to describe fat free mass, since total body mass is largely composed of fat, carbohydrate, protein and water. It must however be remembered that fat free mass measurement also includes essential lipids (fat-like molecules, insoluble in water) and is therefore an estimate.

A number of techniques can be used to assess body composition. However even with the most sophisticated equipment any assessment of body content is difficult. For the assessment of fat and fat free mass the following measures can be used.

- **Densimetry** is used to measure the total mass and volume of the body. Mass is recorded as body weight and volume assessed by looking at the volume of water displaced by a subject when immersed in water. By using a series of equations, we can take into account air trapped in the airways, intestine, etc., and calculate body density using the equation in the margin.

This method is seen as the most accurate body fat assessment. Laboratory based tests involve the used of expensive 'high-tech' equipment such as:

$$Density = \frac{mass}{volume}$$

- **Hydrometry** – assessment of total body water – the most accurate technique to date.
- **Spectrometry** – measurement of radiation using a whole body counter.
- **Ultrasonics** – high frequency sound waves to differentiate between tissue types.
- **Radiographic analysis** – soft tissue X-rays to differentiate between skin, bone, muscle and fat.
- **Electrical conductivity** – distinguishes between the conductance of fat and fat-free mass.
- **Computed tomography** – X-ray scanning technique using cross-sectional images.

Such techniques are time-consuming, expensive and beyond the reach of most coaches and athletes. As a result, field tests, using skinfold measurement were developed in the 1950s. The assumption that there is a linear relationship between the sum of skinfolds and total body density has since been refuted and this form of assessment has been rejected by many sport scientists as too inaccurate to use. However, a number of sport scientists and coaches still use this to give guidelines on body fat values.

For any assessment from skinfold site measurement it is recommended that three or more sites should be used. The main sites used are over biceps, triceps, subscapular, suprailiac and the thigh.

The most accurate equations currently used are the Jackson, Pollock equations for males and the Jackson, Pollock and Ward equations for females.

It is generally agreed that if skinfold assessments are to be used as part of a battery of tests then testing errors can be reduced by using the same experienced tester throughout the monitoring programme.

The accuracy of the equipment used is a key source of error. Plastic skinfold callipers, while inexpensive compared to the calibrated Holtain and Harpenden range, serve only for educational rather than research purposes. It is important to remember that a low or high reading using such equipment may cause unnecessary distress to the athlete and results should be treated with caution.

SUMMARY

- Maximal oxygen uptake can be measured through direct or indirect (predicted) methods.
- Direct methods measure expired air in tests to exhaustion and give precise results.
- Heart rate response and oxygen consumption show a linear relationship for exercise at varying levels.
- Indirect methods are used for large group testing. The results are used to estimate and predict maximal oxygen uptake.
- Motivation plays an important part in all fitness testing.
- Careful preparation for fitness testing programmes is essential.
- For maximum benefit, the sports person must understand and be committed to the testing programme.
- The importance of lean body mass and percentage fat from subcutaneous measurements has caused considerable debate. In general, these results are only used as guidelines.

Questions

1   When using the direct method to assess maximal oxygen uptake, do you have to continue the test to exhaustion? Explain your answer.

2   Why are predicted tests, using heart rate as a response, used to assess maximal oxygen uptake? What are the benefits and limitations of such tests?

3   What key factors need to be taken into account when designing a testing programme?

4   Why are percentage fat and lean body mass procedures using subcutaneous fat measures causing considerable debate amongst sport scientists?

Techniques for performance enhancement

High altitude training

High altitude training is a popular form of training used by long distance runners in their preparation for competition. However, the short- and long-term benefits that were proposed have since been researched over the last decade and it is now suggested that the benefits gained are minimal. The athlete who returns to sea-level encounters the complications of breathing dense sea-level air which can cause extreme difficulties when performing at maximal oxygen levels. It is suggested that the physiological adaptations that occur during acclimatisation mainly serve to prepare athletes for competition at altitude, minimising the distressing effects of altitude sickness.

At altitude, the barometric pressure decreases and the air becomes less dense. In addition, the pressure of oxygen also decreases despite the oxygen content remaining constant at 20.94 % (dry air).

This means that to obtain sufficient oxygen to train at altitude, a number of physiological adaptations need to be made. Above 6000 m, no benefits have been noted and acclimatisation is not possible. The athlete deteriorates rapidly, losing body weight with a decrease in performance levels.

Figure 4.9 Barometric pressure and oxygen pressure of inspired air at varying levels

	Barometric pressure	Inspired oxygen pressure
sea-level	760 mmHg	150 mmHg
2000 ms	596 mm Hg	110 mmHg
4000 ms	462 mm Hg	85 mmHg
6000 ms	354 mmHg	65 mmHg
8000 ms	267 mmHg	50 mmHg
8848 ms	253 mmHg	43 mmHg

A decrease in oxygen pressure of inspired air with a corresponding decrease in the partial pressure of arterial blood results in a decrease in oxygen levels. This is a condition known as hypoxia. The red blood cells carrying oxygen in the form of oxyhaemoglobin show a significant decrease in their saturation levels, that is, the amount of oxygen in the blood.

The immediate response to these lowered levels depends upon the degree of hypoxic stress. Generally, the first response is hyperventilation which is triggered by chemoreceptors in the cardiovascular system.

This lowers the carbon dioxide pressure, initially increases the pH level thus making it more alkaline. The oxygen dissociation curve demonstrates how the body can make minor adaptations to low levels of oxygen within the blood. Once it has detected hypoxic stress, the relationship between saturation levels and the pressure at which oxygen can shift out of the blood into the cells alters. The curve moves to the left meaning that for lower pressure differences oxygen can be given up more easily.

Example: oxygen levels in the blood

Sea-level — 98%

3000 m — 90%

above 8000 m — below 50% saturation

Figure 4.10 The effect of CO_2 and pH on the oxygen dissociation curve of the blood

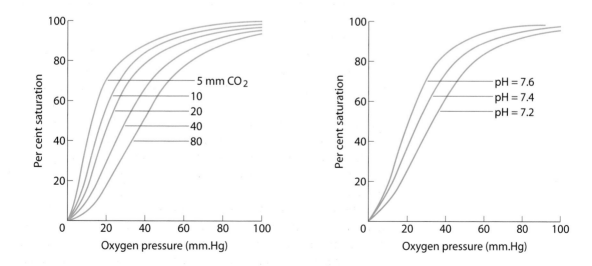

To increase the oxygen carrying capacity of the arterial blood there is also an increase in haemoglobin and red blood cell production by the bone marrow (polycythaemia).

Dehydration also occurs in the cold dry air, increased fluid loss occurs (partly through hyperventilation) resulting in an initial decrease in blood plasma volume. This causes additional stress as the increased viscosity (thickness) of the blood results in increased heart rate and cardiac output. This means that the heart has to work much harder and the ability to work at maximal levels is reduced.

Research has shown that explosive or sprint events are not dramatically affected by altitude. In some events the decreased air resistance can assist performance. Events that involve performance at maximal or submaximal oxygen consumption levels are however, severely affected by altitude. In the 1968 Olympics held in Mexico City (altitude of 2300 m) the distance events were mainly won by athletes who lived at altitude or had completed a considerable period of acclimatisation prior to the games.

Athletes who wish to train or compete at altitude need to decide whether to complete a period of long gradual acclimatisation or a short, rapid, high-quality session. The length of time it takes an individual to acclimatise depends upon the altitude and level of hypoxic stress that an athlete is under.

Above 1500 m maximal oxygen consumption decreases by 3% (compared to sea-level) for each 300 m that you ascend. This means that the higher up you go, the lower your maximal training levels. It takes about three weeks for an athlete to acclimatise to a moderate altitude of 2300 m to 2700 m. However, even after that acclimatisation maximal oxygen levels will still be below 6% to 7% of those obtained at sea-level.

The major problem with altitude training is that the athlete has to train at much lower levels in order to cope with the hypoxic stress and to avoid the complications of altitude sickness. This means that short sessions at altitude do not really allow you to make the necessary altitude adaptations that the sessions are hoping to achieve.

Research has recommended that the athlete who hopes to compete at sea-level trains at moderate altitude (under 2000 m) and combines this with sea-level training. If the competition is to be held at altitude then a gradual period of acclimatisation is recommended. The athlete will start at 1500 m and then ascend 300 m a day. Athletes who have spent months or even years at altitude can increase their red blood cell count by up to 50%.

In the past, some athletes have tried to counteract the rapid loss of the physiological adjustments, gained through acclimatisation, by using a technique called blood doping. Following a period of altitude training, the athlete saves his elevated red blood cells, through a transfusion, then returns the cells to the blood near the competition. This is an illegal practice banned by the Sports Council, but has been associated with endurance events particularly distance cycling.

Before considering a period of expensive training at altitude, the advantages and the disadvantages need to considered. Unless the programme is realistic and well planned, considerable physical damage and distress may be caused to the athlete. In addition to mountain sickness and hyperventilation, other acute illnesses have been recorded which can cause considerable long-term damage, including high altitude pulmonary and cerebral oedema and retinal haemorrhage.

Nutrition

Nutrition and legal substances

Another means of performance enhancement is to adjust and manipulate dietary intake. There are six main classes of nutrients involved in the maintenance of body functions. Consider briefly their major contributions:

Water

The body is 70% water, although these values vary between 60% and 70%. Generally, water has two major roles in exercise. It maintains water balance and controls body temperature.

Minerals

Twenty elements are present in the body; approximately seventeen can be replenished through the diet. They are required in small amounts, assisting in a number of chemical reactions which maintain the stability of the body functions.

Vitamins

Vitamins are essential for metabolic reactions within the cell and for the maintenance of general health. They function primarily as catalysts during chemical reactions in the body and are essential for energy production, tissue building and for controlling the body's use of food.

Proteins

Proteins make up the major structural component of cells, antibodies (immune system), enzymes and hormones. They are necessary for the growth, repair and maintenance of body tissues and, in particular, the production of haemoglobin.

Fats

Nutritionists recommend that fats should constitute 25% of your dietary intake, but generally no more than 30 to 35% of this should be saturated fats. Fat-soluble vitamins are needed in the body as an energy source, heat insulator and as a shock absorber. Also fat stores exist in the spinal canal, eye socket and are situated around the main joints.

Carbohydrates

Carbohydrates exist mainly in the form of sugars and starches and are used as an major energy source. Consider the main sources of energy during exercise. If we know which substances are crucial to exercise performance enhancement then we can consider ways of manipulating stores before, during and after exercise.

There are four main stores used by the body. The energy that they are able to provide per unit weight is expressed in Kcals and is known as the **Atwater Factor**.

Figure 4.11 The Atwater factor

		Atwater factor
Energy sources	1 Ethyl alcohol	7.0 Kcals
	2 Protein	4.1 Kcals
	3 Fat	9.3 Kcals
	4 Carbohydrates	4.1 Kcals

Ethyl alcohol is a by-product of digestion and chemical processes in the cells found in the body tissues and fluids.

From the values it can be seen that there are high energy values in ethyl alcohol and fat. The muscle however cannot use ethyl alcohol for any substantial period of time without impairment to the energy systems.

Protein supplementation is often used by body builders to enhance the building of the muscle tissue and repair processing after exercise. It does not really enhance endurance and is not concerned with energy production during normal levels of exercise. When protein is used while the athlete is in a dangerous state of exhaustion, it can inflict long-term damage on a number of body systems.

The major energy reserves used for exercise are fats and carbohydrates. Each of these substances requires varying amounts of oxygen in order to produce energy via the oxidative pathways. The amount of oxygen used in comparison to the amount of carbon dioxide produced can be expressed as value known as the Respiratory Quotient. A Respiratory Quotient can give us an indication of which fuels are being used during exercise. The ratio of energy stores being used can change during exercise and vary according to pace and duration.

The production of energy for exercise involves quantitative equations. This means that in order for the chemical reaction to occur there must be a specific quantity of oxygen available. The amount needed for glucose (produced from the breakdown of carbohydrates) and fats varies. The pace at which we exercise and our ability to ensure that sufficient levels of oxygen are available will determine which pathway we use. Consider the two chemical equations in the margin.

A quantitative equation also means that the energy produced for each unit of fat or carbohydrate is constant. This is important in

---

The Respiratory Quotient (RQ) is calculated by using the equation:

$$\text{Respiratory Quotient} = \frac{\text{amount of carbon dioxide produced}}{\text{amount of oxygen used}}$$

Glucose oxidation

$$C_{16}H_{12}O_6 + 6O_2 \rightarrow$$

$$6CO_2 + 6H_2O + \text{energy}$$

Thus $RQ = \dfrac{6CO_2}{6O_2} = 1$

Fat oxidation

$$2C_{51}H_{98}O_6 + 145O_2 \rightarrow$$

$$102CO_2 + 98H_2O + \text{energy}$$

Thus $RQ = \dfrac{102CO_2}{145O_2} = 0.701$

assessing the number of calories used during exercise and is used in the design of diets for sport.

In the body we metabolise a mixture of fats with an RQ of 0.706. As we increase the intensity of exercise the demand for oxygen increases and a corresponding change in RQ levels occurs. Figure 4.12 summarises these changes in general exercise levels.

Figure 4.12 The respiratory quotient

Level	RQ value	Energy contribution
Rest	= 0.8	(2/3 Fat : 1/3 Carbohydrates)
Mild exercise	= 0.8	
Intense exercise	= 1.0	(mainly Carbohydrates)

At rest the body is able to take in more oxygen than it needs and can therefore rely on fats to produce the majority of the energy required. As the exercise intensity increases it becomes more and more difficult to obtain sufficient oxygen to continue with the high demands of fat oxidation, that is, 145 molecules of oxygen compared to six for carbohydrate oxidation. As we shift to carbohydrate oxidation the RQ increases. It continues to do so as we struggle to stay in the oxidative pathway and have to rely on the more anaerobic energy systems.

If you continue to exercise at submaximal levels for a length of time the RQ will decrease as the exercise time increases. This indicates that the body has been able to make the necessary metabolic adjustments to the exercise intensity. By using fats we conserve the glucose supply to the brain (normally 60 mg glucose to 100 mg.ml blood). If the glucose level falls to 30 mg.ml then a hypoglycaemic (indicating low blood sugar level) reaction could occur.

Fat is a stable substance and readily mobilised. Generally it is stored as droplets whereas carbohydrate has to be stored with large amounts of water per gram of dried glycogen.

In endurance events fat is a relatively inexhaustible fuel providing 600 Kcals/kg. It is suggested that 50 000 to 100 000 Kcals/kg are produced from fat stores in endurance events, while the maximum use of glycogen is around 2500 Kcals. The major problem of using fat as an energy source is that the excess constitutes dead weight and needs a high oxygen intake.

Consider the effect of exercise intensity and duration on energy pathways and the relative contribution of carbohydrate to exercise intensity, fitness and type of exercise. As duration increases the amount of carbohydrate used increases. At high levels of oxygen consumption (VO_2 max) approximately above 70% max we have to move away from fat metabolism because we cannot match the oxygen demands required. Therefore, if we want to lose fat then we need to consider the intensity at which we are exercising carefully. If we run too fast we will burn sugars (glucose) rather than fats.

Figure 4.13   The effect of exercise on energy pathways

| Time | Energy output in Kcals | | %VO$_2$ max | RQ | % fat | %carbohydrate |
	Anaerobic	Aerobic				
10 secs	20	4	25	0.80	60	40
1 min	30	20				
2	30	45	50	084	50	50
5	30	120				
10	25	245	75	0.87	25	75
30	20	675				
60	15	1200	100	1.00	0	100

NOTE: as time increases so does the aerobic utilisation.

The earliest record of dietary manipulation was of a Greek athlete – Charmus of Sparta – who trained on a diet of dried figs! Eurymeries of Samos in 480 to 450 BC trained on a diet of red meat using the logic that if you eat red meat you can enhance muscular performance.

Can we prepare the body for exercise by dietary manipulation ?

Dietary intake is necessary to:

- renew the supply of energy yielding substances
- facilitate the energy yielding reactions
- counteract the physical or chemical changes accompanying the metabolic processes in the muscle.

Calorie intake should equal energy expenditure. Excess calories will be stored in the body as fat and glycogen. As we age we decrease our basal metabolic rate (rate at which we produce energy) and therefore need fewer calories.

It is suggested that the diet of an athlete should not differ from a non-athlete in terms of the content. However, the nature of the type of work involving strength, speed and stamina should affect the percentage of dietary components.

Research has shown that glycogen is not a limiting factor in sprint events but it is in endurance events. Only after a high carbohydrate diet were glycogen levels exceptionally high. High levels of glycogen within the muscle can increase endurance capacity but do not have an effect on the athlete's pace. Glycogen levels affect the length of time that you can maintain pace rather than allow an increase in speed.

Endurance-trained athletes exercising at a set work intensity gain a larger percentage of their energy from free fatty acids and less from carbohydrate than untrained athletes. This is presumably because they can maintain high oxygen levels. Even at the same work intensity they have lower RQ levels. This means that they have more in reserve for any increase in pace required at the end of the race.

How can diet affect performance?

Can diet influence the form of energy that you use during exercise? If we eat more of a particular energy source will this improve our ability to increase those stores and rely on them during exercise?

Figure 4.14 How diet affects performance

The values show that what you eat influences the level of glycogen stored in the muscle and that this level will affect how long you can keep exercising.

Diet	Exhaustion time at standard work intensity	Amount of fat used at start	Amount of fat used at end
High fat	1	70-75%	95%
Normal	3	50-60%	70%
High carbohydrate	4	25-30%	60%

The use of fat during exercise in relation to dietary fat intake of varying levels was reported by Wilmore (1983).

The values seem to indicate that what we eat will influence what we use as a major energy source. A high fat diet however will mean that you use predominantly fat as an energy source but the time for which you can continue to exercise is considerably reduced.

Does diet have an effect on the length of time for which an athlete can exercise?

As can be seen above there seems to be a relationship between diet and the length of exercise time. Wilmore (1986) analysed varying dietary intakes and looked at the glycogen content in the muscle and the length of time that an athlete could keep going.

Figure 4.15 Diet and the length of exercise

Diet	Glycogen content gm/100gm of wet tissue	Riding time to exhaustion
Mixed	1.93	125.8
High fat/protein	0.69	58.8
High carbohydrate	3.70	189.3

In exercise, glycogen depletion does not occur at a constant rate. Initially it drops rapidly, stimulated by muscular contractions, the release of adrenaline and increased lactate production in the muscles and blood. This is then followed by a constant fall resulting from the circulatory adaptation to exercise. Eventually, a slow rate of glycogen consumption follows where there is a relative lack of glycogen in the muscles. In response there is a release of liver glycogen and an increase in blood glucose uptake.

Muscle biopsies have enabled physiologists to look at the resynthesis of local deposits of glycogen after exercise to exhaustion. They have examined:

- how the muscle glycogen level affects performance
- the resynthesis of glycogen.

As a result of their findings researchers have produced a method by which we can produce high levels of muscle glycogen prior to competition. This is known as carbohydrate overloading. A good example of the many that are in existence is the interval diet outlined by Klausen in 1982. The aim of this diet is to double the muscle glycogen stores. There are four stages to this programme:

Stage 1   Empty the glycogen stores in the muscle by a severe exercise session.

Stage 2   Starve the body of all carbohydrate for 2/3 days.

Stage 3   Deplete carbohydrate stores further by another intensive exercise session.

Stage 4   Consume high carbohydrate stores two to three days prior to the event.

This form of dietary manipulation cannot be used more than two to three times a year. It is known to cause fatigue and in some cases angina (chest pain). In more severe cases myoglobinuria (myoglobin in the urea) has occurred leading to acute kidney failure.

How important is the pre-game meal?

The traditional steak meal is not ideal, mainly because steak has a high percentage of insoluble fat. A main meal should not be eaten three to four hours prior to the event and complex sugars less than two hours prior to the event. The reason for this is that a sharp increase in sugar causes the body to produce high levels of insulin. This in turn causes a sharp drop in blood sugar levels. Generally, liquid meals are better.

Research has suggested that the main aim of a pre-game meal should be to:

- ward off a feeling of hunger
- ensure that the bowel and stomach are empty
- ensure that plenty of food and fluid are digested to avoid dehydration
- ensure that the food is easily digested
- ensure that the meal is comfortable for the athlete.

It has also been suggested that two cups of coffee will help to stimulate the mobilisation of free fatty acids and therefore increase the oxidation of fats. This will protect carbohydrate stores 15 to 60 minutes prior to exercise. The amount that you need to take is a guideline and will depend upon coffee tolerance and usual coffee intake.

NOTE: Caffeine is a banned substance and a large intake of coffee prior to the event may elevate levels to illegal limits

Nutrition during performance

Can I affect performance by eating or drinking during the event?

Research has found that a marathon runner can lose five to seven pounds of body weight in a race. For every 1% loss it is suggested that there is a 0.3 to 0.5 % core temperature increase this will bring about rapid dehydration and fatigue. Therefore, we need to replenish glucose, minerals and water intake.

Strong glucose concentrations are not readily absorbed. It is suggested that a 2.5% glucose concentration in tepid water is sufficient. Drinking 100 to 200 mls every ten to 15 minutes and 30 minutes prior to the start, is a good guideline. This will top up the glucose levels and delay the time at which glucose levels will become critical.

Being thirsty is one of the signs of critical dehydration and should be prevented with hydration before, during and after the event.

Post exercise

The major aim after exercise is to replace energy stores. By taking note of such things as body weight and fatigue levels we can gain an indication of what we need to do. It is important to replace fluid intake and electrolyte fluid levels first. Weighing yourself before and after exercise will give you an indication of how much fluid that you have lost and how much you will need to replace. It is important to take into account the loss of minerals. Isotonic drinks aim to replace lost minerals which are vital to body function. The loss of salt associated with sweating has led athletes to take salt tablets. However, salt tablets are difficult to take because there is always the need to take sufficient water with them.

To replace glycogen stores a high carbohydrate meal two to four hours after the event is ideal.

Illegal substances: their nature and effects

There are six major classes of doping agents identified by the International Olympic Committee and an additional four drug classes which are subject to set restrictions. Research has identified the sites which are affected by these doping agents in the form of a flow diagram.

Figure 4.16 A schema of the 'sites of action' of various drugs

Doping agents

Stimulants

Narcotic analgesics

Anabolic steroids

Beta blockers

Diuretics

Peptide hormones and analogues

Additional drug classes

Alcohol

Marijuana

Local anaesthetics

Corticosteroids

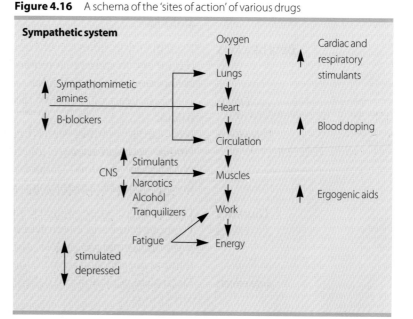

The short- and long-term effects of these drugs are well documented and the list of drugs that are banned are published by the Sports Council and administered within the governing bodies. The aim is to ensure that all athletes are made fully aware of which drugs or doping agents are banned.

Summary of the effects of doping agents

Stimulants
Sympathomimetic amines, caffeine and cocaine bring about the indirect release of adrenaline and noradrenaline.

Effects
Mask fatigue, maintain or improve alertness, increase competitiveness and aggression. Caffeine increases work output through a glycogen sparing effect, mobilising free fatty acids. This will enhance fat oxidation for energy production.

Side effects
Cardiac arrhythmia, anxiety, tachycardia, palpitations, tremor, headaches, insomnia, sweating, vertigo and hypertension.

Narcotic analgesics
Includes derivatives from poppy, the opiates, codeine and morphine.

Effects
They reduce or mask pain and induce euphoria.

Side effects
Respiratory depression, dependence and addiction.

Anabolic steroids
Related to the male sex hormone known as testosterone. This produces secondary male characteristics and is in abundance during puberty. The use of synthetic anabolic testosterone to enhance performance is well researched. It is targeted as a main doping agent used in power, explosive and sprint events in particular.

Effects
Increase in protein synthesis, blocking of the catabolic effect of glucocorticoids, enhancement of aggression. All these combined means that the athlete can work at high levels for longer periods recovering more quickly.

Side effects
Considerable but the main ones are: aggression, euphoria, mania, psycarbohydratesis, changes in libido, acne and alopecia, hypertension, kidney and liver tumours, menstrual disturbances and testicular atrophy.

Beta blockers
Used mainly in submaximal exercise that have periods of high cardiac output and in sports that require the control of hand steadiness such as shooting, darts and snooker.

Effects
Decrease heart rate, systolic blood pressure, cardiac output, reduce tremor.

Side effects
Low cardiac output, sinus bradycardia, cool extremities, muscle fatigue, reduced exercise tolerance, skin rash, exacerbates air flow obstruction (asthma), anorexia, nausea, diarrhoea, depression, insomnia, drowsiness and impotence.

Diuretics
Used in sports where weight control or weight categories are used.

Effects
Promote water and electrolyte loss by acting on the kidneys thereby promoting rapid weight loss. Also used to mask banned substances by diluting the concentration of urine.

Side effects
Electrolyte depletion and dehydration, cramps, muscle strains cardiac arrhythmia.

Peptide hormones and analogues

Used to enhance growth and to balance the effects of anabolic steroids by equalising the ratio of testosterone epitestosterone which is used to indicate drug abuse. The hormone commonly used is the human growth hormone somatotropin which is used in the treatment of children with short stature.

Effects

Promotes amino acid transport, protein synthesis, increases lean bodyweight, cellular growth, increases renal blood flow, accelerates linear bone growth and glomerular filtration rate.

Side effects

Without medical supervision: acromegaly (giantism), articular cartilage hypertrophies and then degenerates, muscle strengthens and then weakens, impotency occurs in males.

Additional drug classes and procedures

Blood doping – Discussed earlier, but involves the administration of erythropoietin in order to stimulate haemoglobin production.

Effects

Increased red blood cell production, increased haemoglobin, increased oxygen carrying capacity resulting in increased endurance.

Side effects

Allergic reactions, acute haemolysis leading to kidney damage, fever, jaundice, transmission of diseases such as viral hepatitus and acquired immune deficiency.

Alcohol, marijuana and sedatives

Effects

Improves relaxation and boosts confidence.

Side effects

Alcohol affects reaction time, hand-eye co-ordination, accuracy, balance and complex co-ordination. Long-term abuse includes pathological changes in the liver, kidney, neural tissue and muscle.

Local anaesthetics and corticosteroids

Effects

Local anaesthetics are injected and used for pain control.
Corticosteroids are used as anti-inflammatory preparations and produce euphoria.

Side effects

Adrenal suppression, sodium and water retention, decreased immune function, osteoporosis, avascular necrosis of the bone.

The detection of drugs involves a wide range of expensive techniques which are designed to isolate the class, type of drug and the quantity detected. However, the life span of some drugs means that detection is difficult when testing. The date and time is often known to the athlete. The need for random testing is being advocated as the only realistic way forward to isolate athletes for whom the cost and risks of drug taking seem minimal compared to the short-term gain.

Bans from sport as a result of varying levels of abuse and conviction against the International Olympic Committee rulings vary from four months to four years at present. There is however a strong belief by some officials and athletes that only a 'ban for life' can be a realistic deterrent and serve to protect young athletes who may see this as the only way in which they can compete on level terms.

SUMMARY

- Sportspersons in their quest to perform at the highest levels look to a variety of methods to enhance performance. These may include dietary and drug manipulation and altitude training.
- The speed and pace at which we train and compete will influence the energy pathways which we use. By understanding the effects of exercise on the energy reserves we can try to ensure that our diet enables the stores to be replenished quickly and effectively.
- Carbohydrate overloading has been used to increase the stores of glycogen within the body, particularly in endurance events.
- The physiological adaptations resulting from altitude training are temporary and quickly lost on the athlete's return to sea-level.
- Drug abuse is seen as an ever growing problem in sport. The reward for success has meant that the health risks associated with drug abuse are often ignored.

Questions

---

1 What are the major nutritional classes?
2 How does exercise intensity influence the energy pathway selected?
3 How can you prepare the body for exercise? Explain the methods you might use before, during and after exercise to enhance your performance.
4 Why do athletes train at altitude? What physiological changes take place in the body while training at altitude?
5 What are the six main doping classes? What is the role of the Sports Council in the control of drug abuse among sports people?

Training, fitness and health

Exercise and training in childhood and adolescence

As children grow and develop, and later go through adolescence to adulthood, their bodies undergo a great many changes. Similarly, their response to training and exercise will alter during this period. Exercise that is suitable for seven- and eight-year olds, will be different to the appropriate exercise for 13 and 14 year olds.

Identifying and accounting for the changes in physical capacity that take place in the period from childhood, through adolescence, to adulthood, is not a simple task. The growth of the body that takes place during this time is not a constant process. Different bodily parts and functions develop at different rates. Individuals have their own pattern of development. Some people will mature early, some will mature later. It is also important to realise that measures used to determine changes in performance in adults, are not always appropriate for determining changes in children. For example, testing for VO_2 max with a graded maximal test does not provide a plateau in oxygen consumption in pre-adolescents. The decline is much sharper with no identifiable levelling off. In children, oxygen consumption drops off much more rapidly, demonstrating a peak. For this reason, it is often termed **VO_2 peak**.

It is important to note that maturation and development, and training all play a part in the changes in exercise capacity. Aerobic capacity develops as part of the growth process. It increases at a slow but even rate up until the onset of puberty. On reaching puberty, the increase is much larger and occurs at a faster rate. When exactly this takes place is not determined by a person's age in years. It corresponds to an individual's maximum growth spurt, the period when they are growing fastest. This can occur anywhere from nine years old in early maturing girls, to age 17 in late-maturing boys.

With this in mind, it is often difficult to decide if changes in aerobic capacity are due to training effects, growth effects, or a combination of both. Children who are active do appear to have higher aerobic capacities than inactive children. So it is possible that aerobic training can produce extra benefits in terms of cardiovascular endurance. But it is almost certain that growth has a far larger influence on an individual's cardiovascular endurance before maturity.

Aerobic power, or capacity, is dependent upon the circulatory and ventilatory systems. Young children have small hearts that respond to the stress of exercise by increasing the rate at which they beat. Because of their relatively small size they have low stroke volumes. Increasing the number of beats per minute is the only way in which the increased oxygen demand can be satisfied. As a result of this, children who are observed at a given exercise work load can display heart rates that are on average 20 b.min^{-1} higher than for adults.

As they grow older the cardiac output is increased by an increase in stroke volume (SV). From the age of about ten years, until about 15 years the stroke volume increases by about 50 to 60%. This allows them to supply more oxygen to the muscles, and perform more aerobic work.

Oxygen is transported in the blood in one of two ways. It is either dissolved in the fluid portion or it binds with a chemical compound known as haemoglobin. The combination of oxygen with haemoglobin is the major method by which it is transported to the active muscular tissues. Each molecule of haemoglobin has the ability to transport a given amount of oxygen.

When a child is two years old, haemoglobin levels in the blood are about 12 g.dl^{-1}. At puberty the level has increased to 14 to 14.5 g.dl^{-1}. At this point it tends to level off in girls, whereas in boys it will continue to increase up to around 16 g.dl^{-1} at full maturity. The changes that take place in haemoglobin levels provide a greater oxygen carrying capacity to the blood, and therefore increased aerobic power. There is little doubt that the increase in haemoglobin levels in boys is a direct result of large increase in testosterone associated with puberty. Girls too, have increased testosterone levels at this stage in their development, but they are much smaller.

The number of alveoli in the lungs increases 12 times as a child grows. By the time an individual reaches adulthood the number of alveoli is 27 times greater than at birth. This means that the surface area over which oxygen can diffuse into the blood is greatly increased as part of the growth process. The younger the individual, the more difficult it is for them to breath.

Figure 4.17 Changes in ventilatory equivalent with age

Children need to inspire a greater volume of air to extract one litre of oxygen from the environment compared to an adult. The amount of air needed decreases as the age increases, along with the growth and development of the lungs. As a consequence of children having to breathe harder to perform the same amount of work, a lot of the aerobic energy produced is used to power the inefficient breathing. This can be seen when examining the ventilatory equivalent, which is calculated by dividing the ventilation rate (Ve) (l.min^{-1}) by oxygen consumption (VO$_2$). This is shown in figure 4.18, where at age six, ventilatory equivalent is 38. This decreases to the low thirties at the onset of puberty, and continues to decline to 28 at 18 years old.

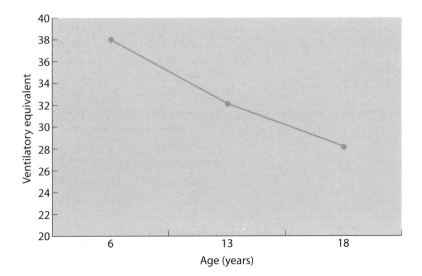

Prior to the beginning of adolescence, both boys and girls function in an aerobic manner. They demonstrate only very small adaptations to strength training. There are a number of reasons for this.

Increases in anaerobic work, such as strength or speed can come about as a result of two factors. The body can become better at conducting and coordinating nerve impulses. As a result, muscle fibre recruitment is better. This implies that there is a skill element involved in many of these activities. Secondly, the ability to perform anaerobic work can also be enhanced by increased muscle bulk. One square centimetre of muscle can produce a force of about four kilograms. If muscle size and circumference are increased, an individual is able to produce a greater force.

A major part of strength training is educating the nervous system to work more effectively to perform a given task. This is one reason why sprinters spend part of their training time practising starts, and performing reaction drills. The nervous system in the human body takes longer to grow and develop than any body part. It does not reach full maturity until the late twenties. As young children have a very immature nervous system, fibre recruitment is not going to be as effective as it would be in an adult. Put very simply, they cannot train what they do not have!

In conjunction with the increase in blood haemoglobin levels, increases in testosterone have an anabolic effect. This means that after adolescence boys are able to produce large increases in muscle mass. This increase in bulk means that they can produce greater forces and as a consequence, they become stronger and faster.

Responses to strength training in young men of this age, come about almost exclusively because of the anabolic effects of increased testosterone levels. It is not uncommon to see cases where individuals have put on three to four kilograms in months, the increase being mostly muscle mass. The increase in muscle bulk is mostly responsible for the increases in strength. There is little adaptation of the central nervous system. In older adults, strength training improves the ability of the nervous system to recruit muscle fibres. This means that they can improve their strength with little, or no increase in muscle bulk.

SUMMARY

- Children undergo a wide range of developmental changes which affect the ways in which they are able to adapt and adjust to exercise intensity and volume.
- It is important to note that maturation, development and training all play a part in exercise capacity.
- Children are naturally aerobic.
- As they reach puberty developmental changes in children accelerate and sharp increases in many aspects of fitness are seen, without any increases in activity level.
- The inefficiency of their physiological system is a major reason why pre-pubertal children respond only slowly to anaerobic training.

Questions

1 How does aerobic capacity develop during childhood and puberty?
2 Why do children find intense exercise difficult? In what ways are they anaerobically different from adults?.

The case for exercise and its long-term effects on the body

Many organisations argue that exercise has benefits that can help prevent the onset of disease and other conditions that are encountered in life. Regular exercise throughout a life time can bring about adaptations to the working systems of the body. This slows down degenerative changes that progress with increasing age. It is important to be aware of the fact that the benefits that are often gained in early life cannot be stored up. They need to be constantly maintained through regular exercise.

Obesity

Increasing body weight is part of the natural process of growth. However, once this is complete, adults still tend to be put on 0.5 kg of fat weight per year after their mid-thirties. This increase in fat weight is often associated with a declining food intake. Indeed food consumption is today about 10% lower than it was 20 years ago, yet the average person is 2.5 kg heavier. It is clear that the increasing weight and fat content of the body is not just due to the energy intake, activity levels have become progressively lower at the same time. Today, most people travel in cars rather than walk or cycle. Also, when they go to work, it is much more likely to be in a office and not require a great deal of physical effort. Hence it is not so much the energy intake that is causing the problem, as the lack of energy output.

Putting on extra weight in the form of fat means that the organs of the body must perform relatively more work. Putting on five kilograms of fat weight means an increase of eight miles of blood vessels through which the heart must pump blood. If fat is increased around the heart itself, it will have to work relatively harder to pump blood around the body and its action becomes relatively less efficient. Increased weight also puts more strain on joints making them more prone to injury.

It must be clear that the there are two sides to the problem, both intake of energy from food, and expenditure of energy. So, to initiate a decrease in body fat the energy intake can be decreased, the energy output increased, or the two factors can be combined.

Regular exercise can be of benefit in a number of ways. For example, running one mile requires about 420 kjoules. A person who is involved in regular exercise will expend more energy, slowing down the build-up of excess fat deposits. If a mile requires 420 joules of energy, then a one mile run or walk, three times per week for a year would expend:

$$420 \times 3 \times 52 = 65\,520 \text{ kjoules}$$

Consider this in terms of the energy contained in 0.5 kg of adipose tissue. Adipose tissue consists of about 87 % fat which will give 14 931 kjoules of energy. By dividing the total energy expenditure of exercise (65 520 kj) by the amount of energy contained in 0.5 kg of adipose tissue it can be demonstrated that the exercise prevented the build-up of 2.19 kg of adipose tissue:

$$\frac{65520}{14931} \times 0.5 = 2.19 \text{kg}$$

Exercise can also produce other benefits to energy output, as well as the energy used to perform exercise. Human adult energy expenditure can be separated into three component parts. These components are the resting metabolic rate (RMR), the thermic effect of food (TEF), and exercise. By far the largest of these components is the RMR. This includes the maintenance of normal bodily functions, and it accounts for about 70% of all energy consumed. The other 30% of energy expenditure is accounted for by the combined effect of the TEF and exercise.

Food intake has a stimulating effect on the energy metabolism of the body. In the process of digesting food and absorbing the nutrients, the body uses energy. The actual amount of energy used in the process depends upon the size and composition of the meal. But anything from 10% to 30% of the total energy intake can be used to simply digest the food.

The problem of weight control can be seen as one of energy balance.

Stable body weight:

Intake of energy = output of energy

Increasing body weight:

Intake of energy > output of energy

Decreasing body weight:

Intake of energy < output of energy

The amount of exercise performed is, without doubt, the biggest variable in human energy expenditure. Increasing exercise levels dramatically increases the energy expenditure. For example, during maximal treadmill running the body's metabolic rate is increased to about ten to 12 times resting values. The increase is so great that a top class sports person can almost double their total energy output by training three to four hours per day.

It must be stated, however, that not all of the increase in energy expenditure is due to the exercise alone. Exercise elevates the RMR, and maintains it at a higher than normal level for a period of about 24 hours. This means that the total energy expenditure will be further increased, and burning more energy means less deposition of fat around the major organs and in subcutaneous storage.

Coronary heart disease

Regularly increasing the heart rate through exercise can have preventative effects against coronary heart disease (CHD). Coronary heart disease begins with the degeneration of the inner lining of the arteries. This in turn leads to the partial blockage of these blood vessels by lipid-rich plaques or fibrous scar tissue. If this pattern continues unchecked, then the muscles of the heart are deprived of blood and a heart attack can occur. Usually for this to happen, the blood flow at rest needs to be restricted by 80%.

It is thought that almost every body has a certain degree of CHD. It is not known if the process begins in very early life, or if it might be hereditary. By the time men reach their thirties, and women their forties, CHD is the largest cause of death. The problem is so inherent in humans that it is very difficult to detect the amount of narrowing in the arteries until it is at least 50% and maybe even as high as 70%.

At least a part of the development process is influenced by the amount of cholesterol consumed in the diet. Although cholesterol is needed by the body to perform certain functions, excess amounts are thought to cause a pre-disposition to CHD.

People who exercise regularly have higher blood levels of high density lipoprotein cholesterol (HDL), and lower levels of low density lipoprotein cholesterol (LDL). LDLs have a high proportion of cholesterol, and as they move through the blood stream, cholesterol is deposited in the veins and arteries. HDLs do the opposite of this, they have a low cholesterol content as they move through the blood stream they combine with cholesterol and transport the cholesterol to the liver where it can be metabolised.

In a similar way to the other effects of exercise, this is another aspect that requires constant maintenance. It would take about six months of regular aerobic activity of about 15 kilometres per week, for an adult to show a marked increase in HDL levels. However, ten to 14 days inactivity after this time, will see them return to pre-exercise levels.

Regular exercise allows less chance for the deposition of

cholesterol and fat in the blood. This reduces the amount of narrowing of arteries, and reduces the chance of a blockage occurring.

Hypertension

Hypertension can be defined as a resting blood pressure reading above 140/90 mm Hg. It is suggested that almost 20% of adult Americans suffer from hypertension, but as people increase in age the condition becomes more prevalent. Those people who have blood pressure in excess of 160/95 mm Hg, have up to a 300% higher incidence rate for conditions such as coronary artery disease and stroke, when compared to similar individuals with normal blood pressure (normotensives).

High blood pressure can be treated in a variety of ways. One method is by use of hypertensive drugs such as beta blockers, another is through regular exercise training. It is suggested that regular bouts of activity can reduce the risk of developing hypertension. They also lower the risk of death in people already suffering from hypertension.

Longitudinal research (studies that follow individuals over a number of years) has shown that people who remain physically active, performing regular aerobic activity, have consistently lower blood pressure than sedentary individuals. Also, those adults who remain physically active throughout adulthood, are between 30 and 50% less likely to develop hypertension.

The detected reduction in blood pressure that takes place, has been observed in both the systolic and diastolic readings. It has been reported that the reduction is in the region of 13 mm Hg for systolic, and 10 mm Hg for diastolic. As is the case with the great many benefits of regular aerobic exercise, the changes have been reported across all age ranges. The decline in blood pressure readings after three months of regular exercise is of a similar magnitude when young hypertensives are compared with adults in the over 60-years old age group.

The intensity of exercise undertaken has been shown to influence the amount of reduction that takes place. Evidence suggest that if activity is at an intensity of 40% to 70% VO_2 max, then the reduction in blood pressure will be greater than if exercise is performed at a higher intensity.

Like many other health benefits that can be gained from exercise training, the lowering of blood pressure is subject to alteration. The largest reductions are seen within the first 21 to 90 days of an exercise programme. Beyond this point the effects are less marked. Any further reductions that take place are small, with some individuals showing no further lessening in blood pressure. In spite of the fact that further lowering of blood pressure after this time is unlikely, the benefits do not remain constant. The changes are evident only as long as endurance training is maintained.

The mechanisms that result in lower blood pressure following aerobic exercise training are to a large extent unclear. However, the lowering of both systolic and diastolic blood pressure by 10 mm Hg, appears to take place independently of alterations in both body fat and body weight. Therefore, it can be reasonably expected that a decrease in body weight and fat mass which also takes place as a result of exercise training, will result in further benefits when considered in terms of reducing the risk of coronary artery disease

Encouraging exercise and activity

It is widely agreed that getting individual fitness to a level where the body gains maximum protection from coronary heart disease, a person must perform vigorous activity for a duration of twenty minutes, at least three times per week. However, finding the time to exercise can cause conflict with other activities, such as work, travel to and from home and other commitments.

Because of the constraints placed on time, it is often difficult for people to set aside time on a regular basis for exercise. The consequence of this is that in England, about 70% to 80% of all people exercise below their age appropriate activity levels. In a school setting only 49 % of boys and 19% of girls undertake vigorous exercise on a regular basis.

Recent initiatives in the United Kingdom and North America have been aimed at those people who are not currently exercising enough. Unlike previous projects, the emphasis has move away slightly from the twenty minutes, three times per week prescription. The new approach can be seen to have a 'two-tiered' structure:

- For people who are currently inactive and the least fit. To improve fitness levels, the aim is to accumulate 30 minutes of moderate intensity activity on most days of the week.
- For people who are already moderately active and moderately fit. The aim is to perform vigorous exercise of 20 minutes duration on three occasions per week.

The overall aim of the strategy is to reduce the total number of people who can be classified as inactive, and increase the number who are classified as active. In this country, the Health Education Authority has declared that their aim is 'to increase the number of men and women aged 16 to 74 taking a minimum of at least 30 minutes moderate physical activity on five days of the week from 18% in 1990, to 90% of the total population by the year 2005.'

Intensity or volume?

With exercise, the emphasis is now being placed on the volume (the total amount of exercise taken), rather than the intensity of exercise. By stating that the level should be 'at least moderate', a whole new list of activities are now available to count towards exercise.

Along with the introduction of new activities which will count towards the daily exercise requirement, there is also the suggestion that the activity does not have to be completed in one session. It is proposed that, the accumulation of 30 minutes activity in three

Vigorous exercise

(>31.4 kj.min-1)

- Aerobics
- Footbal
- Running
- Squash
- Swimming
- Tennis
- Cycling (if the activity makes the participant out of breath and sweaty)

Moderate exercise

(>21 <31.4 kj.min-1)

- Aerobics
- Cycling
- Football
- Golf
- Heavy DIY (e.g. mixing cement)
- Heavy gardening (e.g. digging)
- Long walks at a fast brisk pace (at least 4 mph)
- Social dancing
- Swimming
- Table tennis
- Tennis

Source: Health Education Authority (1994)

periods of at least ten minutes each will have a worthwhile health benefit.

There is evidence to suggest that the benefits of exercise and activity are available to everybody regardless of their age. It is necessary for the preservation of the optimal function of the cardio-vascular system, along with the structure and function of the muscles bones and joints. It can also promote self esteem. Someone who exercises regularly has an increased physical working capacity. So they are able to perform a range of activities with confidence and reduced fatigue levels. For example, a given task say gardening, might require a person to work at a heart rate of 150 b.min[-1]. After training the same work might only require a heart beat of 140 b.min[-1].

Investigations have shown that low levels of exercise are probably more important than other factors (for example, smoking, hypertension, being overweight) when it comes to assessing the risk of coronary heart disease.

To show how important exercise is consider the following example. An obese person is classified as someone who is more than 30% over their correct weight for their height. This condition magnifies the effects of almost all other diseases. These people are more likely to develop heart disease, hypertension, bronchitis and arthritis. However, those obese people who exercise regularly, have been found to be at risk of suffering a heart attack that is no greater than people who are normal weight. Also, in a straight comparison with obese non-exercisers, the obese exercisers are five times less likely to suffer a heart attack.

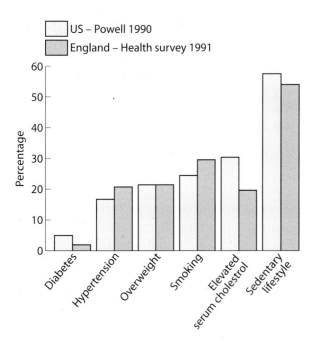

Figure 4.19 Risk factors for coronary heart disease

Exercise is for everyone

It has already been stated that the benefits of exercise are available to all people regardless of age. But it must also be remembered that each specific age group has its own requirements, when it comes to the benefits that are obtainable.

Children and adolescents

During childhood is the best time to begin regular activity. If activity levels are low at this stage of life, it is likely that they will remain low throughout the rest of life. This problem is exacerbated by the fact that the least active children carry the most extra weight. This is true with children as young as four to eight-years old. It is also quite probable that they will continue to be inactive, put on further weight and continue to be inactive.

Even at this early age, exercise has a valuable effect in the prevention of CHD, as in later life, those who exercise least have the highest blood pressure. Even at the age of ten, those with the highest work capacity have lower blood pressure.

One of the major reasons, often quoted, for encouraging children and adolescents to exercise, is that it is habit forming. It is argued that if exercise is a part of the daily routine from very early in life, it will stay that way throughout the person's lifetime. If this argument is examined carefully, it can be seen that it is almost the exact opposite to the pattern described for inactive children above. Essentially, if they are encouraged to be active they will develop habits which involve energetic activity and exercise. If they are allowed to become inactive they will fill their time with activities that do not involve much activity, for example, watching television.

The whole basis of the new exercise recommendations is to encourage the extra expenditure of energy. Quite clearly, walking and running expend greater amounts of energy than sitting.

Middle life

This is the area of life when degenerative conditions begin to display themselves at an increasing rate. As well as the benefits in terms of hypertension, weight control and CHD, exercise can influence the pattern of development of other diseases.

For example, osteoporosis describes a condition in which the density of bones declines. Density decreases with increasing age, and especially in women after the menopause. However, the mineral density of certain bones has been shown to be strongly associated with good stamina. This means that if a person has good endurance they also have stronger bones. Bone tissue is very much like muscle and other tissues when it comes to exercise. If it is stressed, as it is in exercise, it becomes stronger.

Later life

When an individual reaches this stage of his or her life time, it is inevitable that there will be a reduction in activity. However, these reductions can be offset to a certain extent.

Stamina

In endurance terms, maximal heart rate will decline, but the cardiac output can be largely maintained with increases in stroke volume. There is also little doubt that people of this age can show substantial improvements in stamina as a result of exercise training. This has been demonstrated in both men and women over the age of 65. Masters age group athletes who have continued to train, show only small declines in maximal aerobic capacity.

Strength

Strength also declines with age. The decline is largely due to the degeneration of the motor neurones. This causes muscles to become weaker and contract more slowly. As with other functional capacities, strength can be maintained with regular use. In spite of the degenerative loss, the remaining muscular tissue can be strengthened by regular contractions at least once per day. It is not known if increased strength levels come about as a result of better neurological recruitment of muscle fibres or changes within the muscle cells.

Osteoporosis

Some of the problems of this condition have already been described above. When people reach this age group, it is important to try and maintain some of the bone density. With regular light exercise where the body is upright, it has been shown that it is possible to maintain or slightly increase bone density by 1% to 2%.

For this age group, being active is very important. In the later years of life, performing a task such as standing and preparing your own food, can raise energy requirements to two or three times resting levels. It is clear that those with the highest functional aerobic capacities will find a number of everyday tasks relatively less demanding. In terms of strength and osteoporosis, regular training is also very important. Hearing stories of senior citizens who have fallen and broken a hip, is common. With increased strength, there is more chance they will have better motor control to prevent such falls, while the increased bone density will afford a little more protection against fractures.

Exercise throughout life has undoubted benefits. At each particular stage of life, there are specific benefits that can be gained through regular exercise. It must be stressed that to get the most from exercise it must be done regularly and on a life-long basis. The actual activities that an individual can perform may change, but the message is to remain active for a whole lifetime. Do a little exercise and do it often.

SUMMARY

- Exercise has benefits that can prevent the onset of disease and improve the quality of health as we grow older.
- Increases in fat weight will mean that there will be associated increases in the work load of major body systems.
- Regular exercise can help maintain body weight level by burning off the excess fat.
- Adult energy expenditure can be separated into three parts. These are resting metabolic rate (RMR), the thermic effect of food (TEF), and exercise.
- Regular exercise can prevent coronary heart disease. However, gains made through six months of regular aerobic activity can be lost after ten to 14 days of inactivity
- It is suggested that 20 % of adult Americans suffer from high blood pressure (hypertension). This is seen as a major risk factor in coronary heart disease (CHD).
- The latest activity programmes have changed the emphasis away from the twenty minutes of continuous exercise, three times a week prescription, to an accumulation of small exercise sessions giving the same total of exercise time.
- Exercise is for everyone. However, each specific age group has its own requirements in order to achieve desirable outcomes.
- Childhood is the best time to begin regular activity. Exercise at this time has a valuable effect in the prevention of CHD.

Questions

1 How have lifestyle changes brought about changes in our levels of fitness and health?

2 Why is regular exercise useful when trying to control body weight?

3 What is coronary heart disease and how is this linked to cholesterol levels in the blood?

4 Recent initiatives aimed at people who are not exercising enough have suggested a new approach. What is the 'two-tiered' structure currently outlined by these initiatives.

5 What is the difference between exercise intensity and exercise volume? Name five sports which can be classified as vigorous and five as moderate.

6 What are the risk factors of coronary heart disease?

7 Why is it important to encourage children and adolescents to exercise on a regular basis?

References

Astrand P O, Rodahl K, Text book of work physiology: physiological bases of exercise, McGraw-Hill, London, 3rd edition (1986)

British Association of Sport and Exercise Sciences Position statement on the physiological assessment of the elite athletes, 2nd edition (1988)

Fox E L Sports Physiology, Saunder College Publishing (1983)

Hazeldine R, Development of strength and speed, National Coaching Foundation, Leeds (1985)

McArdle W D, Katch F I, Katch V L, Exercise Physiology: energy, nutrition and sports performance, Lea and Febiger, Philadelphia (1993)

Sharp N C C, Developing endurance, National Coaching Foundation, Leeds (1985)

Tartora G J, Grabowski S R Principles of Anatomy and Physiology, Harper Collins (1993)

5 PRINCIPLES OF MOVEMENT

The importance of sport and exercise in modern society is well recognised. The motivation for engaging in physical activity ranges from the pursuit of sporting excellence to the desire to improve our health and well-being. The study of motion of an elite performer may enable us to better understand the key factors which contribute to sporting success. These findings may then be applied to other athletes with the goal of improving their sporting performance. Furthermore, a better understanding of the mechanisms which contribute to sports injuries should enable us to contribute to the important area of sports injury prevention and rehabilitation.

One way of examining sport is through the application of scientific methods of enquiry. The sport and exercise sciences include the disciplines of biomechanics, physiology and psychology. The outcome of any performance is of course due to a complex combination of factors.

Objectives

To understand
- the nature of force and its significance to sporting movement
- the application of Newton's Laws of Motion to explain sporting action
- the meaning of basic mechanical concepts and principles and their importance to our understanding of human motion

Biomechanics

Biomechanics is a modern scientific discipline which is firmly based upon the biological and mathematical sciences. The word element 'bio' means 'living', and thus 'biomechanics' may be defined as the mechanics of living things. More precisely, within the sporting context, biomechanics is concerned with the forces which act on the human body during sporting movement and the effects which these applied forces produce. The role of sports biomechanics is of increasing importance in sports analysis. Reasons for this include the constant pursuit by the coach and elite athlete for the ultimate performance, the need for sound training practices for the ordinary sportsperson and the developing sports technology industry.

A biomechanical analysis of any sport will require a basic knowledge of mechanical principles and laws. However, it is the application of this knowledge to sporting performance that is critical for a better understanding of the control of human movement. This chapter aims to satisfy both of these requirements. It provides an outline of the main biomechanical principles and laws and relates them to specific sporting examples to illustrate their significance.

Biomechanics may be subdivided to provide a framework which may be applied to the study of human performance. Firstly, there are the two major subdivisions of statics and dynamics. There are a further two branches of biomechanics, namely kinetics and kinematics. These terms have specific meanings within the discipline of biomechanics.

Motion may be defined as being either linear or angular in nature, although sporting motion is more frequently a combination of the two. In the latter case, the term general motion is usually applied. Further detailed references to these terms are given in the following sections. It should be noted that the above subdivisions do not exist in isolation from one another. An analysis in this way helps the biomechanical study of sport.

> **Statics** refers to the motion of bodies under the influence of balanced forces.
>
> **Dynamics** refers to the motion of bodies under the influence of unbalanced forces.
>
> **Kinetics** is concerned with the scientific study of the underlying reasons for movement, without regard to the results of movement.
>
> **Kinematics** involves the description of how a body moves, without trying to explain the cause behind the observed motion.

Linear kinetics

Force is the fundamental mechanical quantity which needs to be examined in the study of the cause of movement. Note that the term 'body' is used in biomechanics to represent a defined object or system. Thus, the human body may be the 'body' under investigation, but the term also applies to all the objects used in sport, for example, a soccer ball or a javelin.

Force

A push or a pull due to direct mechanical contact or due to gravitational attraction which alters, or tends to alter, the state of motion of a body is referred to as a force. For a body at rest, forces are responsible for making it move. For a moving body, forces are responsible for speeding it up, slowing it down, and changing its direction.

When a body at rest is acted upon by an external force there is a tendency for it to move. Whether the body actually moves or not depends on specific properties of the force and the body itself.

Under the conditions where a body is already in motion, the application of an external force will change or tend to change its state of motion. As for the body at rest, the actual outcome of the applied force is dependent on the properties of the force and the properties of the body itself (that is, its mass or inertia). For example, a large rugby forward who is running fast may only have his motion altered slightly when he makes contact with a much lighter player. Although the lighter player would exert a force on the larger forward, the force would be of insufficient magnitude to significantly alter the forward's motion properties. However, if the same forward with the same

Internal forces are usually regarded as those associated with muscular contractions which act on the structures of the body itself.

External forces are outside the body and cause a displacement of the body. These external forces include the all-important gravitational force or weight. They also include friction, air, wind and water resistance forces, and forces due to other bodies acting on the body.

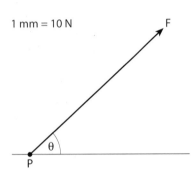

1 mm = 10 N

Figure 5.1 Force (F) as a vector quantity represented by an arrow indicating direction with magnitude represented by the length of the line, acting at point P at angle θ

Newton's law of gravitation

Newton's Law of Gravitation — law of attraction — states that

all bodies attract one another with a force that is proportional to the products of their masses and inversely proportional to the square of the distance between them.

$$F \alpha \frac{m_1 m_2}{d^2} \text{ (equation 1)}$$

[where **F** is gravitational attraction force, **m₁** and **m₂** are the respective masses (kg) of the two given bodies, and **d** is the distance between their centres of mass]

motion characteristics made contact with a much larger tackler, it is likely that he may be significantly slowed down. He may actually undergo a change in direction, or he may be stopped altogether.

It should be understood therefore that forces are responsible for any observed change in the motion properties (dynamics) of a body. They also account for observed relationships between bodies at rest or under balanced conditions (statics). There are numerous examples in sport to illustrate this important quantity called force. Some of these examples will be outlined later in the chapter.

Before considering the significance of force to our understanding of motion, it is necessary to examine more closely its nature and properties. Force may be further defined as that which pushes or pulls through direct mechanical contact, or through the force of gravity, with a resultant alteration in the motion of the body.

Force is a vector quantity, that is, it possesses both magnitude and direction. Magnitude refers to the amount or size, while direction refers to its line of action. These two properties however do not entirely determine the outcome of a force on a body. A third factor in the resultant outcome is the exact point of application of the force on the body. A force (as with any vector quantity) may be represented by accurate construction, whereby a scaled line is drawn, as illustrated in figure 5.1.

The net effect of the magnitude, direction, and point of application of a force will determine the outcome on the body experiencing the force. Since force is a vector quantity it may be resolved into a vertical and a horizontal component. The relative size of these component vectors depends upon the angle at which the force is applied.

Much of our understanding and knowledge of sports biomechanics is the result of the studies over three centuries ago of Sir Isaac Newton (1642 – 1727). Among his many outstanding achievements was his formulation of the law of gravitation and the three laws of motion. These laws may be applied to explain and account for the forces involved and their outcomes in the sports context. Each of the laws is outlined in the margin.

It follows therefore from equation 1 that the greater the mass of one or other, or indeed both of the bodies, the larger the force of attraction between them will be. Conversely, since there is an inverse relationship between force and distance, it follows that the force of attraction decreases as the distance between the bodies increases. There is also a squared effect for this inverse relationship which results in a much reduced force of attraction for linear increases in their distance apart.

The relatively small masses of bodies involved in sport are such that the forces of attraction between them are in actual fact negligible. However, there is one extremely important attractive force which constantly affects all bodies. This is the force exerted on them by the earth or the force of gravitational attraction. Obviously, when the

In algebraic form,

$$F = \frac{G.m_1 m_2}{d^2} \text{ (equation 2)}$$

[where **F** represents the force of attraction exerted on each body; G represents the gravitational constant; m_1 and m_2 represent the masses of the two bodies; and **d** represents the distance between them.]

Newton's laws of linear motion

Newton's First Law – the law of inertia – states that

every body at rest, or moving with constant velocity in a straight line, will continue in that state unless compelled to change by an external force exerted upon it.

Figure 5.2   Effect of an external force

immense mass of the earth is substituted for 'm$_1$' in expression (1) above, and the mass of an athlete, or any other body, is substituted for 'm$_2$', it should be appreciated that 'F' will become significant.

If a known constant (G) is added to the relationships expressed in the law it may be transformed into an equation (equation 2).

It is the constant gravitational force which acts to maintain bodies in contact with the earth's surface in this state. Once contact is broken, as with projectiles, it is this force which pulls or tends to pull them back to the earth's surface. The gravitational force exerted on a body by the earth has a line of action which passes through the body's centre of gravity (COG) in a vertical direction (that is, normal to the earth's surface) towards the centre of the earth. The line of action of any force is an imaginary straight line that passes through the force's point of application on the body. The COG is an imaginary point at which the entire weight of the body may be considered as being concentrated. As such it represents the point where the weight of the body may be said to act. The COG of a body does not always lie within the substance of the body itself. For example, the COG of an air-filled ball lies within the enclosed air space, as it does for the rings used in gymnastics and the hoops used in physical education. The COG of the human body may also lie outside the substance of the body itself, for example in the hyper-extended body position associated with the high jump bar clearance using the Fosbury Flop technique.

The law of gravitational attraction is of central importance to observations on sporting performances. However, it is best understood when considered along with mass and acceleration, as contained in Newton's second law.

For example, consider the rugby football in the pictures shown in figure 5.2. In the first picture, just prior to the moment of impact, the football is at rest. Thus the ball at this moment in time satisfies a set of conditions defined under the term statics, that is, it is under the influence of balanced forces. Moments later, the ball has moved beyond the field of view of the camera due to the player's kicking action. In this rather obvious example, the ball has been compelled to change its state of motion from that of a stationary body to that of a moving body with particular motion properties. This change in the ball's state of motion was brought about by an external force which was the result of the kicking action of the player. It should be noted that there are actually two bodies

Mass represents the quantity of matter in a body which in turn is a measure of the body's inertia. Inertia is the term used to indicate a body's reluctance to change its current state of motion. This discussion of Newton's first law has been concerned with bodies at rest.

interacting in this example. The ball (which may be considered as body 1), is incapable of bringing about this change by itself. Newton's First Law states the requirement of an external force to bring about a change . The player's foot may be considered as body 2 and it is the foot's action which imparts the external force on the ball.

Of course there are a number of other forms of external force which could make the ball move from its stationary position, each with differing resultant motion properties. For example, a gust of wind may blow the ball over. Another gust of wind may not be strong enough to have any observable effect on the ball. However, if it acts on the ball at all it is compelling the ball to change. These compelling or actual outcomes depend on two factors: the characteristics of the force (magnitude, direction, and point of application), and the mass of the ball.

It is also necessary to consider the second part of Newton's first law, which deals with a body moving in a straight line with constant velocity. Under these circumstances, the body satisfies the condition referred to as linear motion, that is, all parts of the body move through the same distance in the same direction in the same time. Under these conditions the body is moving under the influence of balanced forces, referred to as dynamic equilibrium.

Actual examples drawn from sport to illustrate this law are in fact very rare, and at best are only momentary or of very short time durations. However, an understanding of this principle assists in the understanding of Newton's Second Law. Consider the free fall phase of a skydiver, as illustrated in Figure 5.3.

Figure 5.3 Dynamic equilibrium during linear motion

Figure 5.3 represents a free-body diagram, which shows all the forces that act on the body, in this case, the human body. In a free-body diagram, the body is considered as a separate mechanical system, isolated from its surroundings, and with defined boundaries. All the forces acting on the body are represented as vectors by straight lines each having a point of application and an arrow indicating direction.

R

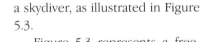

W

In the example above, the skydiver experiences acceleration due to gravity ($g=9.81$ m.s^{-2}), immediately upon leaving the aircraft. However, he also starts to experience the effects of the force of air resistance which brings about a change in his downward acceleration. Air resistance is an external force which acts in the opposite direction to his motion. Due to the effects of an increasing air resistance force, the skydiver's acceleration does not remain constant at 9.81 m.s^{-2}, but rather changes (decreases) due to an associated increase in the force

W = R (equation 3)

[where **W** is the total weight of the system, and **R** is the combined air resistance.]

Figure 5.4 Skydivers in free-fall

of air resistance with increasing velocity. The decrease in acceleration continues until it reaches a value of zero (constant velocity) at which point the weight (W) of the system (skydiver, suit, parachute and associated equipment) is equal to the force of air resistance (R). From this point on (until the skydiver does something to alter his air resistance) he is moving under the influence of two balanced forces (at a constant velocity).

The velocity under these conditions is referred to as the terminal velocity. For the spread eagle position in this example, this velocity may be in the region of 45 m.s^{-1} (100 mph), and is reached in approximately 15 s from the time he leaves the aircraft. However, if he was to 'nose-dive', his terminal velocity would be approximately 90 ms^{-1} (200 mph) attained in a time period of about 20 s. The difference is naturally due to the lesser air resistance (R) in the latter case, since in both cases the weight (W) is identical.

By altering the surface area to the air flow and/or his body position, the skydiver is able to change his speed. He is also able to manoeuvre reasonably well, thus enabling him to link up with other skydivers (figure 5.4). However, such actions result once again in a situation where there are unbalanced forces. Therefore he is no longer moving under the condition referred to as dynamic equilibrium.

At some point, the skydiver opens his parachute. This action has the effect of dramatically increasing the air resistance. Once the period of deceleration caused by this massive increase in air resistance has ended, the parachutist once again moves under the influence of balanced forces, that is, dynamic equilibrium. There is an assumption here that no other external forces are acting, such as cross winds, or the effects of the parachutist's pulling actions on the parachute cords.

In this illustration it has been shown that it is possible, with many assumptions, to satisfy Newton's first law of motion as it relates to

Figure 5.5 Dynamic forces are common in sport

Newton's Second Law – law of acceleration states that:

the acceleration of a body is proportional to the force causing it and takes place in the direction in which the force acts.

Algebraically,

$F = m \times a$ (equation 4)

[where **F** represents the force exerted; **m** represents the mass; and **a** represents the acceleration]

Since the units of measurement for mass and acceleration are kilograms (kg) and (m/s² or m.s⁻²) respectively, the units for force may given as kg.m/s² (kg.m.s⁻²). However, Newton (N) is the unit for force which is conveniently and commonly used (1 N = 1 kg.m.s⁻²).

It follows from equation 4 that the acceleration which a body experiences is proportional to the applied force and indirectly proportional to its mass. That is, since

$F = m \times a$

$a = \dfrac{F}{m}$ (equation 5)

linear motion. However, it is much more common in sport to undergo motion as a result of constantly changing forces, such as that experienced by a wind surfer (Figure 5.5). This is the concern of that branch of biomechanics known as dynamics and to which Newton's second and third laws relate.

The relationship given in equation 5 implies:

- that for a body of given mass, the greater the applied force, the greater will be its acceleration.
- that for a given force, the accelerating effects will vary depending on the mass of the body which experiences that force. Examples drawn from sport will help to illustrate these relationships.

Consider a sprinter leaving the blocks (figure 5.6). During a warm-up or practice start he may choose to apply only some fraction, say about fifty per cent, of his maximum driving force.

According to this second law, the athlete will undergo an acceleration (a) which will be directly proportional to the magnitude of this applied force. If the athlete is capable of exerting his maximum force under race conditions, he will undergo twice the acceleration experienced in the warm-up (2a), that is, he will leave the blocks twice as fast. It is reasonable to assume that the mass of the athlete is unaltered for these two starts.

Assume over a period of time the same athlete maintains the same force generating capacity (F) but manages to lose 10% of his body mass (m). Since F = ma and since m has been reduced by 10%, it follows that the acceleration will have to increase by 10% to balance the equation. Consequently, in theory, the athlete now will be capable of a faster start.

Questions

1 Would this be possible in practice?
2 What other considerations need to be taken into account?
3 What would happen to the athlete's acceleration if he gained weight, that is, his body mass increased by ten per cent? (Assume his force-generating capacity remains unchanged.)

momentum = mass x velocity

or, algebraically,

$p = m \times v$ (equation 6)

[where **p** represents momentum, **m** represents mass, and **v** represents velocity]. When mass is measured in kg and velocity in m.s⁻¹, the unit of measurement for momentum is kg.m.s⁻¹.

Newton's Second Law also takes into account two other important mechanical quantities – **momentum** (p) and **impulse** (J).

Momentum refers to the quantity of motion, or amount of motion, that a body possesses by virtue of its motion. It is equal to the product of the body's mass and its velocity.

A sprinter with a mass of 85 kg and a velocity of 10 m.s⁻¹ has a momentum of 850 kg.m.s⁻¹. Momentum is an important quantity in sports biomechanics, particularly in situations where impacts occur. However, let us first consider its relationship to force and its derivation from Newton's Second Law (F = ma).

Figure 5.6 The acceleration experienced by the sprinter is determined by the force he exerts on the blocks

$$a = \frac{v-u}{t} \quad \text{(equation 7)}$$

Algebraically,

[where **a** represents acceleration, **v** represents final velocity, **u** represents initial velocity, and **t** represents time]

Substituting this expression for a in the equation, F = ma gives,

$$F = \frac{m(v-u)}{t} \quad \text{(equation 8)}$$

Thus:

$$F = \frac{mv-mu}{t} \quad \text{(equation 9)}$$

[where **F** represents the applied force, mv represents final momentum, mu represents initial momentum, and t represents time]

Thus Newton's Second Law may be stated as,

The rate of change of momentum of a body (or the acceleration for a body of constant mass) is proportional to the applied force causing it and takes place in the direction in which the force acts.

Furthermore, equation 9 may be rewritten as

Ft = mv - mu (equation 10)

Therefore,

Ft = m(v – u) (equation 11)

J = m(v – u) (equation 12)

[where **Ft** = **J** represents impulse, and **v** and **u** are the final and initial velocities respectively]

Acceleration in this equation (equation 7) represents the rate of change of velocity, that is, acceleration is the final velocity minus the initial velocity with respect to the time taken for this change in velocity to occur. Equations 8 and 9 illustrate their inter-relationship.

Impulse is the product of force and time. This equation for impulse shows (equation 10) that the product of the force and the time over which this force acts will produce a change in the velocity of the mass. It follows that by increasing either the magnitude of the force or the time over which the force acts (or both), will result in an increase in this velocity change of the mass, or its acceleration. Conversely, any decrease in either of the two quantities on the left hand side of equation 11 will result in a decrease in the velocity, or a deceleration. Note that an increase in velocity over time is sometimes referred to as a positive acceleration while a decrease in velocity is sometimes referred to as a negative acceleration .

Impulse, as the product of force and time, has important implications for sport, particularly where the intention is to maximise the acceleration of an object. Consider, for example, the shot putt event. In this highly technical event the elite athlete not only possesses the physical qualities necessary for high force production, but he also performs a series of highly coordinated body actions finishing in the release of the shot. These actions result in the shot being accelerated from an initial zero velocity (at rest) to a high velocity at the point of release. In order to maximise the time of contact, the athlete is clearly seen to 'follow-through' after the shot has left his hand. The follow- through (which occurs after the shot has broken contact with the hand) in itself does not add to the resultant outcome of the shot. However, it ensures that the athlete has maintained the contact time for the driving force for as long a time as possible prior to release. Of course the athlete has to ensure that his actions do not cause him to foul, for example, by forcing him to step or stumble out of the circle.

Questions

1 Give two examples from other athletics events and two examples from ball games where impulse is important.
2 Outline the body actions which the athlete performs in order to achieve the desired acceleration on the body for the above examples.

Impulse also has important implications for impact situations where there is a potential risk of injury. Consider a cricketer catching a fast ball. As the ball is about to come into contact with his hands, he withdraws his hands in the general direction of the ball's flight until the ball is finally brought to rest. This action has the effect of increasing the time interval over which the ball reduces its velocity (decelerates) from some high value to zero, compared to the short time interval if he was to present his hands as an immovable body. Since the mass of the ball is constant, and the velocity change is the same for both catching methods (from some high value to zero), it follows from equation 11 that by increasing t there must be an equal decrease in F if the equation is to remain balanced. This is best illustrated by a worked example.

Assume the ball has mass (m), an initial velocity of 20 m/s, and a final velocity of 0 for the following two conditions :

1 a deceleration period of 0.5 s.
2 a deceleration period of 0.25 s.

Given that $J = m(v - u)$ $\qquad$ (equation 12)
since $J = Ft$
substituting 1: $F(0.5) = m(20 - 0)$
therefore $F = 40\,m$
That is, there is an impact force of 40 times the mass of the ball.
substituting 2: $F(0.25) = m(20 - 0)$
therefore $F = 80\,m$
That is, there is an impact force of 80 times the mass of the ball, or twice that for condition 1. The potential for injury is thus reduced for condition 1. Also the catcher has greater opportunity to secure a gripping action on the ball and thus to make a successful catch.

Questions

1 Consider the effect of landing from a height with straight legs compared to landing with bent legs with a subsequent further bending action.
2 Account for the actions of a parachutist upon landing.

One body exerts an action force, and the other body exerts a reaction force which is equal in magnitude but opposite in direction to the action force. Consider the swimmer in figure 5.7.

Newton's Third Law – law of reaction – states that

for every action, there is an equal and opposite reaction.

It is important to realise that this law relates to the relationship between two bodies. This law may be rewritten as follows:

for every force that is exerted by one body on another, there is an equal and opposite force exerted by the second body on the first.

Figure 5.7 The action of the swimmer on the blocks causes an equal and opposite reaction force, which projects her into the air

As a result of her body actions involving large muscle groups she exerts an action force on the block. This action force is actually in the opposite direction to the impending direction of her body movement. However, it is the reaction of the block to her action which launches her into the air in the form of a dive. These two forces are illustrated in the free-body diagram in Figure 5.8 below.

Since the action and reaction forces are equal in magnitude and opposite in direction it is reasonable to ask why, in the above example, one body (swimmer) moves and the other body (block) does not. Firstly, note that the block is fixed to the pool side which in turn is firmly embedded in the earth. The explanation then lies in the immense difference between the respective masses of the two bodies

Figure 5.8 The action and reaction forces at the start of a swim race

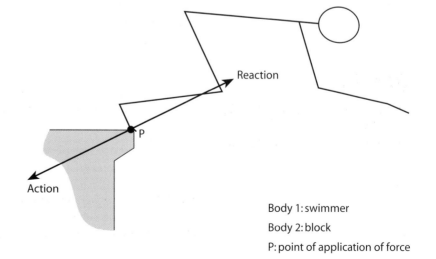

Reaction

P

Action

Body 1: swimmer

Body 2: block

P: point of application of force

and the implication of Newton's second law of acceleration (F = ma). Body 1 refers to the swimmer while body 2 actually refers to the block plus the earth to which it is firmly attached. Obviously the mass of the effective body on which the swimmer acts (the block plus the earth) is so enormous that the force exerted by the swimmer on the block has no noticeable effect. On the contrary, the reaction force of the block on the swimmer clearly results in the swimmer being projected into the air.

Question

What would be the effect if the same action was performed by the swimmer while standing in a canoe? Explain your answer.

It was stated earlier that the vast majority of sporting actions involve constantly changing forces (or dynamics). The reaction force to an athlete's action during sport is of immense interest to the biomechanist. This is because it contains so much valuable information which gives an insight into the reasons behind the observed movement. Thus it is possible to better understand the reasons for excellent, and poor, performances. Such information facilitates better teaching for the learning and development of skills. It also helps to ensure that incorrect techniques which may cause injury are avoided.

The section above on linear kinetics illustrates the importance of forces in bringing about, or changing, the motion properties of a body. The following sections detail these motion properties and their importance within the biomechanical study of sport.

Linear kinematics

Kinematics is the study of movement with reference to the amount of time taken to carry out the activity. It is presented without any reference to the forces which cause the movement to happen. It is however important to realise that a study of sport must include both kinematics and kinetics for a complete understanding. Linear kinematics is concerned with the movement in a straight line (translatory motion) of a body or body part and the time taken for this movement to occur. It is often described as a temporal study of sport or activity. The key quantities in kinematics are distance, displacement, speed, velocity and acceleration. Instantaneous values for these quantities are often determined in quantitative biomechanical studies. In qualitative studies, average values are more readily obtained.

Angular or rotational motion

Since sporting activity cannot be defined purely in translational (straight lines) terms, it is evident that rotation occupies a significant proportion of most sporting movement. For example, in the case of the 100 m sprinter who essentially runs from A to B in a straight line, there will still be a significant amount of rotational movement:

Figure 5.9 Rotational aspect of a sprinter's leg

the rotation of all the leg segments and arm segments about their particular axes of rotation will be included. An example can be seen in the thigh section (upper leg) which rotates about the hip joint of the body (figure 5.9).

In all movements, both linear and angular kinematics and kinetics are involved. In order to initiate motion, overcome equilibrium and start movement, a force in some direction (usually opposite to the movement direction) must be applied. If this force is applied at a perpendicular distance from a joint centre such as the hip, knee or ankle, a resulting moment of force or torque is produced.

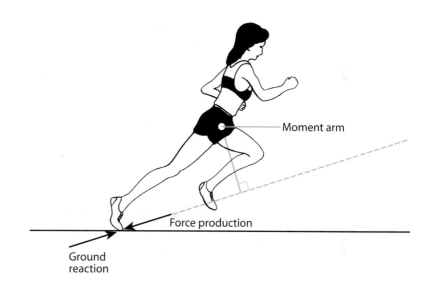

Moment arm

Force production

Figure 5.10 Moment of force production in sprinting

Ground reaction

Moment of a force (Torque)

The moment of force or torque is defined as the application of a force at a perpendicular distance to a joint centre or point of rotation. The moment arm is defined as the perpendicular distance from the force to the joint or rotation centre (figure 5.10).

> Torque or twisting moment can be defined as:
>
> Torque (twisting moment) = force x perpendicular distance from force application point to point of rotation.

Application of moment of force (torque)

In sport, the production of a torque or twisting force has many important applications. The longer limb levers that apply a force to the ground can result in greater and faster horizontal or vertical movement. For example, in the case of sprinting, it is considered that the greater torque generated at the joints of the leg by the muscles together with longer limb levers for the application of force, the faster an athlete will be able to run. This principle can apply in many sporting situations, from discus throwing to high jumping.

Figure 5.11 Force production

In discus throwing, the torque created during the rotational turning preparation movements is imparted to the discus by a long lever arm. As the lever arm length (length of body segments) is essentially fixed, the greater the torque generated in rotational preparation results in a greater force imparted to the implement, and a greater potential distance of the throw.

The production and use of the torque that is created at the joint centre or centre of rotation is an important concept to understand in sport. The torque created eventually results in a force applied at a perpendicular distance from a joint centre.

Angular kinematics

Angular kinematics is similar to the study of linear kinematics, in that it is concerned with distance, displacement, speed, velocity and acceleration. It differs as it is concerned with the angular components of these quantities, namely angular distance and displacement, angular velocity and angular acceleration. Again, remember that most sporting activity is not purely movement in a straight line (translational). The angular components have particularly important implications for the study of sport at all levels. Angular movement is usually expressed in radians, where 1 radian is equal to 57.3°. Furthermore, it is concluded that there are 2 (pi) radians in one complete 360° circle:

  1 radian = 57.3°
  360° = 2 π (pi) radians

In terms of angular movement, which is defined as displacement (vector quantity) and distance (scalar quantity), the same principle as applied to linear kinematics is evident.

In sport, most limb sections will rotate in an angular manner and at the same time often be displaced in a linear manner. An example of this would be a 100-m sprinter with rotational arm and leg movements who undergoes a linear displacement of the body's centre of mass (100 m in a straight line).

Figure 5.12 The javelin thrower

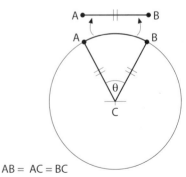

AB = AC = BC

θ = 57.3° = 1 radian

When the section of the circumference is equal to the radius the angle is sustained

Figure 5.13 Determining one radian

Relationship to linear velocity and acceleration

Angular velocity and angular acceleration can also be determined from the linear velocity and acceleration of points on a rotating body by the following formula:

$v = \omega$ (omega) x r (equation 13)
where: v=linear velocity of the point (m/s)
ω (omega) = angular velocity (Radians/s)
r = radius of point of interest from axis of rotation (m)

$a = \alpha$ (alpha) x r (equation 14)
where: a= linear acceleration of the point m/s²
α (alpha) = angular acceleration (Radians/s²)
 r = radius of the point of interest from the axis of rotation (m)

Summation of velocity of segments

In sport the summation of velocity principle is an important concept which must be considered. During most sporting activity movement will occur from a sequential muscle action. In throwing the discus the action will be the muscles in the legs, followed by the trunk, upper body, arms and hand. This sequential movement produces a rapid action at the end of the activity which is imparted to the implement to be thrown.

This action takes place along what is termed the kinematic chain and is involved in most physical activity. Summation of velocity is based on the same principle, whereby the velocity developed at the first segment involved in the movement is transferred through all the segments involved in a sequential order. Usually the better the athlete at performing the skill, the more efficient and fluent this transference of movement pattern.

Figure 5.14 Action of the discus thrower

Figure 5.15 Ice skater (pirouette)

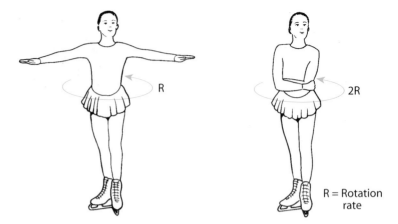

R = Rotation rate

Moment of inertia

In angular terms, the moment of inertia is used to describe an object's ability to offer a resistance to angular motion, that is, its reluctance to start rotating or change its state of rotation. A classic example is in the case of ice skating where the ice skater will rotate much faster (pirouette) when the arms are pulled close into the body (figure 5.15).

In this example, the ice skater has reduced her moment of inertia and reduced the reluctance of the body to rotate. Hence rotation is much greater due to this and the concept of conservation of angular momentum which will be described later in this chapter.

The moment of inertia is usually measured in $kg.m^2$ units and expressed with reference to a particular axis of rotation. It is dependent upon:

- the mass of the object
- the distribution of mass about the particular axis of rotation.

Basically, the closer the mass to the axis of rotation, the smaller will be the moment of inertia.

The radius of gyration can be defined as the distance from a given axis that a particle of the same mass as a rigid body must be placed in order to have the same moment of inertia. For example, in the case of an arm section (such as the lower arm) which is rotating about an axis (such as the elbow joint), the radius of gyration may be at a point nearer to the elbow than the wrist, that is, it is not normally the mid-point between the two extremities (elbow and wrist (closed hand) for our example). This radius of gyration is dependent upon distribution of body mass about each particular segment or object of interest. However, there are specific values established which account for the various segments of the human body. These values express specific points for radii of gyrations depending upon which axis the segment rotates about (the lower arm could rotate about the elbow (in an arm curl) or about the wrist (in a cartwheel)). These values are available in most specific biomechanics text books.

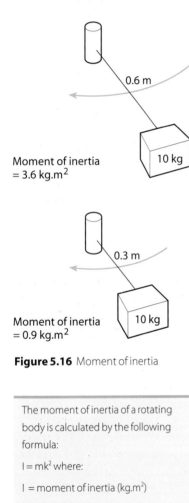

0.6 m

10 kg

Moment of inertia
= 3.6 kg.m^2

0.3 m

10 kg

Moment of inertia
= 0.9 kg.m^2

Figure 5.16 Moment of inertia

The moment of inertia of a rotating body is calculated by the following formula:

$I = mk^2$ where:

I = moment of inertia ($kg.m^2$)

m = mass (kg)

K = radius of gyration (m)

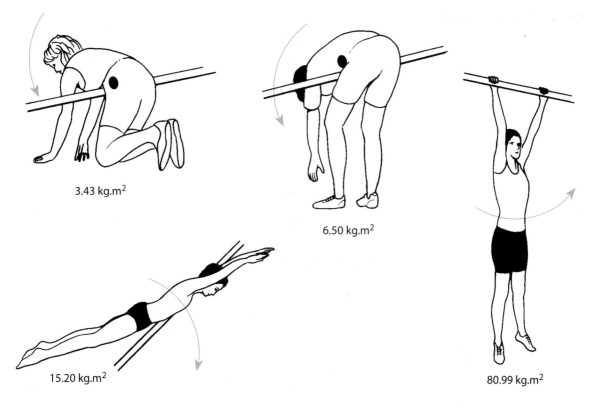

3.43 kg.m^2

6.50 kg.m^2

15.20 kg.m^2

80.99 kg.m^2

Figure 5.17 Moment of inertia for different rotational movements

In sport, moment of inertia has particularly important implications and it is closely linked with the conservation of angular momentum. However, examples of different moment of inertia values for different body positions in sport can be seen with reference to figure 5.17.

Conservation of angular momentum

Angular momentum possessed by a body by virtue of rotation is always conserved. A body will therefore turn about its axis of rotation with constant angular velocity unless an external force or couple (pair of equal and opposite parallel forces) is exerted upon it. In sport, this conservation of angular momentum is critical. The calculation of angular momentum is given by the following formula:

Angular Momentum = I ω (omega) (equation 15)

where: ω (omega) = angular velocity

I = moment of inertia

As a body begins rotation, it will possess a certain angular momentum. This angular momentum is conserved and remains constant provided the body is not influenced by another external force. In sport, it is the transference of momentum that is critical to performance.

Application to sport

Once a body starts to rotate it possesses angular momentum which, providing the body is not acted upon by an external force, remains constant. In the example of a somersault, the body will possess a certain angular momentum.

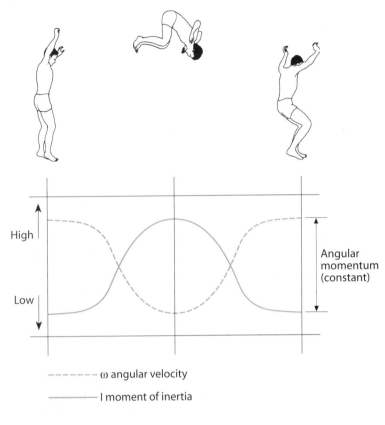

------ ω angular velocity

——— I moment of inertia

Figure 5.18 Conservation of angular momentum

Figure 5.19 Rotational elements of a diver

As the body rotates it will have a certain angular velocity. If, however, the body changes its moment of inertia by redistributing its mass (such as extending the body), the angular velocity will also change. If the moment of inertia increases, the angular velocity decreases, that is, the body slows down in rotation. However, if the moment of inertia decreases (like in a tight tuck for a somersault), the angular velocity increases and the body can perform more rotations in a given time. Throughout this process the angular momentum remains constant and is conserved.

Furthermore, in sport, angular momentum and linear momentum can be transferred from one body segment to another by vigorous arm or body movements. In a 100 m sprint, the athlete will throw the arms forward and drive the lead leg off to start the sprint race, attempting to transfer momentum to the whole body for faster movement. Similarly, in high jumping, the athlete will vigorously drive the lead leg and the arms high at the point of take-off to transfer momentum to the whole body for greater vertical velocity of movement. This principle of transference of momentum and conservation of momentum is one of the most significant principles in terms of the study of sport and is the basis for efficient human movement.

Questions

In the photograph of a diver, discuss the ways in which the conservation of angular momentum is applied. In particular, concentrate on the changes in moment of inertia and the corresponding changes in angular velocity of movement. Finally, describe how momentum may be transferred to enhance efficient performance in this event.

Pressure

Pressure = force/unit area of contact

$$P = \frac{F}{A} \quad \text{(equation 16)}$$

When the unit for **F** is the Newton (N) and for area is square metres (m^{-2}), pressure is given in $N.m^{-2}$ or in pascal (Pa), where 1 Pa is the pressure which arises when a force of 1 N is applied uniformly and in a perpendicular direction over an area of 1 m^2.

As well as the total force applied to a body, it is often important in sport to understand the distribution of that force over the surface of contact.

Pressure (p) is an external force which represents the intensity of a force applied to, or distributed over, a surface, and is measured as force per unit area.

Consider the ballerina in Figure 5.20. If the area of support in this pose is one-tenth that which it would be if she was standing flat on both feet, it follows that the average pressure for this pose is ten times greater than it would be for the two-footed condition. Naturally she would be unable to withstand the force of her body weight over the surface area of the tip of her toes without the inserted block in her ballet shoe.

Many physical activities involve weight-bearing by the feet of the performer, where care needs to be paid to the correct choice of footwear. Therefore, a walking boot is designed to withstand and spread the foot contact forces over the entire sole in activities where sharp stones are often encountered. If this was not the case, as in walking while wearing light shoes, the same impact forces would result in high local pressures where contact was made with the sharp object and could result in injury. Football boots with hard studs and pliable soles are designed to be worn on pitches which allow the studs to penetrate the earth. If the same boots were worn on a very hard surface, the combined body weight and inertial forces normally experienced would result in high local forces corresponding to the stud locations, and could result in pain and injury. Cricket pads, and other protective clothing worn in a variety of sports, not only serve the key purpose of absorbing the impacts associated with the sport, but also help to protect the player by spreading the impact force over a larger area therefore reducing the pressure at the point of contact and consequently the risk of injury.

Figure 5.20 The average pressure is large when the area of support is small

Question

List and detail another five sporting examples where steps are taken to reduce pressure.

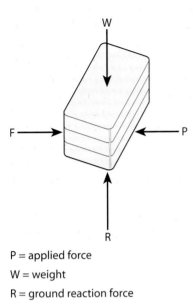

P = applied force

W = weight

R = ground reaction force

F = friction force

Figure 5.21 Friction (F) is the force that opposes the slippage of one body over another

$$\mu = \frac{P}{W} \text{ (equation 17)}$$

where represents the coefficient of friction, **P** represents the applied force, and **W** represents the weight of the box.

Friction

Friction is the external force which represents the resistance of one body sliding, rolling or flowing over another body with which it is in contact. In movements involving contacts with a support surface, friction is the resultant of the two horizontal components of the ground reaction force. In Figure 5.21, friction (F) is the horizontal force that opposes the movement of the box due to the applied force (P).

Maximum friction is determined by:

- the magnitude of the force acting perpendicular (normal) to the surface, which in figure 5.21 is given by the ground reaction force (R)
- a coefficient (referred to as the coefficient of friction (mu) and represented by the symbol μ) which characterises the contact (smooth or rough, lubricated or dry, static or dynamic).

Since μ is a ratio between two forces, it has no units. This coefficient is constant for any two given surfaces. The larger its value, the greater the friction between the surfaces and the more they tend to stick together. Conversely, the lower the coefficient, the lesser the friction and the less they tend to stick together. A theoretical value of 0.0 indicates completely frictionless surfaces.

In addition, the friction between any two surfaces in contact is greater when they are not moving relative to one another compared to when there is relative motion. The former is referred to as starting friction (or limiting friction) while the latter is known as sliding friction. Thus, once slippage commences, the force required to maintain this motion is less than that required to initiate it.

Friction plays a very important role in sporting activities. If there was no friction, movement of the whole body from one point to another would be impossible. However, there are times when attempts are made to increase friction and others when friction is minimised. The studs on football boots and the spikes on running shoes increase friction thus providing the athlete and player with better traction and reducing the chances of slippage. Similarly, the chalk on gymnasts' hands, the glove worn by a golfer and the rubber grip on the club all help to increase friction and give the performer better control over his actions.

Conversely, downhill slalom skiers apply wax to the undersurface of their skis to reduce friction. Wet ice, that is, ice with a thin film of water on its surface, provides less friction to the sliding action of the skater than dry, colder ice. The effect of a skater's body weight on the sharp blade of the skate tends to melt the ice in contact with the blade which reduces friction and therefore permits easier gliding across the ice. Within the joint capsules of the synovial joints of the body, synovial fluid acts as a lubricant reducing friction in healthy joints to a minimal value, many times less than that for ice sliding on ice.

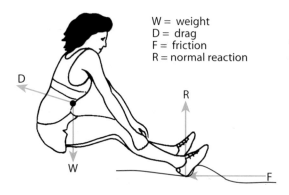

W = weight
D = drag
F = friction
R = normal reaction

Figure 5.22 The application and direction of the external forces which act on the long jump athlete

Figure 5.22 shows a free body diagram with all of the forces acting on a long jumper at the moment of impact with the sand. Her weight (W) is acting downwards through her centre of gravity. The drag force due to air resistance (D) is acting in the exact opposite direction to the motion of her centre of mass (COM) at this instant. The normal reaction force (R) acts perpendicular to the surfaces in contact (that is the feet and the sand). The friction force (F) is acting in the opposite direction to the direction of movement of the feet in the sand.

Although there is friction between the feet and the sand, the sand is soft and 'gives' following impact thus allowing a safe landing. This is proven by the imprints left in the sand which, of course, are used in the measurement of the jump distance.

Questions

1 In the above example, what would be the effect on friction if the sand was wet, hard and impacted.
2 How would this change in friction affect the jumper once ground contact was made?
3 Give another three examples from sport to clearly show how and why an athlete or performer attempts to reduce friction, plus three examples where attempts are made to increase friction.

Fluid forces

Air and water are both fluids, and the laws and principles of drag, lift, and buoyancy apply in both mediums. This has a considerable effect upon the movements of the human body and the implements commonly used as projectiles in sport.

Figure 5.23 The application and direction of the external forces which act on the swimmer

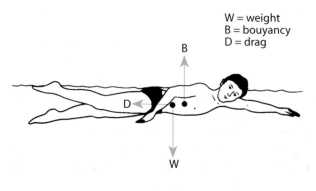

W = weight
B = bouyancy
D = drag

Consider the free body diagram of the forces acting on the swimmer in Figure 5.23. The downward force (W) due to gravity and acting through the body's centre of gravity would cause the body to sink if it were not for the upward force called buoyancy (B). According to Archimedes' Principle, the magnitude of the buoyancy force is equal to the weight of water displaced by the floating body. It acts through a point referred to as the centre of buoyancy (COB). The two points (COG and COB) do not necessarily coincide. The COG takes account of the body composition, that is, the proportion and distribution of lean body tissue and hence body density. The COB on the other hand refers to the volume centre of the body without regard to its constitution.

The other external force acting on the swimmer is referred to as the drag force (D). The magnitude of the drag force depends on a number of factors. These include, among other things:

- the speed of the swimmer
- the cross-sectional area of the body presented to the relative movement of the water
- the shape of the body
- the smoothness of the surface.

Thus, the greater the speed and the greater the cross-sectional (frontal) area, the rougher the surface and the less streamlined the body shape - the greater the drag. The intention in races is to swim as fast as possible. The relationship between speed and drag cannot be modified; the faster you swim the greater the drag.

However, several measures are taken to reduce the other contributing factors to the drag force. The optimal body position will ensure the frontal area is reduced to a minimum. This together with appropriate swimwear helps to reduce skin friction or surface drag. Other practices such as the removal of body hair appear to have more psychological importance to the swimmer as opposed to making any significant contribution to reducing drag.

Air is the other medium in which the majority of sporting activities take place. The force which opposes the motion of body through the air is called air resistance. In sport, the human body experiences air resistance during events such as cycling, running, sky diving and skiing. The implements used in sport are also influenced by air resistance, such as the javelin, discus and golf ball.

The drag force F_D can be given by the equation:

$$F_D = \frac{1}{2} C_D \times \rho \times v^2 \times A \quad \text{(equation 18)}$$

where C_D represents the coefficient of drag, ρ the density of the medium (in this particular case, water), **v** the velocity of the body in the medium, and **A** the cross-sectional area.

Air resistance

The air resistance which is offered to a projectile while travelling through the air can change the shape of the parabolic flight path. In most cases which involve human subjects as projectiles, this air resistance or wind effect is often considered to be negligible. However, it is often the case that jumps can be longer or shorter because of wind or air effects. In 1991, at the World Championships in Tokyo, Carl Lewis broke the long-standing long jump record of Bob Beaman (1968) by clearing 8.91 m. However, this record was not allowed due to wind assistance. Unfortunately for Carl Lewis, shortly after this jump the wind decreased and Mike Powell (USA) cleared 8.95 m (a new world record). Movement through the air will encounter resistance due to the molecules of air interacting with the body and aerodynamic factors due to body shape. This resistance can and does alter projectile motion.

As a body passes through the air, energy is transferred from the moving body to the surrounding air molecules. The amount of energy transferred depends on the extent to which the body disturbs the air, which in turn is dependent on the shape (cross-sectional area) and the velocity of the moving body. The faster the moving body, the greater the magnitude of the air resistance. For example, two types of aerodynamic drag affect the performance of a cyclist – pressure drag and skin-friction drag.

As the air passes the system (cyclist, his equipment plus his bicycle), it fails to follow the contours of the system and air streams separate from its surfaces. Whirlpools are generated, the air molecules in front become congested while behind the cyclist the number of air molecules is reduced. This results in a situation where the pressure in front of the cyclist is relatively higher than the pressure behind him. This pressure differential results in a force (called pressure drag) which acts against the direction of movement of the cyclist. If the system is streamlined the air closes in behind the cyclist thus causing an increase in the pressure behind the system which results in a reduction of the pressure differential and consequently a related reduction in the effects of the retarding force of pressure drag.

Skin friction drag results from the disparity in the motion of the air molecules in contact with the surface of the system (these molecules tend to stick to the surface) and the surrounding air molecules. This results in frictional force between the air molecules which derives its energy as kinetic energy from the moving system, thus causing a reduction in the velocity of the cyclist. The observed fluttering of loose clothing is demonstration of the effects of skin friction. On an ordinary bicycle pressure drag is hundreds of times greater than skin-friction drag. However, skin-friction drag becomes important when the bicycle is streamlined resulting in minimal pressure drag.

On an ordinary bicycle, air resistance riding at 4.5 m.s^{-1} (10 mph) constitutes 50% of all the forces, while at 8.1 ms^{-1} (18 mph) air resistance force represents 80% of all the forces.

As shown above for swimmers, when maximum speed is the aim, drag force must be minimised. This may be achieved to some extent by an alteration of riding position, by lowering the air resistance of the bicycle, and by drafting or riding closely together in a pack.

Question

Outline the techniques and methods used to achieve the lowering of drag force (as given above), and discuss the effect(s) of each of them on the variables in equation 18.

Air resistance also affects runners. For example, on a still day the magnitude of air resistance on an elite sprinter can be as high as 5% of his body weight. For a 800 N sprinter, the retarding force would be equal to 40 N. The force of air resistance has been shown to account for approximately 10% of the total energy expended in sprinting, and 3% of that required for running at 5.4 m.s^{-1}. The addition of wind resistance, or wind assistance, would add to or reduce the effects of the retarding force of air resistance.

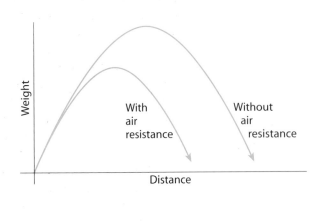

Figure 5.24 Parabolic flight paths

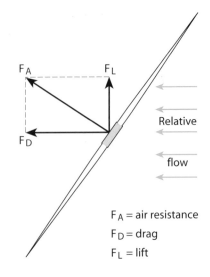

F_A = air resistance
F_D = drag
F_L = lift

Figure 5.25 Air resistance encountered by a javelin

The flight paths through the air, or trajectories, of projectile implements used in sport also depend on the properties identified as lift, drag and weight. Consider the javelin in figure 5.25.

In an actual throw the components of air resistance as defined above tend to simultaneously oppose the forward motion of the javelin (due to the drag force F_D), and to lift it higher in the air than it would go in the absence of air resistance (due to the lift component F_L).

Another important feature in ball sports affecting the trajectory is the spinning nature of the ball and its surface. These features cause a ball to deviate from the path it would follow if it were not spinning. The surfaces of the different balls used in sport (as illustrated in figure 5.26) are all different, yet spinning has a profound effect on each of them.

Figure 5.26 Each of these balls used in sport have different surface properties

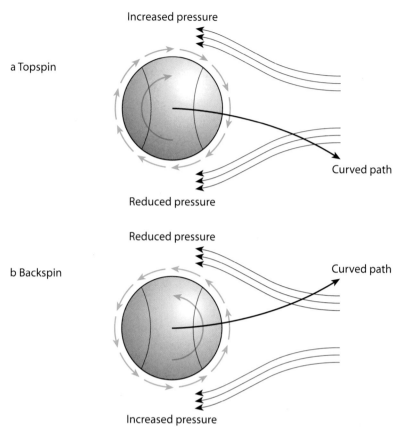

a Topspin

Increased pressure

Reduced pressure

Curved path

b Backspin

Reduced pressure

Curved path

Increased pressure

Figure 5.27 The effect of spin on a ball, causing it to follow a curved path

A ball moving through the air will move in the direction of least air pressure. Air pressure differences occur due to different velocities of the air in contact with the ball's surface, according to Bernoulli's Principle. This law basically states that pressure decreases as velocity increases. Consider the example of the tennis ball with topspin in figure 5.27. The relative movement of the boundary layer of air below the ball is the same as that for the ball itself (due to its spinning characteristics). In contrast, the boundary layer in contact with the top of the ball is opposing the spinning direction of the ball. Thus the relative velocity of the air below the ball is greater than that above the ball, which according to Bernoulli's principle results in a relative reduction in pressure below the ball. The net effect of this pressure difference is the curved path of the ball.

The influence that spin has on a ball is called the Magnus Effect, after the German scientist credited with its discovery. There are numerous examples in sport where advantage is taken of this law. Soccer players can pass an airborne ball around a defensive wall by imparting sidespin on the ball and tennis players often impart high amounts of topspin on the ball to keep it in court and to keep the subsequent bounce low.

Questions

1   Illustrate and account for the curved path of the ball with backspin.
2   Give another five examples of the effects of different types of spin on bodies (implements) used in sport, for example javelin, discus and table tennis.

SUMMARY

- Biomechanics is the scientific discipline which examines the forces responsible for motion and the effects of these forces.
- Statics refers to the conditions under which a body is at rest or is moving under the influence of balanced forces. Dynamics refers to the motion of a body under the influence of constantly changing forces which is commonly the case in sport.
- Biomechanics may be subdivided into two main areas – kinematics, which examines the effects of the forces without regard to their cause, and kinetics, which examines the forces responsible for motion without regard to their outcomes.
- Linear motion is the study of movement with reference to straight line (translatory) motion.
- Quantitative and qualitative analyses are both important forms of assessment in sport.
- Angular motion is the study of rotational movement with respect to time and the examination of such components as angular displacement, angular velocity and angular acceleration.
- Sporting activity cannot be defined purely in translational (straight line) terms and rotation occupies a significant proportion of all sporting movement.
- Forces are both internal (mainly muscular and associated anatomical structures) and external in nature (for example, gravity, air resistance, friction).
- Newton's law of gravitation defines the attraction forces between bodies.
- Newton's laws of motion (three laws) may be used to study and account for observed sporting phenomena.
- Fluid forces (associated with air and water) are extremely important in sporting activities.
- Inertia is the reluctance of a body to start or continue moving and is usually expressed by virtue of its mass.
- Moment of inertia is the reluctance offered by a body to start or continue rotating and is expressed by virtue of its mass and its perpendicular distance from the axis of rotation under consideration.
- In sport the conservation of momentum and angular momentum are particularly relevant and important concepts towards the understanding of efficient human movement.

References

Dainty D A, Norman R W *Standardizing Biomechanical Testing in Sport,* Human Kinetic Publishers Inc., Champaign(1987)

Enoka R M *Neuromechanical Basis of Kinesiology* (2nd ed), Human Kinetics (1994)

Hall S *Basic Biomechanics,* Mosby Year Book Inc. (1991)

Hay J G *The Mechanics of Sports Techniques* (2nd ed), Prentice Hall (1978)

Hay J G, Reid J G *Anatomy, Mechanics and Human Motion,* (2nd ed), Prentice Hall (1988)

Hay J G, Reid J G *The anatomical and Mechanical Bases of Human Motion,* Prentice-Hall (1982)

Luttgens K, Deutsch H, Hamilton N *Kinesiology — Scientific Basis of Human Motion* (8th ed), Brown and Benchmark (1992)

Wade M G, Baker J A W *Introduction to Kinesiology,* WCB Brown & Benchmark Publishers(1995)

Questions

1 a What is the weight at sea-level of a rugby player whose mass is 85 kg?
(Assume $g = 9.806$ m.s^{-2}.)

 b What would his weight be at an altitude of 8 000 m?
(that is, close to the top of Mount Everest where $g = 9.782$ m.s^{-2}).
What are the advantage(s) of this change in weight?
(Ignore physiological concerns)

 c What would his weight be on the surface of the moon?
(where $g = 1.57$ m.s^{-2})

 d Account for the lower value for g on the moon compared to the earth.

2 A weight lifter exerts a force of 2 000 N on a 150 kg barbell.
What average vertical acceleration does it experience?

3 A bowler releases a ball of 7.2 kg mass at 3.0 m.s^{-1}.
At what velocity would a ball of 4.5 kg mass have to be released in order to have the same momentum as the ball described above?

4 An Indian fakir who weighs 500 N lies on a bed of nails so that his weight is supported by a total of 3 000 nails, each having an upper surface area of 0.75 mm^2.
What is the average pressure between the points of contact between fakir and nail?

5 Determine the coefficient of friction for a vaulting horse whose weight is 1 200 N and which required a horizontal force input of 500 N in order to initiate sliding on a dry floor surface. Describe

 a the force required to keep it sliding

 b the force required to start it sliding if the floor surface was wet.

6 Draw a free-body diagram to illustrate the forces which act on a cyclist.

7 A weight lifter performs a dead lift with a 200 kg barbell through a distance of 0.65 m in 3.0 s.

 a What was the average power developed during the lift? (power = work done/time taken)

 b What would the average power be if the lift took 2.7 s?

8 An athlete covers a distance of 18 miles in 2 hours and 20 minutes. Calculate the average speed of the runner.

9 An athlete covers the displacement between the 26.3 m point and the 29.2 m point in a 100 m sprint race in 0.43 seconds. Calculate the average velocity over this section of the race.

10 Plot the displacement-time, velocity-time and acceleration-time curves for the following data and suggest what event it could be.

8. Displacement (m)		8. Time (s)	
9.	0-5	9.	2.1
10.	10	10.	5.8
11.	15	11.	9.7
12.	20	12.	12.2
13.	25	13.	14.2

11 An athlete, at the instant of take-off in the long jump, has a horizontal velocity of 6.2 m/s and a vertical velocity of 3.9 m/s. What is the angle of take-off and the resultant velocity of the long jumper? Comment upon this angle in terms of technique.

12 A volleyball is hit vertically by a player in a gymnasium which has a ceiling height of 22 m. If the initial velocity of the ball is 14 m/s, will the ball hit the ceiling or not in this condition?

6 SKILL ACQUISITION

Objectives

To understand:
- the nature of skilled performance in sport
- how psychological principles and theories of learning apply to motor skill acquisition
- how information processing models explain skilled motor performance in terms of input, decision making, motor output and information feedback
- the ways in which teachers and coaches can present information and organise practice in order to provide the ideal learning environment

Introduction

Human movement can take many forms and is fundamental to every aspect of our daily lives, from talking and eating to running for a bus or participating in sport. These movements are of general interest to psychology, but of particular concern to sport psychologists are those often complex, critical and intricate movements which we perform when we participate in sport. Traditionally, the area of study constituting motor behaviour has been divided into at least three sub-areas of study. *Motor learning* is concerned with the factors that influence learning and the learning process. *Motor control* focuses on how movements are coordinated and controlled, and *motor development* deals with changes in movement competencies throughout life. When reading this chapter it is important to recognise the framework for discussion which is being used and the assumptions underpinning this framework. We will be assuming a distinction between movements which are taken to be learned (for example, sports skills) and movements which are often regarded as being in some way genetically defined (for example, posture, locomotion, and prehension or grasping). Although this distinction could be a topic for lengthy debate, for the sake of convenience it will be the former, learned behaviour, which forms the focus of this chapter. In addition, any discussion of motor learning and motor control must appreciate that there is considerable overlap between the two. Learning, control and performance of skilled motor behaviour form a unit and most recent research on motor skills reflects a fusion of these traditionally separate areas. We will, therefore, deal with both areas under the general topic of skill acquisition.

The nature of skilled performance

Learning or performance

Many early investigations in psychology were concerned with isolating certain components of the learning process and used complex motor skills as the experimental tasks. What is important to bear in mind is that there is a distinction between learning and performance. Performance usually refers to the actual execution of a specific motor skill which can be readily observed and measured. Learning differs from performance primarily in that it cannot be directly observed. It is an internal process which results in relatively permanent changes in behaviour as a result of experience or practice. In order to establish that learning has taken place, it is necessary to chart changes in performance over time. For example, over the course of an eight-week practice period, a basketball coach would expect to see an improvement in the performance of basketball players. If the coach were to graph the shooting scores of players she might expect to see a performance curve like the one presented in figure 6.1.

Figure 6.1 contains three vital elements of a performance curve. The *y-axis* or the vertical axis of the graph represents the measure taken of performance. This measure could be the points scored (as in this example) or it could be the time taken, distance thrown, height jumped, or other measure appropriate to assess the skill being taught. The *x-axis* or the horizontal axis provides a representation of the time over which the skill has been measured. In our example the individual was assessed over eight blocks of trials. Each block may represent any chosen number of individual trials, for example, five, ten, 15, or 20 trials. Time may be represented in terms of hours, days, weeks or months, etc. It is important to notice that the units on both the *x-axis* and the *y-axis* progress equally from smaller to larger values, regardless of the chosen measures. The shape of the curve is determined by marking the average performance measure for each block of trials at the appropriate intersection point on the graph. Each of these points is then connected by a line. The result may not always be a perfect curve shape but we should be able to make some *inference* about what learning has taken place. According to Magill (1993), most motor learning research shows that four generalised performance curves exist, each allowing the researcher to make slightly different inferences about how learning has progressed (see figure 6.2).

Many of the early studies of performance curves established that those representing learning of motor skills exhibited periods where

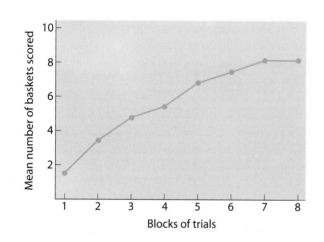

Figure 6.1   A performance curve

A. Linear
Equal amounts of improvement in performance for each unit of time.

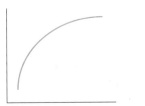

B. Negatively accelerated
Large amounts of improvement in the beginning which then level off later on.

C. Positively accelerated
Small performance gains in the early stages which rapidly increase later.

D. Ogive or S-shaped
Combination curve suggesting slow start, followed by steady improvement which then levels off in later stages.

Figure 6.2 Inferences about learning from four types of performance curve

there was no apparent improvement in performance. Each of these periods was known as a plateau and it was thought that during this time the learner was consolidating knowledge already acquired. Later research failed to replicate the earlier findings, but it is interesting that most books on motor learning still refer to their existence. This is possibly due to the wealth of anecdotal evidence. For example, when you first learn a totally new skill such as playing a video game, you appear to progress very rapidly before passing through a phase when you no longer improve. This is followed by another phase of rapid improvement.

A plausible reason for the failure to replicate *plateaus* in motor learning research is due to the fact that most research examines group performance rather than individual progress. A number of possible solutions to the frustration of learning a new skill have been offered by Robert Singer (1980). He postulated that plateaus are a result of the skill learning process which involves a 'hierarchy of habits'. Singer maintains that when we learn a motor skill we do so in stages. The first stage might involve learning basic actions such as how to strike a ball in a stationary position. In the next stage the player may learn how to strike an object on the move, while a third stage of the hierarchy might see the player develop appropriate movement patterns for an entire game sequence. In theory, a *plateau* may occur at any of these transitional periods from one stage to the next and it is thought that during this time the learner is consolidating knowledge already acquired. Other possible causes of plateaus are listed in figure 6.3 along with Singer's (1980) suggestions for remediation. In general, although a number a causes have been offered for the existence of plateaus it is usually accepted that they do not result in decreased learning and are therefore, more appropriately considered performance 'artefacts'.

Skill or ability

Psychologists have categorised human behaviour into three broad domains known as *cognitive* (knowing), *affective* (feeling), and *psychomotor* (doing). It is generally agreed that such distinctions while convenient for the sake of studying behaviour should not be taken as totally pure as there are obvious overlaps. For example, Sharp (1992) points out that successful athletes are skilful in all three domains: they must know and understand many vital aspects of their sport (cognitive skill); success depends on mental attitude and developing psychological skills to cope with stress (affective behaviour); excellence in sport demands the execution of precise, fluent, effective movement patterns (psychomotor skill). Despite the apparent simplicity conveyed by the elegance and grace of a skilled Olympic performer, for example, there is an underlying complex interaction between mental and physical processes necessary for movement production. Many motor skills actually rely heavily on sensory-perceptual elements, such as detecting where the opponent is going to kick the ball, how team members will involve each other in

Figure 6.3   Causes and solutions for performance plateaus (Singer, 1980)

Cause	Solution
1 Loss of interest Loss of novelty Loss of motivation	Make practice appealing; be creative; look for alternative approaches; be enthusiastic; be supportive and encouraging; use reinforcement.
2 Focus on wrong cues	Maintain the learner's attention to the appropriate cues so that practice is meaningful; provide knowledge of results.
3 Fatigue	Be alert to situation; stop practice or practise something else.
4 Emotions	Let learner progress slowly; provide security.
5 Lack of physical readiness	Analyse the task demands and the learner's physical development; he or she might possess physical capacities to perform a task at a certain level of proficiency but will need further development if higher order skills are to be demonstrated.
6 Low level of aspiration	Help the learner to establish realistically high but attainable goals.
7 Lack of understanding of directions; Lack of ability to recognise and adapt skills	Make a task analysis, breaking down the activity into smaller units so that transitions are smooth and logical from one performance level to a higher level of expectation; allowing the learner to progress too fast in a complex activity places hardships on one's ability to apply lower-order learned skills to higher-order ones and to comprehend and use instructions and directions effectively.

the named play, or how the weather conditions and course will influence the choice of golf club, for example. The sensory-perceptual aspect of many skills is important as the resulting decisions will often determine the success of the action taken.

There is frequently confusion surrounding the exact nature and distinction of the terms skill and ability. For example, the word 'skill' can mean a specific action (such as kicking a ball) or may refer to the level of performance of the individual (a player has attained a high skill level or has skill). Furthermore, in common language, the word 'ability' is sometimes used to convey a similar meaning, such as 'that player has good ability in sport'. Given these various interpretations it is important for us to carefully define these terms as they are used by sport psychologists. Most classic definitions of skill agree that '*skill consists of the ability to bring about some end result with maximum certainty and minimum outlay of energy, or of time and energy*' (Guthrie, 1952). By using such a definition we are emphasising a number of key elements:

- Skill implies action directed towards some specific objective or goal, for example, executing a forward drive in tennis or holding a headstand in gymnastics.

- Skilled performance implies achieving the end result with maximum certainty, that is, reliably and on demand, rather than haphazardly or due to good luck.
- Skill results in economic and efficient movements where energy is generally conserved.
- The apparently effortless performance of the skilled player is the result of learning and practice which results in efficient use of both physiological and psychological energy. This last feature of skilled performance, the importance of practice, is a key distinction between skill and ability.

'Ability' is generally defined as an inherited and relatively enduring, stable trait of the individual. Abilities are therefore presumed to be more general attributes that can help performance in a variety of skills or activities. Because abilities are believed to be genetically determined it is unlikely that they can be modified by practice or experience. It has been suggested that ability may set the limits on performance. For example, if you are 6'2" with poor balance, it is unlikely that you will become a successful gymnast or if you have poor manual dexterity you might be better suited to a sport which does not require object manipulation. At present, around 25 abilities have been identified which are relevant to sport performance. All individuals are thought to possess all of these abilities, but each individual will have a different pattern of strengths and weaknesses depending on his or her unique genetic make-up. Examples of a few of these abilities and the skills to which they might contribute are provided in figure 6.4.

Figure 6.4   Abilities and the skills

Ability	Skill
Reaction time — involves quick response to a single stimulus.	Sprint start
Response orientation — quick choice among numerous alternative movements	Goalkeeper in hockey
Speed of movement — underlies tasks where limbs must move quickly	Swinging a cricket bat
Manual dexterity — underlies tasks where large objects are manipulated by hands	Dribbling a basketball

It was originally presumed that a single inherited general ability underlies all sport tasks, called a *general motor ability*. It was believed that a person who possessed strong motor ability would be effective at nearly all motor tasks attempted. However, very little scientific evidence was found to support this notion of single general motor ability and therefore, arguments were put forward for the existence of numerous more specific abilities. This became known as the *specificity hypothesis* (Henry, 1961). The specificity hypothesis suggests that there are many specific abilities, unrelated to each other and that different sports skills are supported by different patterns of these abilities. Recent suggestions also introduce the notion of a possible

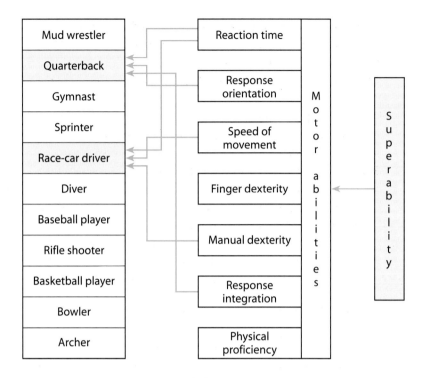

Figure 6.5 Relationship between superability, motor abilities and selected sports skills

weak general factor underlying most movement skills known as a *superability*. This superability is *not* the same as general motor ability, as it is the pattern of specific motor abilites which is more important in determining skilled performance. It has been suggested that we may possess a broad general *superability* which underlies and contributes to the various *specific* motor abilities which are fundamental in the production of skill. This concept is illustrated in Figure 6.5.

Skill classification

One of the problems faced when studying motor behaviour is the amazing diversity of sporting activities. The fact that activities such as hockey, windsurfing, pool and athletics appear to differ so greatly might encourage scientists to conduct separate and unique studies to understand each specific sport. However, this is not the case, as such a piecemeal approach would overlook the common processes involved in learning and performance which hold across a variety of activities. In order to highlight the common factors between apparently different motor skills, a number of classification systems have been devised. These classification systems group together skills which share some key elements and they have been shown to influence how the skills should be learned. It is useful to consider each classification system as lying on a continuum with the extreme examples at either end. All other motor skills fall somewhere between the two extremes.

Open and closed skills

This classification system is based on the nature of the environment in which the skill is performed. Sports such as soccer, hockey, rugby, netball and other fast ball sports usually involve open skills. These are skills performed in an environment which is constantly changing and there is uncertainty about what to do or when to do it. Making decisions about action is often difficult due to the unpredictable nature of events. For example, a hockey goalkeeper is uncertain about which opponent may take a shot at goal, when the shot will be taken, and from what area of the field it will be directed. Conversely, closed skills take place in stable, predictable environments where the performer knows in advance exactly what to do and when to do it. Examples of closed sports skills include archery, gymnastics, shooting a freethrow in basketball, serving in squash, tennis or volleyball.

Figure 6.6 Open and closed skills

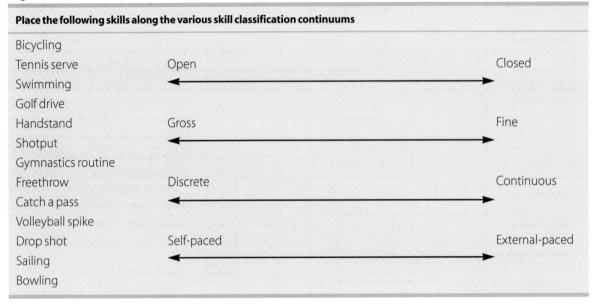

Place the following skills along the various skill classification continuums

Bicycling
Tennis serve
Swimming
Golf drive
Handstand
Shotput
Gymnastics routine
Freethrow
Catch a pass
Volleyball spike
Drop shot
Sailing
Bowling

Open ←————————————————→ Closed

Gross ←————————————————→ Fine

Discrete ←————————————————→ Continuous

Self-paced ←————————————————→ External-paced

Gross and fine skills

This classification system is based on the precision of the movement. The two extremes of the system are gross and fine motor skills. Gross skills are skills in which the major muscle groups are involved, for example, running, jumping and swimming. Fine skills are those which require the use of very small muscle groups, for example, typing or playing a piano. While these examples show the extremes of the continuum, there are many sports which include skills which fall somewhere between these two extremes, such as shooting a basketball, playing snooker or throwing a dart.

Discrete, serial and continuous skills

Another classification system is based on the distinctiveness of the beginning and end points of the movement. The two end points of this continuum are discrete and continuous.

- **Discrete skills** are usually identified as very brief, well-defined actions which have a definite beginning and end point. Examples include a large number of separate skills which make up the actions involved in a variety of sports, such as hitting, kicking, throwing and catching.
- **Continuous skills,** on the other hand, do not have distinct beginning and end points and could be stopped at any point during the performance of the skill. Examples include swimming, running, roller skating and riding a bike.
- Activities which fall between these two have been categorised as serial tasks. **Serial skills** are usually thought of as a group of discrete skills strung together to make a new and more complex

movement. Examples include playing a tune on the piano (discrete notes strung together), or performing an ice skating or gymnastics routine (discrete actions strung together).

Self-paced and externally-paced skills

The final classification system to consider is based on the timing or pacing of the action. Self-paced movements are under the performer's own control. For example, in golf, both the performer and the ball are static, the initiation and execution of the movement are decided by the golfer. Externally-paced skills require the performer to pay greater attention to external events in order to control his rate of movement. For example, in skipping rope, the performer must time his movements depending on the speed of the moving rope, or in ball games the performer must time his actions in accordance with the actions of other players and the ball.

SUMMARY

- Performance refers to observable action whereas learning refers to an unobservable, internal process.
- Performance curves allow us to assume that learning has taken place.
- Skilled performance covers the key elements of being goal-directed, consistent and efficient, whereas ability refers to more general underlying attributes of an individual.
- Skill classification systems allow us to group together sports skills which share key common elements in order to make more general statements about learning and performance.

Principles and theories of learning

Motivation

It is generally agreed that there can be little learning without motivation, therefore, it is vital that we consider the effects of motivation on the process of skill acquisition. There are numerous theories to explain motivation (or lack of it), but it is beyond the scope of this chapter to outline them all in full. However, we will briefly summarise current thinking on some fundamental aspects of motivation relevant to the learning process.

Motivation is what influences our decisions to participate in sport and our subsequent persistence and effort in the selected activity. Although motivation is fundamental to learning, there is no easy relationship between amount of motivation and sporting performance. In fact, more in this instance rarely means better. There is an optimal level of motivation which is right for each individual and task. This issue will be discussed in more detail in the next chapter. The two main types of motivation are intrinsic motivation and extrinsic motivation.

- **Intrinsic motivation** is defined as coming from within the individual, for example, participating in sport for the sheer joy, pleasure, fun and personal mastery associated with the experience.

- **Extrinsic motivation** refers to the external reasons for participating in an activity, for example, seeking social approval, status, or material rewards such as badges.

Research suggests that intrinsic motivation is better and leads to more satisfying and long lasting results than extrinsic motivation. It has also been shown that young children rate intrinsic factors such as fun, excitement, skill improvement as more important motives for participation than extrinsic factors such as trophies and praise. However, it is also agreed that motives may change with experience, and coaches may wish to encourage a shift from extrinsic motivation to intrinsic motivation. Most people are now familiar with the many award schemes organised by the various governing bodies of sport, for example, BAGA Awards and Athletics Gold Top Awards. While these award schemes have their merits in attracting children to a sport, it is generally more desirable that the extrinsic motivation be replaced by internal reasons for participating in order to encourage persistence and effort.

A term which is often linked with motivation is **reinforcement**. It is often difficult to distinguish between extrinsic rewards and reinforcement, although psychologists have attached specific meaning to the term 'reinforcement' in the learning process. In particular, they distinquish between different types of reinforcement and their effect on the learning process.

A final distinction should also be made between negative reinforcement and punishment. Punishment refers to the presentation of an aversive event in order to discourage the previous behaviour. For example, a student is made to do 50 sit-ups because he forgot his PE kit. Although punishment can be effective in suppressing unwanted behaviour, it is usually not as effective as rewarding desirable behaviour. For example, punishment often leads to dislike of the punisher (PE Teacher) and the situation (PE, Sport), so the child who is made to do 50 sit-ups as punishment may decide to withdraw from future physical education classes.

In the past there were two main groups of theories proposed to explain learning: the behaviourist or stimulus-response (S-R) theories and the cognitive or field theories.

Behaviorist theories

The behaviourist theories, in general, emphasise the importance of strengthening the connection or bond between stimulus and response. Individuals are said to be *conditioned* when they repeatedly strengthen the bond between stimulus (S) and response (R). Edward Thorndike (1931) was a forerunner of S-R psychology of learning. Thorndike's main influence was in contributing three laws of learning which are still acknowledged for their impact on education. The *law of*

Positive reinforcement is defined as any event which increases the probability of a particular response or behaviour occuring. Examples of positive reinforcement would be praise, encouragement, or attaining a good grade. Their effect, hopefully, is to encourage the student to repeat the response and persist in trying to improve.

Negative reinforcement is defined as any event which, when removed, increases the probability of the response or behaviour occuring. Some performers are used to having a coach who constantly yells loud criticism at them; if the performer has a particularly good session and therefore escapes any criticism, then the removal of the *aversive stimulus* acts as a negative reinforcer. The important thing to remember here is that reinforcers always serve to strengthen the response.

exercise maintained that by repeated practice, a bond or connection is established between S and R. This law was later modified to state that more effective learning takes place when the bond is reinforced in some way. A second law, the *law of effect,* emphasised the importance of rewarding the desired response by stating that 'satisfiers' after the response will strenghten it, whereas 'annoyers' will weaken the response. Thorndike's third *law of readiness* dealt with the individual learner's personal state of satisfaction or frustration. He maintained that the learners experienced satisfaction if they achieved their intended objective (things go well), but if the objective is not achieved or is annoying, then frustration is experienced.

Another influential forerunner of the conditioning theories was Clark Hull (1943) who developed the *drive theory*. This theory uses a very formal, precise and mathematical approach to explaining the many variables which interact and influence human learning. In particular, Hull described factors such as need, drive, incentive, reinforcement and *inhibition.* The latter factor, *inhibition*, is important in explaining a phenomenon often observed in sport. According to Hull, when a person repeatedly practices the same thing she builds up *inhibition* which works as a depressing effect on the strength of the performance. However, this inhibition was shown to be offset by a period of rest. For example, a netball player who practices 100 shots is more likely to have better performance in the middle of her practice than at the end yet, when she returns to shooting after a rest period, her performance will be better than at the end of the previous session. This is a good example of a situation where it is important to draw a clear distinction between observed performance and actual learning.

Two of the most popular conditioning theories are Pavlov's Classical Conditioning and Skinner's Operant Conditioning.

Pavlov's classical conditioning

Ivan Pavlov was a Russian physiologist who, during the course of his experiments on digestion, noticed that the laboratory dog he was using began to salivate at the mere sight of food. In other words the dog had learned to connect the sight of the dish with the taste of the food. Pavlov then set out to explore whether the dog could be taught to associate other elements with food. The various steps of classical conditioning are presented in figure 6.7.

Food is considered to be an unconditioned stimulus and the natural tendency to salivate is said to be the unconditioned response. A second stimulus (the conditioned stimulus), such as a light being turned on, is presented just before the food on many occasions and eventually the dog salivates only when the light is turned on in the absence of food. The dog has learned to associate the light with food and therefore salivates. This is a conditioned response. Classical conditioning techniques are sometimes used by sport psychologists to assist performers in controlling anxiety. For example, many of the

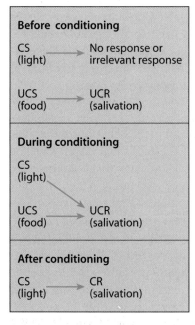

Figure 6.7 Classical conditioning

relaxation and meditative exercises recommended rely on controlled breathing exercises during which the individual repeatedly uses a calming phrase such as 'breathe easy' or 'steady'. Eventually, when the performer is in a highly anxious situation she can induce muscular relaxation by calling up the phrase.

The difficulty with the classical conditioning theory is that it does not really help to explain what happens when you teach someone to do something new. For example, what unconditioned stimulus would make a dog sit-up and roll over? Usually what happens is that you first try to persuade the dog to do the trick and then you have to reward it each time it comes close to producing the desired behaviour.

Skinner's operant conditioning

In operant conditioning, the association or connection is not between stimulus and reponse but between the action and the consequences of that action. According to Skinner, most human be-haviour is thought to be operant., that is, we operate on our environment and it is the nature of the consequences of action which dictates whether the action will be repeated or not. This led Skinner to suggest that the role of reinforcement is crucial to learning. Desirable actions which are reinforced will be strengthened and responses which are not reinforced will eventually disappear. A teacher should be able to shape behaviour by progressively reinforcing successive approximations of the desired action. For example, suppose the desired action is a lay-up shot in basketball, the teacher would need to successively reinforce correct performance on a number of intermediate steps before the desired action would be possible for a novice (see figure 6.8).

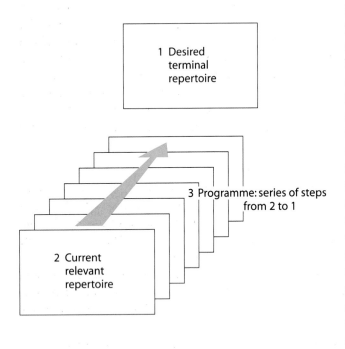

Figure 6.8 Shaping behaviour

Cognitive theories

Cognitive theories of learning, in contrast to the behaviourist theories, emphasise the thought processes of the individual rather than the importance of stimuli and responses. The Gestalt psychologists were influential supporters of the cognitive viewpoint. They originally proposed the notion of insight or intuition as a means of learning. In numerous studies of the learning process, the Gestaltists demonstrated that while skill acquisition is usually quite slow in the early stages, it is then followed by a point of very rapid progress. They suggested that the intial period of 'trial and error learning' causes the learner to organise and reorganise cognitive information until the learner suddenly discovers the relationships necessary to solve the problem. This kind of 'eureka' phenomenon is often very evident in young children when they are trying to figure out how a toy works and then suddenly they discover the key relationships. Similarly, beginners in sport, when given initial instruction and then left to practice, can often be heard to shout 'I've got it' as they suddenly discover the key essential relationships to ensuring successful performance.

The Gestalt dictum, *'the whole is more than the sum of the parts'*, highlights the importance that these theorists placed on understanding the whole action. In teaching motor skills they would argue that skills should be taught as a whole rather than broken down into parts, as only by experiencing the skill as a whole will the learner establish the true relationships between elements. For example, if a child is taught a swimming stroke by breaking the skill down into arm technique, leg technique and breathing pattern it does not help the child perform the stroke in its entirety because the essence of the relationships between the parts is missing. Rather, the learner should be allowed to experience the stroke in its entirety and focus on the whole action. Although interest in Gestalt views of psychology has waned over the years, it is important to appreciate that cognitive theories and models are very much in evidence in the field of motor behaviour.

Adams closed loop theory

A cognitive theoretical approach which has had the most profound influence amongst motor behaviourists was Adams' (1971) Closed Loop Theory. As a reaction to behaviourist ideas based on experiments conducted on animals, Adams outlined ways in which humans are set apart from the rest of the animal kingdom.

- Immediacy of reinforcement is less critical for humans than other animals. With particular reference to sport, humans may continue to produce a response or performance without a teacher or coach reinforcing it.
- We have the capacity for speech and often guide or mediate our motor responses through verbal instructions.
- Humans tend to use information to correct errors and vary their subsequent responses accordingly whereas animals tend to continually produce the same response until it is rewarded.

Adams' theory has two key elements: the **perceptual trace** which is essentially a reference standard acquired through practice, and the **memory trace** which is responsible for initiating movement.

A key feature in the theory is the role played by feedback. Accord-ing to Adams, the memory trace works by way of

Figure 6.9 Adams Closed Loop Theory (1971)

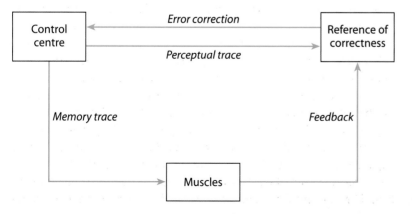

237

recalling the appropriate response from memory of previous correct responses. The memory trace simply selects and initiates the response but it does not control it. Feedback is provided both during and after movement production and over many practice attempts a perceptual trace is laid down. The perceptual trace is like a record of the movement which then operates as a reference of correctness in subsequent efforts, for example, serving in tennis. The learner compares feedback and knowledge of results of his action with this reference of correctness and any appropriate error adjustments can be made. This gives the theory it's closed-loop character.

Schmidt's schema theory

A second theory put forward specifically for motor learning was Schmidt's schema theory (1975). It moves even further away from traditional behaviourist concepts, turning instead towards cognitive psychology and the idea of the schema or set of complex cognitive relationships. Schmidt argued that every time movement is produced, four items of information are stored:

- the initial conditions, for example, *what was the starting position in a throw?*
- certain aspects of a general motor programme for action, for example, *how much force was used?*
- knowledge of the results of the action, for example, *did you hit the target?*
- sensory consequences of the action, for example, *what did the movement feel like?*

Abstract relationships are then made between these items of information and it is these relationships which make up the recall schema and the recognition schema. The recall schema is based on both knowledge of the goal of the task (initial conditions) and knowledge of results of previous attempts. It is responsible for generating a motor programme for the action which is appropriate for novel circumstances. The recognition schema is based on the relationship found between the actual sensory feedback experienced during movement and the consequences of movement. The recognition schema is thought to guide move-ment production by comparing expected sensory consequences with the actual consequences.

A key distinction between this approach and that proposed by Adams is that, for Schmidt, the

Figure 6.10   Schmidt's (1975) Schema Theory

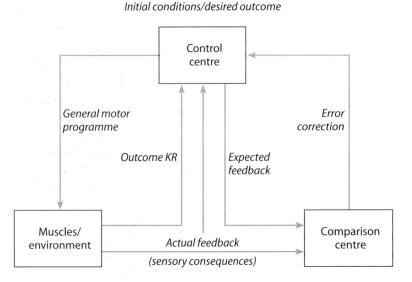

Initial conditions/desired outcome

Control centre

General motor programme

Error correction

Outcome KR

Expected feedback

Muscles/ environment

Comparison centre

Actual feedback

(sensory consequences)

individual actions are not stored. Rather, we refer to abstract re-lation-ships or general rules about movement production. In this way it is predicted that learners will be more able to cope with new situations where they are required to adapt already existing movements, rather than necessarily devise new patterns of movement. The most signifi-cant implications for teachers and coaches relate to the value of varied practices and routines, as opposed to specific practice for one movement or performance. Schmidt and others have conducted studies in which one group of learners practice a motor task in a variety of conditions and the other group is required to practice the specific task. When both groups are then asked to produce a response in a third and different situation (the transfer task), the group with varied practice produced the best performance. This finding was stronger for children than for adults. For teaching programmes, it is important, therefore, to practise the skill under a variety of conditions.

Phases of skill learning

Paul Fitts, an American psychologist, detailed the kinds of changes and phases that learners go through when acquiring skill. As a result of both laboratory experiments and interviews, he proposed that there were three phases to learning a skill.

The early or cognitive phase

The beginner relies heavily on cognitive processes. Her first concern is to understand the task and this often means attaching verbal labels to movement responses. The learner is primarily concerned with what to do and how to do it. The beginner in dance typically has to verbalise the required actions. For example, 'side, together, side, hop'. The learner also has to pay attention to the details of action, so for example, beginners in a variety of sports tend to look at the limbs involved rather than freeing their attention to watch what is happening around them. As a result of this high cognitive involve-ment, action in this phase often has a large number of errors which leads to very variable performance. The kinds of errors made are usually quite gross, that is, novice tennis players may completely miss the ball when swinging to hit, or basketball players may walk into the bouncing ball as they attempt to dribble. An associated problem for beginners at this stage is that although they tend to realise when they have committed an error, they usually are not aware of what needs to be done in order to correct the problem. Therefore, teachers and coaches need to supply plenty of appropriate feedback which could be visual (demonstrations), verbal (instructions), or manual (physical guidance), in order to assist the learners in developing their own 'reference of correctness'.

The intermediate or associative phase

The next phase of learning is primarily concerned with practising the newly-acquired skill. During this phase the learners can usually produce the basic mechanics of the skill and make associations with previously learned material, allowing for some degree of transfer (see next section). Performance is characterised by fewer errors, usually caused by difficulties in controlling speed, force or timing of movements. In addition, the learners become proficient at identifying their own errors although they may still require assistance in correcting them. A key element of this phase is the change in type of feedback control from visual/verbal to more reliance on internal/kinesthetic. The intermediate phase can last a long time, particularly in the absence of regular practice, with some performers never reaching the final phase.

The final or autonomous phase

The autonomous phase is so named because the performers are now capable of producing skilled actions automatically with little or no conscious control to movement production. The lack of conscious control to movement production enables the performers to free their attention mechanisms to deal more effectively with environmental information, such as player and object postions, or how a particular strategy is developing. Physical performance is characterised as being highly consistent, efficient and having few errors. Performers are now capable of identifying their own errors and correcting them themselves without needing additional feedback from others. The key role for the teacher or coach at this level is in assisting with finer details of technique or focusing on strategy and mental preparation. Performers should also be encouraged to contribute to their own improvement through self-analysis.

Transfer of learning

Transfer of learning is basic to so much of teaching and coaching. Rather than assuming that learners start with a clean slate when learning new skills, teachers often assume that transfer will occur from previously learned skills. For example, most boys will have played soccer at some stage and therefore teachers may sometimes assume that the skills of kicking and heading may transfer to new situations. Such teaching and coaching practice procedures actually support very early psychological thinking regarding learning where it was assumed that identical elements (or skills) readily transferred to new situations. (This idea was first brought to attention by Edward Thorndike, 1931.) More recent approaches explain transfer in terms of the degree of similarity between the stimuli and responses required by the tasks being learned.

- **Positive transfer** is thought to occur when the task being learned is assisted by the

Figure 6.11 Negative transfer: sometimes tennis players find it difficult to bend their arms when playing squash

learner's previous experience in tasks with similar elements. For example, someone who has played soccer is likely to grasp the tactical requirements of field hockey fairly quickly.

- **Negative transfer** is thought to occur when a previously learned skill interferes with learning a new skill. For example, tennis players sometimes find it difficult to bend their arms when playing strokes in squash. Despite numerous practical examples of negative transfer in sport, it has been very difficult to establish this in the research setting. Typically, any initial negative influences are hidden by the effects of positive transfer, such as racket to ball coordination or strategy development.

- **Zero transfer** is said to occur when experience in one sport has no impact on learning a new sport. For example, little transfer either positive or negative might be expected in an experienced swimmer learning to play basketball.

Transfer and generalisation

Psychological terms such as *stimulus generalisation* and *response generalisation* are sometimes used to explain how transfer occurs. *Stimulus generalisation* refers to a situation where a variety of similar stimuli can evoke a previously learned response to one specific

Figure 6.12 Design of transfer experiments

There are various different experimental designs to test for transfer of learning. Here we present two basic types which test for Proactive and Retroactive transfer:

Proactive transfer is so named because effects seem to occur forward in time. Task A has a positive or negative effect on subsequent learning of Task B.

Proactive transfer of learning design		
	Transfer task	*Test task*
Group 1	Task A	Task B
Group 2		Task B

Retroactive transfer is said to occur if the effects seem to work backwards in time. For example, in the design below, two groups both practise the same task. One group is then given another task while the second group does nothing. Subsequently, both groups are tested on the initial practised task. If the performance for Group 1 is better we say that positive retroactive transfer occured or if it is less effective we say negative retroactive transfer occured.

Retroactive transfer of learning design		
Initial task	*Transfer task*	*Test task*
Group 1	Task X	Task Z	Task X
Group 2	Task X		Task X

(similar) stimulus. For example, if you have already acquired the skills of squash you would probably experience stimulus generalisation if placed in a four-walled court and asked to play racquetball, handball or paddleball. Having already learned to respond to a ball rebounding off a wall, you would experience stimulus generalisation and respond by intercepting the ball. **Response generalisation** occurs once a particular response has been learned to a given stimulus. Subsequently, that stimulus will evoke a variety of possible alternative responses. For example, in tennis beginners typically learn to hit the ball back over the net without worrying about placing it, yet as they become more proficient they can generalise to vary their return down the line, cross court, lob, volley or smash.

According to Schmidt (1991), the concept of similarity between skills falls into the three common areas of perceptual features, movement patterns and strategic elements. The popularity of his Schema Theory has led to renewed interest in the issue of transfer. The theory suggests varying the practice conditions so that learners learn more than just the basic movements of the task. It is assumed that what is learned is a set of relationships between particular conditions or sets of circumstances. Learners are given practice conditions involving a range of requirements regarding distance, location and speed. The underlying assumption is that when they are next faced with new circumstances in a game situation, transfer will occur. In addition to providing variable practice, Schmidt suggests that teachers and coaches can assist transfer of learning by highlighting the similarities between skills, especially in the early phases of learning, by pointing out similarities in cognitive aspects such as rules, principles and strategies, and by questioning the learners on their understanding of how these apply to various situations.

Bilateral transfer

In **bilateral transfer**, the focus is on transfer of learning between limbs rather than between tasks. Research has shown that learning can transfer from one muscle group to another. For example, beginner soccer players are often told that is advantageous to learn to dribble the ball with either foot, and basketball players are likewise encouraged to dribble with either hand. Motor learning research supports the proposition that learning a task with one limb will improve the performance of the non-practising limb. However, it is not altogether clear why this should be, although various suggestions would indicate that both cognitive and motor control aspects are influential. Cognitively you 'know what to do' when you attempt the task with the previously unpractised limb. Motor control explanations suggest that practice on one limb enables the development of a generalised motor programme (non-muscle specific). When you attempt the task with the non-practised limb, you simply adapt the generalised motor programme.

SUMMARY

- Motivation is what influences our decisions to participate in sport and our subsequent persistence and effort in the activity.
- Intrinsic motivation is believed to be better and leads to more satisfying, long-lasting results than extrinsic motivation.
- Behavioural association or S-R theories of learning emphasise the role of repetition and reinforcement to establish a bond between stimulus and response.
- Cognitive theories of learning emphasise the importance of the learner's thought processes.
- Adam's Closed Loop theory and Schmidt's Schema theory deal specifically with the process of motor skill acquisition and emphasise the importance of feedback and variable practice conditions, respectively
- Three stages of motor learning have been identified: cognitive, associative and autonomous.
- Transfer of learning can be positive, negative or zero.

The information processing approach

Welford's information processing model (1968) was designed to examine the limitations of the human performer in terms of perception, memory, decision making, feedback and attention. According to this approach, the brain functions in a similar way to a computer with input, translation and output facilities.

- The **input stage** is concerned mainly with the detection of available sensory information. For example, does a player see a white tennis ball against a black background?
- The **central stage** of the model is concerned with perceiving and making sense of the information, making an appropriate decision and planning the necessary action. For example, the player identifies certain characteristics of the ball coming towards her, including direction, speed and spin. Decide how to return the shot and then issue the appropriate muscle commands.
- The **output stage** of the model is concerned with actual movement production. Once a decision has been made, the appropriate instructions are issued to the body and limbs and action results.

The sense organs appear at the input stage of the model and these include the five familiar sensory receptors (the eyes, ears, nose, skin, tongue) as well as the less familiar proprioceptors (for example, the muscle and joint receptors) and the vestibular apparatus adjoining the inner ear. Together they are responsible for sensing movements and body position. A sport performer's sense organs are continually bombarded with stimulus information from the environment but not all of this information is likely to be useful at any one time. For example, a footballer playing outdoors on a grass pitch will have many different environmental cues available. These include such things as visual information about the positions of teammates, opponents, ball,

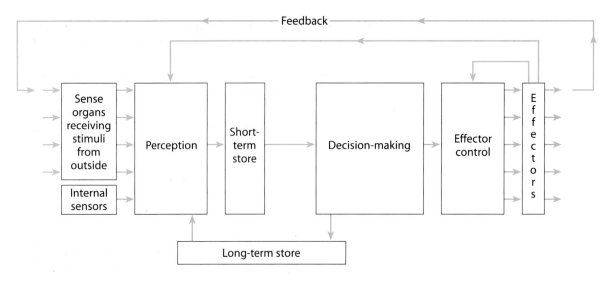

Figure 6.13 Welford's (1968) information processing model

pitch markings; auditory information from teammates, coaches or spectators; tactile information from contact with other players or the ball; kinesthetic information (body-awareness) from proprioceptors and vestibular apparatus regarding positions and movements of body and limbs as he runs over uneven ground, keeping his balance, while attempting to kick, pass or tackle an opponent.

All of this information is subjected to a pre-attentive analysis which the performer conducts by comparing incoming information to knowledge available in his or her memory about similar situations or events. Previous experience has an important role to play in establishing the importance of incoming information. The more familiar the person is with a situation the more likely it is that she will process such information automatically and without conscious control. As a result of this process the stimulus information transmitted to the perceptual mechanism for detection is usually drastically reduced. The remainder of the stimulus information is stored in memory for future reference. At this early stage of the process it is not thought that much meaning is attached to the pre-processed information. In fact, meaning is only attached when the information makes contact with previously stored knowlege in the memory.

The information now arrives at the perceptual mechanism and it is here that further meaning is acquired within the context of the current situation. The person begins to interpret the environment. For example, a wind surfer must 'read' the situation quickly in order to establish which stimulus cues are most relevant to him or her with regard to making the best possible decision.

The perceptual system is thought to function as a kind of filter which allows meaningless information to be filtered away, allowing the performer to selectively attend to the most relevant information. This information is then forwarded to short-term memory for further processing. Simultaneously, information from the long-term store is also advanced to the short-term store to enable the individual to have readily available all relevant information. For example, a netball player might recall that when faced with a similar situation in a previous game she used a particular technique effectively. For this reason the short-term memory has more recently been referred to as 'working memory' due to the amount of processing that actually occurs at that site. The working memory is responsible for receiving all the information from the perceptual mechanism and from the long-term store, and then organising it for appropriate decisions or further storage.

The short-term store is believed to have three main functions.

- It provides the performer with a 'working memory' to process current information.
- It is largely responsible for the cognitive processes of thinking, problem-solving and decision-making.
- It combines both of the functions and decides which information will then be forwarded to long-term storage for future reference.

Despite the many functions of this system, the short-term store does have limitations. Originally it was thought that the amount of information which can possibly be stored is limited to 'seven plus or minus two' items or chunks of information. The size of an item or chunk will largely depend on experience or familiarity with the information. For example, it has been shown that there are considerable differences in the amount of information which experts and novices in various sports can pick up at a single glance. One explanation for this superiority in recall of experts over novices is that the experts have knowledge of the structured game situations. This allows them to chunk the information into meaningful units whereas the novice presented with similar information attempts to recall each individual item and therefore reaches the limit of their short-term store very quickly.

The next stage of the model is concerned with decision-making. This involves using perceptual information about the current situation, such as where the ball and other players are, as well as information held in memory, such as previous success with a particular move, to determine what response, if any, is required. A key method of measurement which is relied upon when working within this approach is that of reaction time, as it is believed to indicate the speed and effectiveness of decision-making.

Reaction time is typically defined as the amount of time between the presentation of an unanticipated stimulus and the start of a response. It is important to emphasise that RT does not include any movement time. Figure 6.14 illustrates three factors which typically occur when RT is measured. For example, the subject is often (not always) given a 'warning signal' which alerts him or her that a 'stimulus signal' will occur, to which the subject must respond (initiation of response). The warning signal and the stimulus signal could be in any sensory modality, for example, vision, hearing or touch, and the required response can be any designated movement involving part or

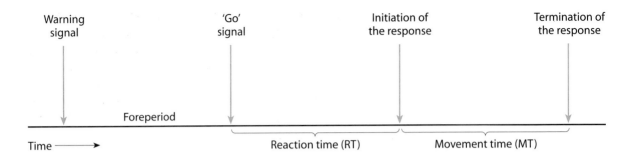

| Warning signal | 'Go' signal | Initiation of the response | Termination of the response |

Foreperiod

Time ⟶   Reaction time (RT)   Movement time (MT)

Figure 6.14 Magill's reaction time (1993)

all of the body. The purpose of the fore-period which usually ranges from one to five seconds, is to guard against the subject anticipating when the stimulus signal will arise.

Although there are examples of reaction time to single stimuli, such as the starter's gun in a sprint race, sport also provides us with situations where we must react quickly and choose among a variety of stimuli, for example, the hockey goal-keeper trying to anticipate where the shot will come from. **Choice reaction time** gives us a measure of this ability to discriminate among several stimuli and decide on the response. A primary factor influencing decision-making is the number of possible stimuli, each requiring a specific response, that are presented. It has been found that reaction time gradually increases as the number of possible alternatives increases. This finding forms the basis of **Hick's law**, which maintains that there is a linear relationship between reaction time (decision-making time) and the amount of information to be processed. While the law itself may seem clinical, it can be translated into very practical suggestions. Many sports skills require rapid decision-making situations, for example, defending against a punch in boxing, intercepting a pass in netball, or blocking a shot in basketball. By deliberately increasing the number of stimulus-response alternatives you present to your opponent, you automatically delay his or her processing time (RT will increase). A sensible strategy would be to develop various shots, strokes, or moves from a given situation, rather than always producing the one alternative which your opponent can process quickly. The more alternatives the opponent has to process, the longer will be the RT to the final move.

Another factor which affects CRT is stimulus-response compatiblity or the extent to which a stimulus and the required response are matched in a 'natural' way. For example, in a typical experimental situation, a subject may be required to respond to a flashing light by pressing a key of the same colour or on the same side of the display. This is a compatible situation. However, if the display and instructions are altered so that the subject has to respond to a flashing light by depressing a key on the opposite side to the light,

Figure 6.15 Hick's Law

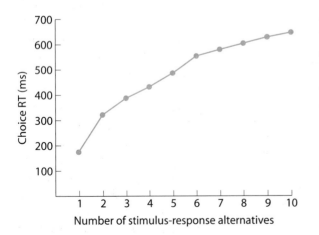

then we have less natural pairing. This is considered to be an incompatible S-R display. The basic finding from the research literature is that increasing compatibility decreases CRT. Practical examples of incompatible situations might be in sailing when you have to move the tiller to the right for the boat to go left, or the aerobics instructor who faces the class while demonstrating movements left and right. The learner has to actually move in the opposite direction (unless the teacher has already reversed the moves).

A final element which influences CRT is the nature and amount of practice. Research suggests that although practice does not greatly affect simple RT, it can have a pronounced effect in reducing CRT, especially when there are a large number of alternatives or when compatibility is low. Essentially, highly skilled performers have spent many hours practising the myriad alternatives available to them so that they appear to almost process information automatically (see section on attention). The actual stimulus situation is no different, but the links between stimuli and responses appear more natural or compatible, thus reducing CRT.

It is also during the decision-making process that a phenomenon known as the **Psychological Refractory Period** (PRP) sometimes occurs. According to Welford, there is only a 'single-channel' through which all information must pass and this sometimes means that delays in processing will occur if there is more than one stimulus to be processed. Support for the PRP has been found in experiments where subjects are presented initially with one stimulus (S_1) to which they have been instructed to respond (R_1) as quickly as possible. During the processing of this stimulus, the subject is then presented with a second stimulus (S_2) to which they must also respond (R_2). Typically, the second stimulus (S_2) will have to wait until the first stimulus (S_1) has been processed. This causes a longer

Figure 6.16 Information processing bottleneck

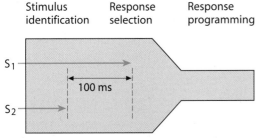

Stimulus 1 enters, followed in 100 ms by stimulus 2. Both are processed in parallel until stimulus 1 reaches the bottleneck in the response-programming stage, where

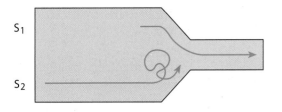

Stimulus 2 must wait until the response-programming stage is cleared for further processing, so

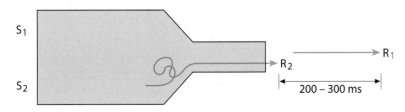

Response 1 and response 2 are separated by far more than 100 ms

[SOURCE: Schmidt, *Motor Learning and Performance*, 1991]

This type of central control, **motor programme selection**, was first proposed early this century when a medical doctor discovered that a patient with a gunshot wound to the back experiencing total anaesthesia of the lower limbs could still accurately move his leg when deprived of visual feedback. This suggested that the information about movement control was still being fed to the limbs via the intact efferent nerve pathways (brain to periphery), with little need for sensory feedback from the severed afferent nerve pathways (periphery to brain).

reaction time to (S_2) than if it had occured alone. This delay in reacting to (S_2) is known as the PRP and is a common phenomenon in sport, for example when a player sells a dummy or fake. A basketball player may fake (S_1) to jump-shoot but she remains firmly on the ground. Meanwhile her opponent jumps (R_1) to try to block the faked shot. Once the opponent has begun her movement the player can then dribble the ball past the airborne defender (S_2), by which time the defender realises that she must quickly respond to the actual play (R_2). Despite the application of the concept to sport and its intuitive appeal, to date there has been little field testing of PRP in sport itself and most of the findings tend to come from more mainstream psychological experiments.

The next stage of processing is known as **response selection** or more specifically **motor programme selection,** implying the selection of an already formulated response from memory. During this phase the performer must select the most appropriate re-sponse from the many possibilities available to him or her. For example, a soccer player may decide that he needs to pass the ball to a teammate who is in a better position than he is. However the question is, how does he select the most appropriate action? Classical explanations of this phenomenon assumed the use of a motor programme. This is a predetermined set of neural commands which are structured before a movement begins and which controls the execution of each particular movement. It is now thought that rather than calling up a specific motor pro-gramme from a central store, the performer calls upon an abstract programming rule. This is applied to a given situation by considering the initial starting conditions of the individual, the repertoire of similar responses, and the expected sensory con-sequences of the action.

Evidence for the existence of motor programmes has mainly been provided the three sources of investigation: there are deafferentation studies involving animals (where it is shown that movement planning and production is still possible when the afferent pathway to the spinal cord is severed and no feedback is available); research investigating the relationship between movement complexity and reaction time (RT) is available (more complex movements have longer RTs because more time is required to plan the response); and there are studies which record the muscle activity patterns of human performers producing rapid actions. In the latter studies, when the performer is mechanically prevented from completing the action, a similar EMG trace emerges suggesting that even though the limb does not move, a similar movement organisation process occurs.

Strict interpretations of the motor programme have since been modified to incorporate less rigid formulations, and current program-ming notions include more abstract and generalised concepts. The schema notion, for example, is thought to account for the use of feedback during movement execution and storage (where are programmes stored?) and novelty problems (how do programmes develop?) associated with motor programmes. This more economical view of motor programming suggests that rather than recalling a detailed response specification for each and every action performed, instead an abstract programming rule is applied to the specifics of a given situation in terms of the task requirements, the intitial starting conditions of the individual, the repertoire of similar responses, and the expected sensory consequences of the action. This abstract rule has developed on the basis of numerous repetitions of similar actions within general classes of movements. For example, an overhand throw may have similar specifications to other types of throwing action in terms of speed, force, and sequencing requirements.

It has been suggested that these programming rules form a 'grammar of action' which functions at the interface between thought and action. Much of the research on behavioural aspects of motor control over the past decade has concentrated on establishing the structure of such generalised motor programmes, that is, exactly what is specified in advance by the programme. It is generally agreed that two processes are involved in the programming of movement: planning the action and specifying parameters. In this view, the acquisition of motor control is proposed as being synonymous with the acquisition of programming rules, rather than in terms of muscle-specific motor programmes.

Attention

The concept of attention forms an intricate part of information processing models although it has been researched and discussed under a variety of different headings and within a number of theoretical frameworks. In this section we outline the concept of attention from three related perspectives.

Several references were made to the fact that performers selectively choose some informational cues over and above other stimuli. This phenomenon is commonly referred to as *selective attention* and many theories have been proposed to account for it, each with the common notion that a bottleneck or filter operates somewhere in the early stages of processing. In sport, selective attention can be seen to function at any time when a player screens out irrelevant stimulus information and focuses solely on selected cues. For example, a hockey goalkeeper attends to the penetrating play by the opposition's forwards by 'gating out' the movements of players who are in less threatening positions; the volleyball player who blocks a dig focuses solely on the shot rather than being distracted by movements of other players on court; the doubles partner in badminton selectively attends to the server while ignoring the sights and sounds of other players or spectators. Given the speed of so many sports, the whole process of selective attention becomes fascinating as performers are continually faced with situations which involve extremely restrictive time constraints. A number of sport psychologists have focused their research efforts on examining the role of

Planning an action is believed to include rules for action regarding the orderly sequence of events, including the relative timing and the relative forces which are to be specified.

Parameter specification refers to the addition of context-dependent and task-dependent information, including the overall duration of the movement, the overall force of the contractions and the specific muscles to be used.

selective attention in developing anticipation in fast-ball sports. In general, this work suggests that selective attention can be improved through practice and experience, with more mature performers from a variety of sports including basketball, volleyball, tennis, badminton and hockey, all showing an ability to focus on selected relevant information very quickly and being able to process this information accurately before making rapid and accurate decisions.

In addition to considering attention as a selective process, psychologists have focused on our ability to attend to more than one thing at a time in some circumstances. For example, a soccer player is described as having good vision when simultaneously he can dribble the ball, read the defensive pattern, spot holes in the defence, indicate to a teammate where to receive the ball and accurately pass the ball. However, we are also familiar with instances where we have difficulty doing two things at once, such as throwing a ball with the right hand while accurately catching a ball with left hand. Various *capacity theories* have been proposed to account for situations where information processing space appears to become either limited or more flexible, in some cases allowing for the performance of two tasks simultaneously while in other situations prohibiting this. An early proposition was that there is a single pool of attention available which can be allocated flexibly as required to any number of tasks. No detriment in performance should occur providing the total capacity is not exceeded. More recent theoretical developments suggest multiple resources or several pools of attention each with its own limited capacity. Within this theory it is possible to perform more than one task if the separate tasks require different attentional resources. If the demand for resources overlaps, then performance will be affected if any given pool of attention reaches its limit. For example, if two tasks both involve the same output resources (perhaps limb coordination), there is an increased likelihood that there will be resource limitations.

We have already suggested that one difference between novices and experienced performers in sport is in the type of attentional processing conducted. During the early stages of skill acquisition it is thought that attention involves *controlled processing*, a slow and cumbersome method which re-quires conscious attention to all details in order to make decisions. The role of a teacher or coach in these early

Figure 6.17 Attention allocation strategy

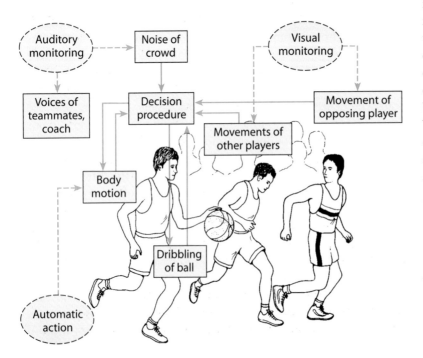

Figure 6.18 Relative information processing space

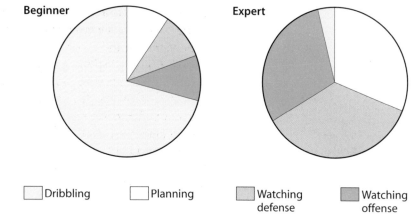

Beginner | Expert

☐ Dribbling ☐ Planning ▨ Watching defense ▨ Watching offense

stages would be to help the player realise which information is more pertinent and relevant to effective decision-making. The novice's attentional capacity may also be greatly limited by the nature of this cumbersome controlled processing, with much attention being allocated to motor output (the actual mechanics of throwing, catching, dribbling, running, etc.), leaving less resources for reading the play and making decisions. As a performer gains experience and improves in terms of skill acquisition, it is thought that attention involves more *automatic processing*, a fast and effortless procedure not under conscious control. Motor response elements in particular are thought to be performed under this type of subconcious control, freeing attentional resources to be allocated to evaluating the opposition's strategies and planning future responses.

In addition to the notions of selective attention and attentional capacity, the third aspect of attention considered within the information processing framework involves the concept of *arousal* or *alertness*. The phenomenon of attentional narrowing as a result of increased emotional arousal was first highlighted by Easterbrook (1959). Easterbrook maintained that in normal (non-threatening) situations, the performer uses as many cues (or stimuli) as are available to her or him, selectively attending to the most relevant information. As arousal increases (which will happen as an event increases in importance) so attention narrows, making the selection process to relevant information even more effective. However, if arousal continues to increase beyond an optimal level then the performer is in danger of narrowing attention to a point where some relevant information is discarded along with irrelevant cues – the blinkers come on. Sport offers many examples of situations where players who have become over-aroused fail to see team mates who are in good receiving positions, fail to see the positions of defence players and barge through them, or fail to see easy scoring opportunities. A sport psychologist, Dan Landers, has conducted some research into Easterbrook's notions in the sports context and has found considerable support for the suggestion that increased emotional arousal results in a deterioration of performance due to increased attentional narrowing (see Figure 6.19).

251

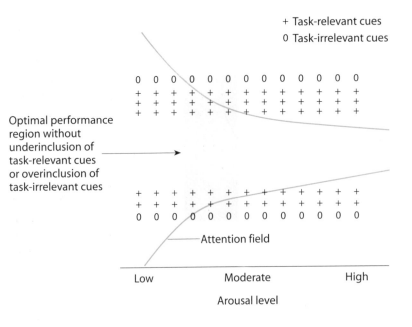

+ Task-relevant cues

0 Task-irrelevant cues

Optimal performance region without underinclusion of task-relevant cues or overinclusion of task-irrelevant cues

Attention field

Low   Moderate   High

Arousal level

Figure 6.19 Cue utilisation and the arousal-performance relationship

Feedback and knowledge of results

Information available during and after movement can be fed back into the system both during the course of movement and after actions have been completed. The term feedback is used to describe the information received by the performer as a result of the movement produced. For exam-ple, when a tennis player serves the ball she receives information about how the movement felt, looked and sounded, as well as information about the result of the movement. Information received as a direct result of producing a movement is referred to as **intrinsic feedback.** A performer is sometimes able to use this type of feedback, at a subconscious level, to control ongoing movement. A soccer player may be running over uneven or wet ground and may have to momentarily correct his stride to ensure that he does not slip or fall.

A distinction is made between this type of information and that known as **extrinsic** or **augmented feedback**, which refers to any additional information not inherent in the movement itself but which improves intrinsic feedback. For example, a performer may be given instructions from the coach about what to do on future attempts or she may be shown a video replay and given advice as to how to improve. There are a number of areas of extrinsic feedback but sport scientists have focused mainly on one category, known as **knowledge of results** (abbreviated to **KR**). There are many examples of KR in sport, both in practice and competition. For example, a coach might shout split times to swimmers as they train over a number of lengths, or in com-petition a gymnast receives a visible score from a judge after completion of a routine. In general, feedback is essential to the entire system if learning is to take place and performers are to benefit from previous experiences. Feedback about perceptual information, movement decisions, selected motor programmes and programme execution is all fed into the memory systems. This enables performers to establish a reference of correctness for various movements and thereby assist in the regulation of future actions.

In recent years movement experts from a variety of dis-ciplines have expressed dissatisfaction with a possible overemphasis on KR. In particular, the **knowledge of performance** (KP) has become a popular means of differentiating between information given about the actual movement pattern produced and information given regarding

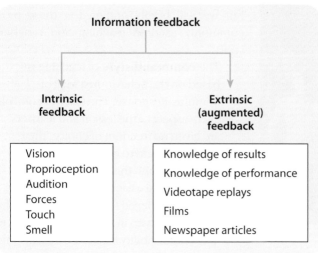

Figure 6.20 Types of information feedback

the end result or movement outcome. Typically, in laboratory experiments, learners are shown kinematic information (information about the mechanics of the movement itself) without reference to the forces involved. Several recent studies show that learners receiving kinematic information (KP) perform better than learners who only receive outcome knowledge (KR). Coaches and teachers of motor skills do not usually have access to highly technical equipment with which to measure and present kinematic information. However, most schools and clubs now have video cameras and monitors which can be used instead. Reviews of studies utilising videotaping as a means of providing knowledge of performance, suggest that more will be learned by directing the performer's attention to specific aspects of the performance or even segments of the movement sequence, rather than simply reviewing the tape.

SUMMARY

- The information processing model was designed to examine the limitations of the human performer in terms of perception, memory, decision-making, feedback and attention.
- Reaction time is defined as the amount of time between presentation of an unanticipated stimulus and the start of a response.
- Hick's Law states that there is a linear relationship between decision-making time and the amount of information to be processed.
- Feedback is an essential element for skill learning and can be either intrinsic or extrinsic.

The learning environment

Now that we have considered the various underlying elements of motor skill acquisition, let us turn our attention to the actual learning environment. Teachers and coaches have direct control over a variety of features which influence learning effectiveness. In order to facilitate the best learning outcomes, teachers and coaches need to consider strategies for the provision of information, the organisation of practice sessions and the scheduling of practice and rest time.

Teaching styles

Teachers and coaches generally adopt a specific style of teaching which can vary in terms of who makes most of the decisions about the learning environment. It has been suggested that teaching styles lie on a continuum: at one end the teacher makes all the decisions and at the other end the learner makes all the decisions. A variety of styles have

Figure 6.21   The learning environment in educational gymnastics

been identified as falling along this continuum but we will briefly outline the three most commonly used in teaching and coaching sport.

- The **command style** of teaching is based on the behaviourist idea of Stimulus-Response. The teacher controls every aspect of the lesson and learners are given no freedom of choice, they simply respond to commands given to them. Although this style of teaching is thought to be easier to implement, it is generally believed that it is less successful than other styles in motivating learners to take responsibility for their own learning.

- The **reciprocal style** of teaching is based on cognitive theories of learning. Typically learners work in pairs with one person designated as the 'doer' and the other as the 'observer'. Although the teacher decides which aspect of performance will be worked on, students are encouraged to interact with each other and make decisions about possible performance adjustments. This style of teaching is quite common in gymnastics where learners work together using such cognitive operations as observing, comparing and contrasting, concluding and communicating results.

- **Problem solving** is also sometimes used in sports situations. This style is even more firmly based on the cognitive theories of learning and students are expected to take much more responsibility for their own learning. This style is concerned with the discovery process of learning. The teacher sets open-ended questions and all answers which meet the general criteria of the problem are considered to be correct. This is often the approach used in educational dance and gymnastics classes where students are set movement problems but no restrictions in terms of right or wrong solutions. In general, more and more teachers and coaches are adopting cooperative styles of teaching which consider the student to be in control of their own learning. It also assists in developing intrinsic motivation which is important for continued involvement in sport throughout life.

Forms of guidance

There are a variety of ways in which a teacher or coach can impart information about the skills to be learned. Typically such information can take one or a variety of forms which we will consider under the headings of visual, verbal and manual guidance.

Visual guidance

One of the most common methods of teaching sports skills is the 'watch me – do it this way' approach which relies heavily on the use of demonstrations. This phenomenon has arisen for two reasons. One is that vision tends to dominate the other senses. The other is the natural tendency for human beings to learn by imitation. Demonstrations provide an efficient way to transmit information about what needs to be done at all stages of skill learning. In the cognitive phase, demonstrations give the learner a general idea of the action. At later stages of learning the demonstration may be used to highlight specific problem areas. Factors such as physical arrangement, timing and nature of emphasis of demonstrations need to be considered for maximum benefit of this form of guidance.

Verbal guidance

Giving instructions is a fairly traditional way of teaching and coaching and can serve the purpose of identifying what needs to be done and how the learner should do it. However, one of the problems with verbal instructions is that they are not always the most efficient way of describing the subtleties of movement. Nevertheless, when used in conjuction with an appropriate model of action they can be very useful, particularly in guiding a learner's attention to specific elements. For example, coaches are frequently heard giving direct verbal instructions such as 'point your toes', or 'keep your eyes on the ball', or 'turn your shoulder into the shot'.

Manual guidance

The main aim of manual guidance is to physically guide the learner through the required movement pattern and by doing so, reduce any errors. Manual guidance is particularly useful in learning dangerous moves, such as a gymnast using a spotting belt, and in situations where a learner may be experiencing fear, such as a swimmer using a flotation device. In general, research suggests that manual guidance is not a very effective technique for learning. Although it is designed to ensure that learners produce correct action and reduce errors, manual guidance does not actually assist the learner in developing the proper 'feel of the movement'. In order to develop kinesthetic perception, learners need to actually produce the movement themselves rather than being passively guided through an action. Therefore, it is suggested that if manual guidance techniques are used, learners should be encouraged not to rely on them too much and to quickly move on practice without them.

Structure and type of practice

Massed and distributed

Practice is an essential element in acquiring any motor skill. The distribution of practice conditions may have varying effects on how much is learned or how well a skill is learned. Distribution of practice refers to the spacing of practice either in an individual session or the spacing between different practice sessions. For example, a coach could advise

Figure 6.22   Factors which influence the choice of mass or distributed organisations

	Shorter and more frequent	Longer and less frequent
If the task:	is simple, repetitive, boring	is complex
	demands intense concentration	has many elements
		requires warm-up
	is fatiguing	is a new one for the performer
	demands close attention to detail	
If the learner	is young or immature (unable to sustain activity)	is older or more mature ·
	has a short attention span	is able to concentrate for long periods of time
	has poor concentration skills	has good ability to focus attention
	fatigues easily	tires quickly

a young gymnast to spend one hour of a two-hour practice session trying to improve a handspring vault (massed practice). Another coach might favour having gymnasts practice the vault during three, 15-minute blocks interspersed with other practice activities (distributed practice). Similarly, one coach may favour one two-hour session per day whereas another may prefer to use two one-hour blocks. A number of early studies attempted to address the effects of massed as compared to distributed practice within individual practice sessions. The majority of these studies looked at organisation within one session and showed that distributed practice is more beneficial than massed practice. These studies have not been without criticism, the most telling concern is the distinction which is offered between learning and performance. Later investigators have pointed out that massed practice may result in a lower level of performance at the end of a session. However, reminiscence may be equally high for both massed and distributed practice groups when next performing the task. Clearly, the relative merits of massed or distributed practice need to be considered in the light of individual circumstances surrounding the skills being learned, the total amount of time available and the amount of time available per session.

Whole and part methods

Another issue which is of considerable importance to teachers and coaches concerns the best method of practising the skills being learned. Should skills be presented and practised in their entirety (whole method) or should they be broken down into smaller component parts (part method)? Should some combination of these approaches be used (whole-part or part-whole)? Most people who have been involved in sport are familiar with instances when they had to simplify a skill in order to grasp precisely what was required of them. Similarly, many school children are familiar with the days and weeks spent on skills, practices and short routines rather than just playing the game. So, should whole or part methods be the mainstay

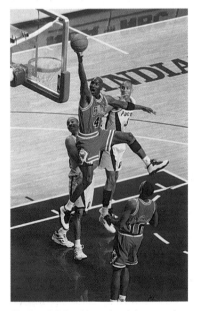

Figure 6.23   How should we teach skills?

Research study

A study frequently cited for its practical utility was that conducted by Baddeley and Longman (1978). These investigators were required to train postal workers on a task similar in many respects to typing. It was initially decided that sixty hours of practice would be required for workers to become proficient but the question concerned how this amount of time should be scheduled. Four practice conditions were devised, namely one- or two-hour sessions conducted once or twice a day. Results favoured the one-hour practice session offered once per day. Individuals in this group learned the typing task in the least number of hours and nine months after the study, they were still the most proficient workers. This study clearly suggests that motor skills are best learned during shorter amounts of practice time per session. However, even with this 'real life' skill, arguments could be lodged as to how representative a typing task is of the kinds of motor skills involved in sport and exercise. Furthermore, in considering the results of this study we need to take into account the fact that the one hour per day scheduling would have to be spread across almost three months in order to complete sixty hours of training, whereas the two hour, twice per day scheduling would be completed within three weeks.

Figure 6.24 Factors which influence the choice of whole vs part

	Wholes	Parts
If the task:	has highly dependant (integrated) parts	has highly independent parts
	is simple	is made up of individual skills
	is not meaningful in parts	is very complex
	is made up of simultaneously performed parts	if limited work on parts or different segments is necessary
If the learner	is able to remember long sequences	has limited memory span
	has a long attention span	is not able to concentrate for a long period of time
	is highly skilled	is having difficulty with a particular part
		cannot succeed with the whole method

of teaching practice? Research suggests that the deciding factor has to be the nature of the task which is being learned. Let us consider two sports skills, a swimming stroke (arm action, leg action, breathing) and a lay-up in basketball (dribble, approach, take-off, shot). Each of these skills appears to be made up of individual parts which could be practised separately. However, a fundamental difference between the skills is that in the swimming stroke, the parts ultimately occur simultaneously whereas in the lay-up, the parts occur sequentially. Generally speaking, the whole method is preferable for skills in which elements are performed simultaneously, whereas the part method may be used for skills which are performed sequentially. When using the part method caution should also be taken to ensure that the performer also learns to integrate the part into the whole skill (or game or routine). Failure to do this may result in destroying the fundamental unity of action.

Physical and mental practice

Mental practice or rehearsal, of which visualisation and imagery are sub-sets, has long been regarded as an effective aid to skill acquisition and maintenance. If actions are seen as reflecting thoughts, then the benefits of mental practice are almost self-evident. *Mental practice* refers to a situation in which the learner thinks about or imagines performing the task rather than physically practising it. A recent review of the many studies related to the effects of mental training on motor skills concluded that performance can be improved by mental practice. Mental practice was better than no practice, but physical practice was found to be better than mental practice. It has also been suggested that

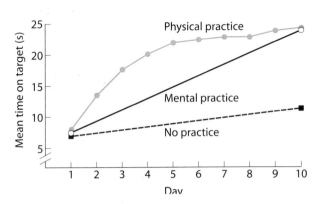

Figure 6.25 The effect of physical and mental practice

the type of task being practised will affect the usefulness of mental practice. Tasks with a large cognitive component seem to benefit more from mental practice than tasks which require large amounts of strength. This would affect sports such as gymnastics, ice-skating or dance, where the performer has to remember long sequences of movement, or indeed any team sport where the performer is attempting to learn a new game play or strategy. It appears that learning the sequence of actions is facilitated by mental practice, but that learning the actions themselves benefits more from physical practice. Given these findings, it would be unwise to suggest that teachers and coaches use mental practice to replace physical practice. However, it is wise to encourage use of mental practice, particularly in the early stage of learning when the learner is establishing the correct sequence of action. By using breaks in physical practice efficiently, the time taken to learn new skills may be shortened. There is less scientific evidence for the use of mental practice at the élite performer's level, but there are a great many anecdotal reports of the use of imagery by top-class athletes. There is also extensive research literature available which examines the role of imagery as a pre-competitive 'psyching-up' strategy.

SUMMARY

- Teaching styles can be either command, reciprocal or problem solving.
- Teachers and coaches can provide visual, verbal or manual guidance. Learners should not become dependent on guidance.
- Decisions regarding the structure and type of practice conditions largely depend on the nature of the sports skills being learned and the age and ability level of the performer.

Questions

1 In teaching and learning motor skills, a number of decisions need to be made regarding practice variables. With reference to the sport of your choice, outline the important conditions of practice which a teacher or coach should consider.

2 Analyse one team or individual sport in terms of Welford's Information Processing model.

3 Outline and describe the various types of information feedback available to sports performers. To what extent may feedback be regarded as an essential element of skill acquisition and performance?

4 What are the three stages of motor learning described by Fitts and Posner (1967)? Describe the kinds of performance levels and the ways in which the performer appears to control his actions in each stage.

5 Define the terms 'simple reaction time' and 'choice reaction time'. Discuss the limitations imposed on players in open sports due to the speed of play.

6 Outline three views of attention. How would your knowledge of attention as a limited capacity assist you in designing effective practice conditions?

7 Choose a particular sport and describe various different conditions of practice which you might want to consider in designing effective coaching sessions.

References

Adams, J A A closed loop theory of motor learning *Journal of Motor Behavior*, 3 (1971)

Baddeley, A D and Longman, D J A The influence of length and frequency of training session on the rate of learning to type. *Ergonomics*, 21 (1978)

Easterbrook, J A The effect of emotion on cue utilisation and the organisation of behavior. *Psychological Review*, 66 (1959)

Guthrie, E R *The psychology of learning* Harper and Row (1952)

Henry, F M Reaction time-movement time correlations. *Perceptual and Motor Skills*, 12 (1961)

Hull, C L *Principles of Behavior* Appleton-Century-Crofts (1943)

Magill, R A *Motor Learning: Concepts and Applications* Brown and Benchmark (1993)

Schmidt, R A A schema theory of discrete motor skill learning. *Psychological Review*, 82 (1975)

Schmidt, R A *Motor Learning and Performance* Champaign, Human Kinetics (1991)

Singer, R N *Motor Learning and Human Performance* Macmillan (1980)

Sharp, B *Acquiring Skill in Sport* Eastbourne: Sport Dynamics (1992)

Thorndike, E *Human Learning* Appleton-Century-Crofts (1931)

Welford, A T *Fundamentals of Skill* Metheun (1968)

7 SPORT PSYCHOLOGY

Objectives

To understand
- the nature of individual differences in relation to performance in sport
- the role of intervention techniques in controlling anxiety and optimising performance
- the social influences affecting sport participation and sporting performance
- the impact of group motives and group dynamics on sporting processes such as team cohesion, leadership, competition and cooperation

Professional sport psychologists work with performers and coaches alongside other sport scientists as part of a team, devising packages and programmes which aim to improve player performance. However, sports psychology does not give instant solutions to complex sporting situations.

Physical preparation for sport in the 1990s has become quite scientific, structured and time-consuming. In contrast, you may notice how haphazard most athletes' mental preparation still is, despite the fact that the mental side of sport is so often acknowledged as the crucial difference between winning and losing. According to golfer Jack Nicklaus, his own sport is 70% mental and 30% physical. Anyone associated with sport will recognise just how important psychology can be to achieving sporting excellence and understanding the dynamics of sporting performance.

Despite this recognition, it is surprising how long it has taken for sport psychology to be taken seriously in the UK. Elsewhere this has not been the case. For example, as early as the 1920s, the Chicago Cubs baseball team employed a sport psychologist called Coleman Griffith to identify the psychological profile of the sporting champion. Back in 1956 the Brazilian squad brought a sport psychologist with them to the World Cup soccer finals in Sweden. Since the 1960s sport psychologists have routinely accompanied teams from what was the Soviet Union and other eastern European countries to the Olympics.

In the United Kingdom, recognition of sport psychology has taken longer, but we are now moving to a position where resistance and scepticism is weakening and the contribution of sport psychologists to performance improvement is more readily accepted.

Individual differences

One area of concern throughout the history of sport psychology has been an understanding of individual differences within and between sports. This section will consider these differences in terms of personality and gender issues in sport.

Personality

In a systematic and scientific fashion many sport psychologists have set themselves the task of finding the psychological recipe for sporting success. This is one of three issues in particular which have dominated work in this area, the others being comparisons between athletes and non-athletes, and between athletes in the same sport. Within psychology, a number of personality theories continue to offer alternative explanations as to what makes us human. These include Freud's pychodynamic approach, cognitive behavioural approaches and various theories of the self. Freud argues that we are biological beings, driven by selfish needs but also having to co-exist with others in a social world. Our personalities reflect on this ongoing conflict between the selfish and the social.

Cognitive-behavioural or social learning theories, including that of Albert Banduro, suggest that our personality is shaped primarily by our interactions with the social and physical environment. According to Bandura, either through direct experience or observational learning, we both influence our environment and in turn are influenced through a process known as reciprocal determinism. One cognitive element is especially important here: self-efficacy, or our belief that we are capable of a specific action which is required to produce a desired outcome in a given situation. Through observation and action, we learn to believe that our efforts will or will not lead to success. Those who believe they can achieve, will then strive for further success (high self-efficacy), and thus 'success circles' are created.

Self or phenomenological theories of personality, including those of Carl Rogers and George Kelly, place emphasis on the unique qualities of each individual and their unique experiences, and their idiosyncratic interpretation of these experiences. These are known as idiographic approaches, in contrast with nomothetic approaches which emphasise generalities across populations.

One psychological theory of personality has dominated this field. This, the trait theory, sometimes known as dispositional theory, is based on the idea that our personality is made up of a finite number of characteristics or traits, and is one of the oldest and most controversial mainstream personality theories. At one level, the theory is very appealing as it answers simple questions such as what makes us different, and what names can we give to the psychological characteristics which make us different people. Many psychologists would now argue that a trait approach is fundamentally flawed because of its simplicity; it is unable to deal with our complexity as unique individuals,

> A **trait** is defined as a continuous quality that individuals possess in different amounts (for example, sociablity, dominance, extraversion)

Thomas Tutko and Bruce Ogilvie argued that certain characteristics marked out successful sportspeople and listed these characteristics:

- aggression
- coachability
- conscientiousness
- determination
- drive
- emotional control
- guilt proneness
- leadership
- mental toughness
- self-confidence
- trust

Research

One famous study using Cattell's 16 PF was carried out in 1977 by Schurr and his co-workers. They looked at a sample of approximately 1500 young American students using the personality inventory known as the 16 PF (the dependent variable), with student year, type of sport, level of success and sport involvement as the main independent variables in the experimental design. They concluded that those who took part in team sports tended to be less independent, self-sufficient and stress-free than those participating in individual sports, and that certain athletes scored higher on extroversion and independence, and lower on anxiety. Overall however, no single profile could be established to distinguish those who took part in sport from those who did not.

or how our personalities may change over time and place. Trait theory argues that we are all constructed from a certain number of psychological traits; other personality theorists argue that we are unique individuals who each continue to develop and change in unique ways which defy measurement by standardised questionnaires.

Sport psychologists have routinely used psychological inventories in order to categorise and differentiate athletes. One of the earliest attempts was made by Thomas Tutko and Bruce Ogilvie of San Jose State College in the USA in 1966.

They subsequently developed a questionnaire, called the Athletic Motivation Inventory (AMI), to measure these traits and this scale became very popular in North America as a way of categorising athletes. Unfortunately, it was not developed on the basis of sound psychometric principles, that is, the measurement of psychological characteristics. Neither was it validated (shown to actually measure what the psychologist claims it is measuring), nor checked for reliability (accuracy in terms of producing the same result on a number of different testing occasions). The AMI was not grounded in scientific methods.

Since then more rigorous attempts have been made by sport psychologists to identify winning traits using existing and well validated psychological inventories. Prominent amongst the tests and inventories which have been used are Raymond Cattell's 16 PF and Hans Eysenck's EPI. Cattell's scale is based on sixteen personality factors (16 PF) which he identifies as forming the core of primary, while the British psychologist Hans Eysenck based his Eysenck Personality Inventory (EPI) on three independent surface traits (extraversion-introversion, neuroticism-stability, psychoticism).

In a further study in 1982, this time using the EPI, Eysenck himself argued that '*extroverts and high psychoticism scorers are more likely to take up sports and excel in them, because their low arousal levels lead them to seek sensory stimulation . . . and they are more tolerant of the pain associated with sport.*'

Later work has been far more critical of this standpoint and has led sport psychologists to adopt one of two attitudes: **the credulous**, who believe that traits can predict sporting success, and the **sceptical**, who do not believe that traits predict success.

From the credulous perspective there is some evidence to suggest that athletes in certain sports may be less anxious and more extroverted, with the largest differences between team and individual sports. Also, specific personality types can be shown to cluster in particular sports and in particular positions within sports. However, both the sceptical and the credulous camps would agree that when it comes to comparing those who succeed in their chosen sport and those who do not, psychological scales have so far failed to find the winning formula. There is no comprehensive psychological recipe for success.

If personality differences do exist, were these differences present before the individuals took up their chosen sport or did they develop through the experience of this sport? On the one hand, longitudinal

POMS measures six dimensions of mood:

- anger-hostility
- confusion-bewilderment
- depression-dejection
- fatigue-inertia
- tension-anxiety
- vigour-activity

research (carried out over a long period of time) has found little evidence of change in personality as a result of sport. On the other hand, taking up exercise (but not necessarily competitive sport) has been shown to influence aspects of mood state and personality, for example, depression. It could be that sport in itself is not the crucial variable here but rather the associated changes in lifestyle which come about through a healthy involvement in a sport or recreation.

Most sport psychologists now recognise that a simple trait approach will inevitably fail to capture the subtleties of personality. At the very least, an interactional approach is the only sensible way to proceed. The interactional approach does not ignore personality traits but instead places as much emphasis on the context within which the athlete must compete. Behaviour (B) is then represented as a function (f) of the personality (p) and the environment (e), or:

$$B = f(p,e)$$

Sports psychologists admit that their ability to predict performance would be limited without expert knowledge of the physical and motor potential of the performer. For this reason above all others, personality tests should never be used to select people for teams in sport.

Mood state and performance

The relationship between mood and performance in sport has been studied by a number of psychologists. William Morgan used a questionnaire called the Profile of Mood State Questionnaire (POMS) to consider the relationship between mood and performance.

Consistently, it has been found that a particular pattern of POMS scores can predict above average athletic performance. Low scores on tension, depression, anger, fatigue and confusion, together with a high score on vigour indicate superior performance. This pattern became known as the 'Iceberg Profile', which is the shape produced when scores on each mood state are plotted in turn to make up a line graph. The profile in figure 7.1 compares the mood states of athletes subsequently chosen for the 1976 US Olympic Wrestling team with those who were not selected.

If athletes were asked to record their mood state prior to competition in a range of sports including swimming, wrestling, rowing and track athletics, it would be shown that those whose moods match the Iceberg Profile will often, but not always, perform well.

SUMMARY

- Sport personality theorists fall into two camps: the credulous, who believe that traits can predict sporting success, and the sceptical, who disagree with this view.
- The interactional approach offers a way forward by emphasising the context within which athletes must compete.
- It is suggested that a particular pattern of mood states can predict above-average sporting performance.

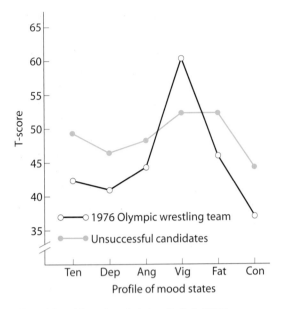

[SOURCE: Test of Champions: the Iceberg Profile by W P Morgan, 1980, *Psychology Today 14 (2)*]

Figure 7.1   Iceberg Profile

Competitive anxiety

One dimension of personality above all others has interested sport psychologists over the years, that is, how the individual copes with the psychological demands of competition, called competitive anxiety. A number of terms are used to describe this state. The terms stress, arousal and anxiety are difficult to distinguish but here they can be defined as:

- **Stress**: the entire process of activation or readiness to respond to a stressor.
- **Arousal**: the physiological or somatic response to a particular stressor.
- **Anxiety**: the psychological and physiological antecedents to these responses.

There is a great deal of overlap between each, because they all deal to some degree with both cognitive (mental) and somatic (bodily) responses.

Measurement

In order to begin to understand and measure competitive anxiety, sport psychologists have tried using a range of psychometric tests or questionnaires. In 1966 Charles Spielberger argued that it was necessary to make a distinction between momentary states and more permanent traits. Anxiety states (A-state) are subjective, consciously perceived feelings of tension. Anxiety traits are a motive or acquired behavioural disposition (A-trait). Spielberger developed a 40-item Likert scale known as the STAI or State-Trait Anxiety Inventory. At the same time, sport psychologists began to develop anxiety questionnaires which were tailored specially to sport, for example, Marten's Sport Competition Anxiety Test (SCAT). This 15-item scale was described as 'a sport-specific A-trait inventory', and is designed to measure trait anxiety in competitive situations.

Martens also recognised that any measure of sport anxiety must take due regard of its multi-dimensional nature. This includes not only the distinction between underlying predispositions (A-trait), and behaviour and emotion in the present (A-state), but also the two types of anxiety, which sport psychologists call cognitive anxiety (negative thoughts, worry) and somatic anxiety (physiological response). It is A-state which is the concern of the scale now most widely used for looking at competitive anxiety, the second version of the Competitive State Anxiety Inventory, or CSAI-2. The CSAI-2 measures competitive anxiety. This scale takes into account the difference between A-state and A-trait. It also distinguishes between cognitive anxiety (worry) and somatic anxiety (physiological symptoms).

The scale is recommended to be administered within an hour of competition, and does appear to identify different dimensions of anxiety. For example, research using the CSAI-2 has shown that cognitive anxiety may be high for several days before competition,

CSAI-2 examines:

•cognitive A-state, for example: 'I am concerned about this competition.'; 'I have self doubts.'

•somatic A-state, for example: 'I feel tense in my stomach.'; 'My body feels tight.'

•self-confidence state, for example: 'I'm confident I can meet the challenge.'; 'I feel comfortable.'

State anxiety refers to a temporary condition which is produced in response to the immediate perception of threat or challenge.

According to drive theory, performance (P) was regarded as a function of habit (H) multiplied by drive strength (D), or

$$P = f(H \times D)$$

while somatic anxiety tends to rise quickly in the few hours before the event itself.

We now know more about anxiety before competition but what happens during competition itself remains a mystery. Some athletes, and particularly élite competitors, report that their A-state drops quickly, while others find it more difficult to 'come down', but who, why or how has yet to be answered. For this reason pre-competition measures of A-state remain poor predictors of performance.

Anxiety therefore includes state and trait dimensions, both of which can show themselves in both cognitive and somatic symptoms. An individual with high trait anxiety will be more likely to look upon a great many situations as threatening and will be likely to become over-anxious in stressful situations.

Anxiety – performance relationship

The relationship between arousal or anxiety and performance has been researched. As drive increases so performance should improve so long as that performance is well-learnt and well-rehearsed. According to classical drive theory, if athletes are already skilled then 'psyching up' or increasing drive will help them perform well. Unfortunately, research has failed to support this claim.

A second approach which followed from drive theory is known as the Inverted-U hypothesis. This theory has enjoyed a great deal of support over the years, mainly because of its simplicity and ease of application. The Inverted-U hypothesis predicts a curvilinear relationship between arousal and performance, approximating an inverted-U shape. Therefore, increasing arousal will lead to an increase in sporting performance but only up to a certain point. As arousal continues beyond this point so performance will then become worse.

The inverted-U hypothesis

The basic model for the inverted-U hypothesis has been modified and refined over the years. For example, as early as 1970, it was argued that the hypothesis must take into account the activities associated with particular sports. An American sport psychologist called Oxendine argued that high levels of arousal would be likely to improve performance when the sport relied on gross

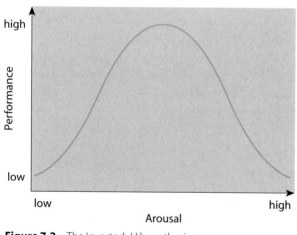

Figure 7.2   The Inverted -U hypothesis

Figure 7.3   Oxendine's taxonomy of sport

Optimum arousal	Sport
5	American football blocking; 200/400 metres race; gym exercises; weight lifting
4	Long jump; sprints/long distance; shot putt; swimming races; wrestling/judo
3	Basketball; boxing; high jump; gymnastics; soccer
2	Baseball; diving; fencing; tennis
1	Archery; bowling; golf putting/chip; figure skating

motor skills (for example, weightlifting) but would interfere with performance of complex motor skills involving coordination, steadiness, concentration and fine movement (for example, snooker or golf). Oxendine actually developed a classification system for matching sport skills with appropriate levels of arousal, although the system largely remains untested.

The inverted-U hypothesis has been unable to explain the complexities of competitive anxiety although the general inverse relationship between arousal and performance has been explained by Easterbrook's cue utilisation theory (the more aroused we are, the less able we are to attend to a range of stimuli) or signal detection theory (greater arousal, greater neural noise). Instead the inverted-U has been replaced by models which deal with the multi-dimensional nature of anxiety. Multi-dimensional anxiety theory is based on the distinction between cognitive anxiety and somatic anxiety. It suggests that anxiety shows in two responses: a somatic response based on physiological arousal, and a cognitive response which includes worry about performance, inability to concentrate, disrupted attention and fear of failure. The theory then makes a series of predictions:

1 There will be a negative but linear relationship between cognitive state anxiety and performance.

2 The relationship between somatic anxiety and performance will resemble an inverted-U.

3 Somatic anxiety should decline once performance begins but cognitive anxiety may remain high so long as fear of failure remains.

4 Cognitive anxiety will generally be stable across time whereas somatic anxiety will tend to rise dramatically prior to competition.

British sport psychologists have developed an alternative approach to understanding competitive anxiety. This is based on a theory known as the Catastrophe Theory. Hardy and Fazey argue that the effects of physiological arousal on performance may be either relatively mild or they may be catastrophic. These effects depends on cognitive anxiety (both state and trait acting together).

When cognitive anxiety is low, for example during training, and when the athlete has low trait anxiety then an increase in arousal will normally help performance up to a certain point (an inverted-U). When cognitive anxiety is high, for example, immediately prior to competition, or when the athlete is of a nervous disposition then the dangers of increasing physiological arousal are that much more serious.

Figure 7.4 Catastrophe model of the effects of anxiety upon performance
The model is often described as shown below, where the surface of the three-dimensional model represents performance. In the background, increasing arousal leads to marginal improvements in performance within limits (the inverted-U); in the foreground, increasing arousal leads the performer over the edge of a cliff with a rapid decline in performance and a climb back to adequate performance which is almost impossible.

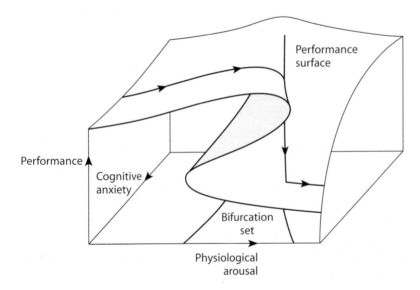

The catastrophe model suggests that:

- stress and anxiety will influence performance
- each individual will respond in a unique way to competitive anxiety
- this will ultimately reflect in their performance in a unique way which may be difficult to predict using general rules or formulae.

One practical approach which deals with these three simple messages and neatly bridges the gap between theory and practice is Yuri Hanin's Optimum Arousal Theory. He argues that each athlete has a zone of optimum functioning or ZOF. According to Hanin, athletes will perform at their peak when their level of arousal or competitive anxiety falls within their ZOF. The task of the applied sport psychologist is to get to know their athletes and to help them understand what state they perform best in, and then use techniques to move them to that state prior to competition.

Controlling anxiety

Many sport psychologists spend their time using intervention techniques of various kinds to make the athlete feel most at ease and comfortable prior to and during competition. When the athletes are performing well within their ZOF, they will feel comfortable being in that state. The range of intervention techniques include:

- mental skills (cognitive)
- physical relaxation (somatic)
- elements of cognitive and somatic
- long-term change, where the aim is to develop a range of psychological skills to be used as and when necessary (for example, time management, stress management, goal setting, interpersonal skills, life-style management, self-confidence, relaxation techniques and imagery)
- preparation for a specific event where a programme is put together to build an athlete towards a goal over several years, for example, the Olympic games
- short-term or crisis interventions where counselling is offered immediately in response to one issue, for example, a physical injury, an inexplicable loss of form, or when the build-up to a major competition goes awry.

One popular anxiety and stress management somatic technique is known as self-directed relaxation. This aims to release tension in each of the body's major muscle groups while emphasising slow, easy breathing, and encouraging visualisation of stress flowing away from the body. Over time and with practice athletes require fewer self-instructions to relax each muscle group, and the muscle groups can be slowly combined, so that eventually only a few seconds are needed to achieve full body relaxation. An example of a self-directed relaxation script is provided. (You may wish to make an audiotape of this script for your own use!)

Self-directed relaxation script

Close your eyes and adjust your body so that you are stretched out, making maximum contact with the ground. Raise and lower your head to stretch your neck, making sure your head is not tilted backwards. Flatten your back and push away with your heels to stretch out your legs. Take a deep breath and let it out slowly. Feel the weight of your body on the floor. Take another deep breath and let the floor support the full weight of your body:

- Now take a good deep breath and then slowly breathe out. Think of the word 'calm' then pause. Breathe in deeply . . . then out slowly . . . [and repeat twice].

- Concentrate on your head. Feel any tension in your forehead then consciously let the tension flow away from your forehead. Feel the tension flow away to the floor and think of the word 'calm'.

- Feel any tension in your jaw then let the tension in these muscles flow away. Breathe in deeply . . . then breathe out slowly.

- Feel the relaxation in your facial muscles. Relax . . . then pause. Breathe in deeply, breathe out slowly [pause]. Enjoy that feeling of warmth as you relax and feel calm and rested.

- Now feel any tension in your arms, fore-arms, and hands. Let that tension go and feel it flowing away. Again, breath in deeply . . . and out slowly.

- Feel any tension in your hands, fingers, or arms, and then release the tension in these muscles. Feel the warmth as the tension flows out your body. Breathe in deeply and out slowly.

- Feel the relaxation in your arms and hands. Think of the word calm . . . [pause]. Breathe in deeply . . . breathe out slowly [pause]. Allow yourself to drift into deeper and deeper relaxation and enjoy the feeling of warmth and calm then breathe in deeply . . . breathe out slowly.

- Now focus your attention on your neck and upper back. Feel any tension in the muscles of your neck and upper back. Release the tension in these muscles. Feel the tension flow out of your body. Breathe in deeply . . . breathe out slowly. Feel the warmth and relaxation in these muscles. Feel calm and peaceful . . . [pause]. Breathe in deeply . . . breathe out slowly [pause]. Let yourself relax even deeper . . . and deeper . . . and deeper.

- Remember your facial muscles, your arms and hand muscles, your neck and upper back muscles. Keep that feeling of warmth and relaxation. Breathe in deeply . . . breathe out slowly. Feel the warmth in all these muscles. Feel the relaxation even deeper . . . and deeper.

- Now feel any tension in your lower back and stomach muscles. Focus all your attention on these muscles and get them to relax.

Let yourself relax these muscles fully. Feel the tension flow away. Breathe in deeply . . . breathe out slowly. Feel the relaxation in your lower back and stomach muscles. Relax . . . [pause]. Again breathe in deeply . . . breathe out slowly [pause]. Think of 'calm' and relax even deeper . . . and deeper . . . and deeper.

- Feel any tension in your upper legs, both the front and back. Focus all your attention on these muscles and let them relax. Feel the muscles relax; feel the tension flow away. Breathe in deeply . . . breathe out slowly. Feel the relaxation in your upper legs. Relax . . . [pause]. Breathe in deeply . . . breathe out slowly [pause]. Relax even deeper . . . and deeper . . . and deeper.

- Now feel any tension in your lower legs and your feet. Focus all your attention on these muscles and ask them to relax. Relax these muscles fully. Feel the tension flow away. Breathe in deeply . . . breathe out slowly. Feel the relaxation in your lower legs and feet. Relax . . . [pause]. Breathe in deeply . . . breathe out slowly [pause]. Relax even deeper . . . and deeper . . . and deeper.

- Now relax your entire body. Relax it completely. Feel all the tension flow away from your facial muscles . . . your arms and hands . . . your neck and upper back . . . your lower back and stomach . . . your upper legs . . . and your lower legs and feet. Breathe in deeply . . . breathe out slowly. Feel the relaxation in all your body. Relax . . . [pause]. Breathe in deeply . . . breathe out slowly [pause]. Relax even deeper . . . and deeper . . . and deeper.

Self-directed relaxation is especially effective for those who find it easy to focus their attention on different muscle groups and who are able to turn on and off the tension when directed to do so. However, if this is difficult or the athlete is constantly distracted, he or she may be a better candidate for more active techniques such as progressive relaxation training (tensing then relaxing muscle groups), autogenic training (involving self-hypnosis), or a combination of self-directed relaxation with imagery relaxation (for example, imagining yourself in a very comfortable, favourite environment).

Other techniques for controlling anxiety place an emphasis on how the mind can influence the body (rather than vice versa). These are known as cognitive stress management techniques and include goal-setting and imagery. In imagery, the person imagines himself or herself in a particular situation or activity in the absence of physical practice. It is a technique which utilises all the senses but primarily the visual sense. Many sport psychologists currently recommend the use of imagery for a wide variety of purposes, including skill acquisition, skill maintenance, competition preparation, self-confidence and anxiety control. Practical examples from the sport of golf are provided for the latter two purposes.

Imagery in practice

Imagery to develop self-confidence

Recall as vividly as possible a time when you performed very well on the golf course. Picture how you looked when you were playing well. Notice any differences in how you looked when you played well as opposed to when you play poorly. You walk differently, carrying your head and shoulders differently. When a golfer is confident on the inside, it shows on the outside. Try to get as clear a picture as possible of what you looked like when you were playing well.

Listen in your mind to the sounds you hear when you are playing well, particularly the internal dialogue you have with yourself. There is often an internal silence that accompanies your best performances. Listen to it. What is your internal dialogue like? Recreate all the sounds as vividly as possible.

Now, recreate clearly in your mind all the bodily sensations you have when playing well. How do your feet and hands feel? Do you have a feeling of quickness, looseness, speed or intensity in your body? Often, your clubs have a distinctive feel when playing well. How does your club feel on a drive, a chip, a putt? Focus on the bodily sensations that are associated with playing well. Finally, focus on the feelings you have as you are playing well.

Imagery to control anxiety

Most golfers have problems with tensing up, becoming angry, losing concentration or losing confidence. Picture yourself in a situation that usually brings out one of these emotions. It may be missing an easy putt, or going out of bounds and dropping a shot. Recreate the situation and especially the feelings that accompany that situation. For example, feel the anxiety experienced when putting under pressure at an important stage of the game, but use one of the stress management techniques you have learned. Feel the tension drain out of your body and focus on what you need to do to sink the putt. Again, the focus should be on controlling what you see, hear and feel in your imagery.

Practical investigations of imagery have tended to focus on the role of mental practice in skill acquisition, the role of imagery as a pre-competition cognitive 'psyching-up' strategy and comparisons in the use of imagery by successful and unsuccessful athletes. Findings generally point to the effectiveness of imagery in improving skill acquisition and as an effective psyching-up strategy. Where comparisons have been made between successful and less successful competitors it has been suggested that the former claim to use imagery more than unsuccessful athletes. Psychologists actually working with athletes are currently using techniques based on this work to good effect. At the same time, the research has been criticised for lack of scientific rigour.

SUMMARY

- The concepts of stress, arousal, and anxiety are very closely linked but need to be defined in order to help our understanding.
- Measures of anxiety distinguish between trait anxiety and state anxiety, cognitive and somatic components of the stress response.
- Theoretical approaches to explain anxiety-performance relationships include drive, inverted-U, catastrophe and optimal level theories.
- A range of intervention techniques have been proposed to develop anxiety control.
- Somatic techniques include various relaxation methods and cognitive techniques focus and goal-setting imagery.

Gender

When looking at individual differences other than personality types, gender immediately comes to mind. In discussion of gender and sport, our biological sex (man; woman) has been found to be less important than our gender or psychological sex (male; female) or our sex-role orientation (masculine; feminine). According to recent writers, each of us, men and women alike, have two sides to our personality, the masculine and the feminine. Traditionally, these are measured by sex role inventories, including the Bem Sex Role Inventory or BSRI. Contrary to what many believe, these are not inversely related or opposite but are actually independent dimensions of personality. Hence, men and women can be either masculine (low feminine; high masculine scores), feminine (high feminine; low masculine scores), androgynous (high feminine; high masculine scores) or undifferentiated (low feminine; low masculine scores).

Studies have compared the sex-role orientations of men and women between sports, in and out of sport, or in terms of specific sports-relevant characteristics. They have found that those who succeed in sport tend to have more masculine or androgynous traits, and that feminine traits can be associated with poor motivation in sport and high levels of competitive anxiety.

It remains the case that competitive sport sits most easily alongside the traditional masculine stereotype which is built around attributes such as dominance, assertiveness, aggression and competitiveness itself. Men run towards their stereotype but women may experience sex-role conflict if they feel that their sporting lives contradict what their culture or society dictates is appropriate for their sex or their traditional sex role. For example, in many western societies women have been reluctant to take up field events in athletics, including the shot putt and discus, but in eastern European and Slavic countries this has rarely been a

Figure 7.5 Gender stereotyping in tennis

271

problem. These cultures value the manual work which women carry out, especially in the fields but also in industry. Many of the body traits associated with athletic strength are not seen as being out of step with women's sex-role stereotype.

Stereotypes therefore are not fixed but are culturally and socially determined, and they do change over time. Up until the late 1980s in the United Kingdom it would have been exceptional to see women lifting weights in a gym, or taking part in many sports which were naturally seen as men's sports, for example, marathon running, rugby or even boxing. There have been considerable and rapid changes in patterns of sports activity, and these changes in behaviour have gone hand-in-hand with fundamental shifts in sex-role stereotypes. It is argued that the traditional stereotype of the woman as carer, homemaker and provider is gradually being replaced by the 'superwoman ideal', especially among young women. Now women are given greater freedom to experience multiple roles and make choices about lifestyles. This shift has its positive side but it also has its downside. For example, the increase in eating disorders, including anorexia and bulimia nervosa, has been linked to women's need to strive for the superwoman ideal, to be masculine yet feminine, thin yet curvaceous, nurturant yet independent, instrumental yet expressive. In turn, women's relationship with sport and exercise needs to be looked at afresh, asking basic questions such as why do women in the 1990s choose to exercise, and what benefits do they hope to derive.

When considering sport socialisation during childhood and adolescence, it appears that despite early interest (to the age of 11), girls are less interested in sport as they approach adolescence while in contrast, boys' enthusiasm grows. Again, whether these patterns will change over coming years remains to be seen but this is clearly a fascinating area of research, and one which is likely to become increasingly important as the sport and leisure industry continues to grow.

Attitudes

A final area of individual differences which we need to consider relates to peoples' attitudes toward sport and physical activity. Sport attitude research is criticised because its findings rely mainly on practical research without a firm theoretical base. Despite these criticisms it should be recognised that attitude development and change represent important concepts for anyone hoping to affect change in the individual's patterns of sport and exercise participation.

There is no single definition of attitude but most definitions include reference to them being relatively stable predispositions which influence an individual's response to an 'attitude object' (examples might be people, events, ideas). Furthermore, most definitions highlight the fact that attitudes are learned and organised through experience. In terms of measuring attitudes there are three common types of attitude scale.

The Thurstone scale (1929)

In the 1920s, Louis Thurstone devised a method for constructing an attitude scale. Initially, a large number of statements about an attitude object are produced. A group of judges then rates each statement on an 11-point scale from highly negative to highly positive. The statement is then awarded a 'scale value' which is the mean value of all judges' ratings. A pilot test is then conducted with subjects who score the scale value of each statement agreed with and a mean attitude score can then be calculated.

The Likert scale (1932)

The Likert Scale is one of the most common attitude measures. An equal number of favourable and unfavourable statements are made about the attitude object and the subject is asked to indicate, for each item, whether they: (a) strongly agree (b) agree (c) are undecided (d) disagree (e) strongly disagree.

The semantic differential scale (1957)

The semantic differential scale requires the subject to mark on a scale between bi-polar adjectives, the position which corresponds to their feelings about the attitude object. For example, rate how you feel about jogging for exercise:

    good _____ bad
    valuable _____ worthless
    foolish _____ wise

When the semantic differential scale is subjected to statistical analysis eventually all the bi-polar scales give rise to three factors which account for most of the meaning we give to attitude objects:

    Activity (active/passive)
    Potency (strong/weak)
    Evaluative (good/bad)

The relationship between attitudes and behaviour was originally believed to be important because it was thought that attitudes directed behaviour. Thus, if you hold a positive attitude toward exercise it may be reflected in your behaviour by exercising every day and encouraging your friends to take exercise. If you have a negative attitude toward exercise you may be inclined to avoid many kinds of physical activity and actively discourage others from participating in exercise. Various social psychologists have further examined the attitude – behaviour relationship. They generally agree that the following three factors need to be considered when attempting to predict behaviour:

- Certain attitudes towards specific activities (attitude to running) are better predictors of behaviour (running) than general attitudes (to exercise).

- An assessment of an individual's beliefs about social situational factors (Does anyone else run at lunchtime? What would others think if I did?), in addition to specific attitudes, predicts behavioural intentions (intention to go running or not).

- The best predictor of behaviour (actual running) is an individual's behavioural intention (intention to go running) which in turn is predicted by their belief system (cognitions) and their affective response (emotion).

Taking these factors into consideration means that teachers, coaches and other organisers of sports activities need to explore the individual's attitudes to sport and exercise. They also need to look at the situational factors which will influence their intentions regarding participation and actual behaviour patterns.

The problem most sport and exercise enthusiasts face is how to change attitudes toward sport in order to encourage increased participation in programmes. One of the most influential theories of attitude change is based on the notion of 'cognitive dissonance'. This arises when an individual has cognitions (thoughts, beliefs) and behaviours which contradict each other. Having inconsistent beliefs and/or behaviour causes a state of psychological discomfort which motivates the individual to do something to achieve consistency. Changing attitudes is seen as a key way of resolving cognitive dissonance. For example, if you believe that you should exercise three times a week in order to be healthy, yet you also know that you never exercise more than once a week, then you have cognitive dissonance! A fitness programme instructor might actually try to make clear this dissonance in order to motivate individuals to take the appropriate action to resolve the conflicting notions. There are various tactics people use when faced with cognitive dissonance:

- Changing one belief to make both more consistent. For example, exercising three times a week is only essential if you have spare time.
- Reducing the importance of one of the beliefs. For example, exercising three times a week is only essential if you are not already fit and healthy.
- Adding more consistent cognitions. For example, certain types of exercise are actually damaging to your health/ will cause injuries/ will cause exercise addiction, etc.

It has been suggested that these ways of reducing dissonance show humans not as rational creatures but as rationalising beings. These examples also show that convincing people to change their beliefs or take particular courses of action is not particularly easy as they tend to distort information to maintain their own perceptions. Unfortunately, while the applications from social psychology seem obvious, very little detailed research has ever been conducted into attitude change in sport and exercise.

SUMMARY

- Studies on gender issues have found that those who succeed in sport tend to have more masculine or androgynous traits and that feminine traits are often associated with poor motivation and high anxiety.
- Women may experience sex-role conflict if they feel that their sporting lives contradict what society dictates is appropriate for their sex role.
- Stereotypes are not fixed but are culturally determined and change over time.
- The relationship between attitudes and behaviour is complex and should consider specific attitudes, social-situational factors and individuals' intentions.

Motivation

As well as basic individual and personality differences, sport psychology has long had an interest in the whole area of how we are motivated to take part in sport and what rewards we derive from our experience in sport. Some of this work considers personality types in relation to motivation (specifically, achievement motivation). Other research deals with how we all cope with success and failure (causal attribution). A third branch considers participation motivation, including the factors which influence take-up, continuance and drop-out from sport. These three areas are the focus of this section.

Achievement motivation

Achievement motivation, competitiveness and self-confidence (together with competitive anxiety) form a cluster of very important characteristics which are relevant to our understanding of sport performance. Achievement motivation and competitiveness have been investigated for a number of years, with early research still regarded as important.

In the 1960s Atkinson proposed a model of achievement motivation which is still used today. He regarded the need to achieve (nAch) as being the sum of two independent factors, the motive to achieve success (Ms) and the motive to avoid failure (Maf). These are affected by the probability of success (Ps) and the value attached to success, otherwise known as the incentive value of success (1 - Ps). This relationship is normally represented by the following formula:

$$n\,Ach = (Ms - Maf) \times (Ps \times [1 - Ps])$$

The formula for achievement motivation shows that in order to be motivated to achieve, the motive to achieve success must be higher than the motive to avoid failure. Enough value must be placed on the rewards associated with success and those rewards should be regarded as being attainable. While the formula is difficult to test in practice, the most important probability is that high achievers, those who strive for success and yet do not fear failure, will be drawn towards competition and difficult yet realisable challenges. Low achievers will avoid personal challenges, for example, by only playing weaker opponents or setting unattainable goals where, because failure is a high possibility, it is not particularly threatening.

In terms of applied sport psychology, this model can be a useful way of diagnosing problems, particularly those afflicting young athletes. A simple way to present this model is to talk about a number of basic categories or types of athletes, as shown overleaf.

For young athletes, achievement motivation may be developed if experiences of success and failure are handled correctly. If mastery attempts are rewarding then the positive emotions which are aroused

Need to achieve: How much do you want to win?

Being as truthful with yourself as possible, on a scale from 0 to 10, how would you rate your interest in winning or need for achievement? (0 = no interest; 5 = moderate interest; 10 = crucial) _____ out of 10.

Now in terms of your fear of failure, how would you rate your fear of losing or failing? (0 = fear not important; 5 = moderately important; 10 = crucial) _____ out of 10.

What type are you? Are you:

TYPE wF — Low interest in winning; High fear of failing

Things are often left unfinished or you lose interest in activities. You will avoid genuine competition whenever possible but enjoy playing against someone who you know you can beat easily and impress.

TYPE wf — Low interest in winning; Low fear of failing

You are not really bothered about competition and can not really understand why people get so worked up about winning and losing. After all, it is only a game!

TYPE Wf — High interest in winning; Low fear of failing

You really enjoy competition, especially when you are presented with a real challenge. You are always well motivated and enjoy taking risks. You love to win but don't lose much sleep if you don't always succeed. There's always next time!

TYPE WF — High interest in winning; High fear of failing

You enjoy competitive situations and take personal responsibility for what happens around you. You sometimes find failure hard to take. It raises self-doubt and lowers your confidence. You can sometimes come across as a bad sport and as unwillingness to take risks, perhaps with a superficial air of arrogance. You often feel that you haven't played to your potential.

will encourage future attempts, and a 'success circle' will develop. This idea has developed from the work of Susan Harter on perceived competence, which in turn has close ties with Bandura's theory of self-efficacy. Bandura argues that success breeds success, or more correctly, it breeds self-efficacy and self-confidence, and hence future success. He maintains that an individual's performance will be determined by the level of self-efficacy so that, the higher the level of self-efficacy, the higher the level of performance.

An important message to be taken from this and other related work is that the rewards which are given for performance may have a very significant effect on motivation. Extrinsic rewards (tangible or concrete factors such as trophies, prizes, badges) may actually do more harm than good. Intrinsic motivation is said to be enhanced when the individual feels in control of his or her environment and when he or she feels competent at the task at hand. Intrinsic rewards follow in the form of enhanced self-esteem, competence and self-confidence. Interestingly, external rewards may actually detract from intrinsic motivation by providing an external justification which takes away from personal feelings of pride and competence. This is a very important message for coaches and sport administrators.

Causal attribution

Our interpretation and explanation of success and failure can also be very important in determining our willingness to continue to take part in sport. A group of theories of causal attribution have been developed which consider how we explain or interpret events, and especially success and failure.

Some of the most fundamental questions which arise in sport concern the attributions (the explanations) we associate

Figure 7.6 Extrinsic rewards in sport may actually detract from motivation

with success and failure. One of the more popular ways to classify these attributions is shown below, taken from the work of Bernard Weiner. The four major attribution elements are labelled here as ability, effort, task and luck.

Despite some methodological and theoretical problems with the attribution model, Weiner's basic ideas continue to generate a great deal of interest at both a practical and a research level. For the applied sport psychologist, it is possible to use the model to understand if the athlete is favouring particular attributional styles, and what effect this may have upon motivation. For example, the athlete could be helped to greater psychological satisfaction from success. This could be achieved by explaining success and achievements with reference to stable, internal factors. For example, 'You did it because your backhand is so improved.' Failures can also be redefined in ways which may be less damaging or which will at least present optimistic ways forward. For example, this is making use of the internal, unstable dimension of attribution. 'In future we should work on your serve to make it more reliable.'

Figure 7.7   Weiner's Attribution model

The two dimensions which combine to make up these four cells are stability (stable/unstable) and locus of control (internal/external). Explanations or attributions then fall into one of the four cells. For example, effort would be classified as an unstable, internal factor. More recently, Weiner has added a third dimension, controllability, but it is the two-dimensional model which is still most popular.

		Locus of control	
		Internal	**External**
Stability	Stable	**Ability** "My backhand was just too good for her"	**Task** "It was a very high standard tournament"
	Unstable	**Effort** "My serve needs practice to improve"	**Context** "It was too windy for me to play my shots well"

Probably the single-most popular attribution topic to be empirically investigated is known as the **self-serving attributional bias**. It seems that we are all naturally inclined to attribute success to internal causes, and to blame failure on external factors. Research has shown that successful performance in sport is more likely to be attributed to stable, internal factors (such as ability) especially in sports involving larger teams and where the attributions relate to team performance. At the same time however, there is little evidence to suggest that failure is always attributed to external factors (task difficulty or luck). While there is some inconsistency in the literature, it would appear that we may often subconsciously make internal attributions and thus reward ourselves for success. This is especially true of younger athletes who are better able to protect their egos from the psychological consequences of failure.

A related body of research has examined a phenomenon known as **learned helplessness**. This has been defined as a psychological state in which individuals feel that events are out of their control.

A common factor among learned helpless individuals is their tendency to attribute failure to internal stable causes such as lack of ability rather than unstable factors such as lack of effort. By repeatedly making such inappropriate attributions these individuals come to see subsequent failure as the most realistic expectation for the future. Coaches and teachers could play a very important role in encouraging learned helpless individuals to make appropriate attributions. This would enable children to recognise that failure is not inevitable, if the cause is not stable. Such attribution retraining can also assist in the development of self-confidence by emphasising the importance of taking credit for success.

A final body of research has considered the differences in attributions between actors or participants and observers. It is found that participants tend to attribute their own behaviour to external causes whilst observers tend to attribute others' behaviour to internal factors, also known as the **fundamental attribution error**. The next time you are listening to a post match or competition discussion involving players, coaches, managers and commentators, bear this fundamental attribution error in mind!

Participation motivation

The work on attribution and achievement motivation focuses on the behaviour of people who are already involved in sport. Another branch of sport psychology deals with the factors which encourage people to take up sport in the first place and then make them either continue or drop out. Over recent years there has been a massive growth of interest in this field. This work has demonstrated the significance of personal expectancies and values in determining sport participation. According to recent authors, three principal clusters of factors can be identified. These are:

- Personal attributes (including expectancies, values and attitudes)
- Significant others (family, peers, siblings, teachers, coaches and role models)
- Socialisation situations (or opportunity sets).

Of the three clusters, the effects of significant others have received the most attention and here the influence of social learning theories becomes immediately obvious. Social learning theories focus attention on children's capacity for learning by observing others and imitating their behaviour. This process is evident when examining the influence of significant others on children's sport involvement. It has been shown that the family, and especially the father, has a considerable effect on whether or not a child becomes involved in sport. If a child is used to seeing his or her parents involved in sport then it is more likely that the child will see involvement as natural. At the same time, other influential factors contributing to this socialisation process will include the role of teachers and coaches, together with the influence from siblings or peers. The influence of socio-economic status on the opportunities for involvement in more expensive sports is also significant.

It appears that an individual's motivation to take up sport will be influenced by the reinforcement which is offered, the rewards (both intrinsic and extrinsic) which build up and the feedback which is received.

Gender must also play an important part in the sport socialisation process. Numerous studies point to the different ways parents treat sons and daughters. When a small boy hurts himself playing football he is told 'big boys don't cry' but when a young girl goes out to play with her friends she is told not to get dirty. It is statements like these which quite unintentionally influence children's perception of what are appropriate gender roles and hence, sporting roles. Often it is the boys who are given greater encouragement and more opportunities to become involved in a wider range of competitive sports.

Two popular reasons which young children give for becoming involved in sport in the first place are 'fun' and 'improving skill' but not competition, or health and fitness. These move higher up the list as we grow older, but at the same time, the drop-out rate from children's organised sports programmes remains worryingly high. In the USA, it is maintained that drop-out is the most serious problem facing contemporary children's sport. An estimated 80% drop-out rate between the ages of 12 and 17 years across all sports is found. Statistics from elsewhere confirm this depressing picture worldwide.

To understand why children drop out, Daniel Gould has proposed a motivational model applicable to youth sport. He found that when children were asked why they became involved in sport, the reasons centred on improving skills, having fun, being with friends, enjoying the excitement, experiencing success and developing physical fitness. More significantly though, those who had ceased involvement in sport gave motives such as conflicts of interest, lack of playing time, lack of success or skill improvement, competitive stress, lack of fun, dislike of the coach, boredom, and injury. Gould then developed a motivational model of youth sport withdrawal, a model which has three main components.

- **Sport withdrawal** deals with the way in which children withdraw from a sport. Often they do not stop participating in all sport but instead withdraw from a specific sport. So, for example, 80% of swimming drop-outs in the USA re-entered or planned to re-enter sport at a later date. In contrast, other work has found that 59% of American school sport dropouts did not subsequently re-enter any organised spot. Hence drop-out may be sport specific and will range from complete withdrawal from organised sport to cessation of one particular sport.

- The young athlete engages in a **costs-benefits analysis** (based on a theory known as social exchange theory). Individuals weigh up the perceived benefits or costs by comparing outcome (in terms of reward or cost) against two standards. The first standard is known as the comparison level (CL) and can best be described as the person's expectations about a given activity. Satisfaction or

attraction to an activity is determined by comparing outcomes with CL. The second comparison is known as comparison level for alternatives (CLalt), and is the lowest level of an outcome that a person uses to judge something as being attractive or otherwise. Motivation to continue an activity or sport is predictable by CLalt as it represents the individual's best alternative to the current activity. Gould suggests that an individual will withdraw from sport if the perceived costs of involvement outweigh the perceived benefits and if the alternative activities (for example, other sport, schoolwork or discos) are seen as more attractive.

Figure 7.8 *Parents often put too much pressure on children who participate in sport*

- Motivation for withdrawal considers the explanations which are given as well as theoretical frameworks for understanding these explanations. These include the argument that withdrawal from activity is based on a number of factors. The factors are the individual's achievement goals and their perceived chances of success, the suggestion that an individual's perception of competence will affect their decision to withdraw or participate, and the idea that burnout (and drop-out) occurs when competitive stress is not handled correctly and becomes too much.

According to the model, it is necessary to establish the individual's achievement orientation in order to predict both sport involvement or subsequent withdrawal. Applying the model, it becomes important for those involved with youth sport to recognise individual differences in motivational patterns, their level of perceived competence, their level of trait anxiety and their ability to cope with stress. Once this is achieved it is proposed that coaches should be responsible for structuring the environment so that motives are fulfilled and confidence remains high, the costs and benefits should be openly discussed and the reasons for departing discussed.

One commonly-held belief is that involvement in sport is good for building character, but the research evidence here is not strong. This is not to say that no good comes of involvement in sport; it merely points out that not all sport is always good. Four main points emerge here:

- Parent-child relationships can be affected either positively or negatively through involvement in sport; what may have started as initial enthusiasm and encouragement from a parent may later be interpreted as pressure by a child if that child perceives that

Practical goal setting: SCAMP

S Specific

Do not set vague goals such as 'improve performance'. Specify exactly how much you want to improve and how you can measure it. Predict the extent of your improvement and you will work hard to achieve it.

C Challenging / Controllable

Set performance goals at a level slightly ahead of your current ability; this means that goals are within the realms of possibility but also provide challenges. Keep goals within personal control rather than depending on performance of others.

A Attainable

Do not burden yourself with an impossible goal. All goals should relate to where you are now and you should aim to improve yourself step by step. Do not be afraid to reassess goals if they prove unrealistic.

M Measurable / Multiple

Sense of achievement is greatest and motivation enhanced most when progress can actually be seen. Goals are best expressed in a form which can be measured objectively, such as seconds off time. Failing that, measure performance or characteristic on a subjective rating scale of 1 to 10, for example, rate ability to cope under pressure on a scale of 1 to 10. Multiple goals increase probability of achievement.

P Personal

The goals you set (in conjunction with your coach) must relate to you as an individual. Decide what you want to achieve; do not borrow other people's goals. This will enhance your commitment to these objectives.

the parent is spending a lot of money and time on the his or her involvement in sport.

- There is some evidence to suggest that involvement in organised formal sports programmes may interfere with and undermine children's abilities to create, develop and organise their own play and games.
- There is concern that children involved in organised formal sport may become obsessed with winning and playing well, rather than with being fair and having fun.
- The influence of the coach on children's sport experiences is considerable. Coaches can become significant role models for young athletes, particularly if the children are lacking family role models who are involved with sport.

It is pleasing to end on a positive note here, for research suggests that most coaches have a positive rather than a negative influence on children's involvement in sport.

Setting goals

One technique which is used widely within sport to enhance motivation and self-confidence is goal setting, a technique pioneered by Edwin Locke, not in sport but industrial psychology. According to Locke, goals affect performance in four ways.

- Goal setting focuses attention.
- Goals mobilise effort in proportion to the demands of the task.
- Goals enhance persistence.
- Goals encourage the individual to develop strategies for achieving their goals

Furthermore, Locke and his co-workers claim that a number of features relate to these performance effects.

- More difficult goals lead to a higher level of performance than easy goals.
- Specific goals are more effective than general subjective goals or no goals.
- To be effective, goals must be accepted by the performer.
- Goals will not be effective in the absence of feedback.

Goal setting has been embraced enthusiastically by applied sport psychologists who often employ it as an integral part of psychological skills training programmes. One practical example is the widespread use of the acronym SCAMP as a way of teaching athletes simple goal setting procedures.

Working from the SCAMP principles, it is relatively easy to come up with programmes to deal with a wide range of sports related skills. One example, in this case a soccer goalkeeper, is shown below as a practical way of introducing the principles of goal setting to other athletes.

A practical example: goal setting for goalies

A goalkeeper wishes to improve his dead ball clearance accuracy. The biggest obstacle to achieving this is recognised as simple practice of the skill. He has decided that he is committed to increasing the accuracy of his clearances and will devote the time which is necessary to achieve this. At present, he works out that he is able to hit a ball from thirty-five metres into a six metre circle three times out of ten (his baseline). He then sets himself a realistic goal of hitting the target seven times out of ten by the start of the season. How does he achieve this?

He works out a training programme which involves going out to a field three times a week, marking a circle and hitting thirty shots each from thirty-five metres. He records his success rate on each occasion and charts improvement over time. In the light of this continual feedback he is able to check whether he is on line for achieving his goal and can adjust his practice over the weeks if necessary.

Unfortunately, while goal setting is now widely used and supported, unless used carefully it may be demotivating, for example, when goals are too high or too distant. In addition, too ambitious goals may be positively dangerous for athletes who are already experiencing stress or low self-esteem, or are not genuinely committed to the task. Considerable assumptions about the athlete's or coach's ability to analyse current performance and predict future performance are also made. These assumptions should not be taken for granted especially when dealing with young athletes or those who have enjoyed fewer educational opportunities. So, goal setting may increase intrinsic motivation but not always. It should be used with care.

SUMMARY

- Theories of motivation deal with the impact of personality types on motivation, how our experience of success and failure affects subsequent motivation and which factors influence selection of sport, adherence in and drop-out from sport.
- Achievement motivation may be developed if experiences of success and failure are handled correctly.
- It seems that we are all naturally inclined to attribute success to internal causes and to blame failure on external factors (self-serving bias).
- Participation in sport is largely determined by a variety of influences, including the significance of personal attributes, significant others and socialisation situations.
- Goal setting, a cognitive intervention technique pioneered in industrial psychology, is frequently used as a method of enhancing motivation and self-confidence.

Social influence

When people participate in sport, they are almost always taking part in a social event; there are other people physically present or their presence is felt. Because this is the case, sport psychology has spent some time dealing with social influence, the effect of real, implied or imagined others on our behaviour, whether these be fellow athletes, the opposition or spectators.

Social facilitation

As early as 1898, an American psychologist and amateur cyclist called Norman Triplett carried out research using cycling records to compare the times of cyclists training alone, with others and in competition. He found that those in company consistently rode faster and those in competition had the fastest times of all. This work then launched a programme of experimental research which gave rise to the term 'social facilitation'.

Social facilitation means that the presence of others will lead to enhanced performance on certain tasks, and most specifically tasks which involve well-learnt, dominant responses. So, if you can do something well, the presence of others will improve performance. On the other hand, if you are incompetent, learning a skill or attempting something for the first time, then you may perform worse in company than alone.

Traditionally, one theory has been used to explain these findings, a theory built on research with both humans, animals and even insects such as cockroaches and ants. Zajonc's (pronounced Zionk) Drive Theory of social facilitation argues that the mere presence of others increases arousal which in turn causes social facilitation (but only with dominant, well-learnt responses) or social inhibition (with non-dominant or new responses). According to later writers, the reason why this happens may be due to distraction. When others are present, we are torn between concentrating on the task and concentrating on the other people. This creates a conflict which increases arousal, which in turn leads to social facilitation, as shown in the model in figure 7.10.

More recently it has become apparent that it may not be presence alone but the type of presence which is significant. More specifically, social facilitation effects increase in proportion to the extent that we feel we are being evaluated by those around us, whether these are spectators or fellow competitors. Even accomplished performers may crack when playing in front of a crowd which they know has high expectations or is highly evaluative. It is now accepted that evaluation apprehension plays a central role in explaining social facilitation. In turn, this apprehension has been linked to heightened self-awareness, self-consciousness, self-presentational concern, self-monitoring or self-attention.

Figure 7.9 The Tour de France

Research

In 1982, Michaels and his co-workers set up a field experiment in an American pool hall. Players were secretly rated as being of above or below average ability, on the basis of the percentage of shots which went into the pocket. Subsequently, groups of four people were paid to casually stand by the tables to see how their presence influenced performance. In the presence of spectators, players of above average ability increased their shot accuracy from 71% to 80%; the below average players slipped from 36% to 25%.

Figure 7.10 Baron's model of distraction-conflict theory

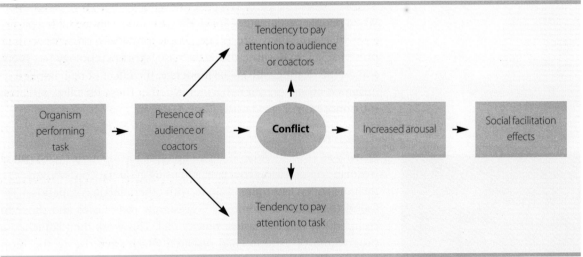

Social loafing

Social facilitation means that performance improves in the presence of others. Another example of social influence which has interested psychologists has a less positive effect. This is known as social loafing. In 1913, a French agricultural engineer called Max Ringelmann discovered that, on average, one man pulling on a rope attached to a strain gauge was likely to pull twice as hard (on average, 63 kg) as when his efforts were combined as part of a team of eight (31 kg). Later experiments confirmed this finding, using tasks (for example, hand clapping) where subjects worked alone but in the presence of others (hence avoiding possible coordination losses) and were not aware that individual contributions were being monitored. The term social loafing then came into play.

The Ringelmann effect or social loafing is defined as the reduction of individual effort when working as part of a group or team. As with social facilitation, it has been shown that many factors affect the extent of social loafing. These include:

- the size of the group
- the identifiability of individual effort
- the strength of group identity
- the nature and attractiveness of the task
- the degree of trust between group members
- the interdependence of group members
- the extent of involvement with the group
- group cohesiveness
- intergroup comparisons
- personal responsibility.

Various theories have been offered to try to explain why social loafing occurs. Some explain social facilitation and social loafing as being related aspects of social behaviour. Other explanations focus on what happens when we place people in situations where they know their efforts are not easy to identify and where they are not being personally evaluated. In a group we feel able to share responsibility with other group members and this may well lead to less effort. Other researchers have emphasised the strategies which people will use to 'get by' in groups. It is assumed that we are motivated to exert the minimum effort for the maximum reward, otherwise referred to as the allocation strategy. Yet others place greater emphasis on group cohesiveness, arguing that the more closely we identify with the group, the less likely we are to loaf. Which explanation is right remains to be decided, but it is probably true that each in their own way helps us to understand something about the phenomenon.

Home and away

One practical example of the effect of social influence in sport is how home advantage influences performance. We would all probably believe that playing at home brings an immediate advantage, but this is not always true. To test this hypothesis, Schwartz and Brasky collated and catalogued the results of thousands of professional games in the USA. They found home advantage did exist in the major professional American sports of baseball (53% home wins), ice hockey (64%), American football (60%) and basketball (64%). This effect does appear to depend on a number of factors, including the type of sport. For example, it was found that professional English soccer players from a particular club were increasingly likely to be either booked or sent off the further from their home town they played. Also, American professional basketball players displayed functionally aggressive behaviour (within the law) at home, whereas away players were more likely to exhibit dysfunctionally-aggressive behaviour, that is, they accumulated more recorded fouls.

While home advantage may be important in early rounds of competitions, other research has shown that the further into the tournament the team progresses, the less significant venue becomes. When defending champions are playing at home, in front of fans with high expectations, then there is actually more chance of a team cracking under the pressure and losing.

SUMMARY

- Social facilitation means that the presence of others will lead to enhanced performance on well-learned tasks. If you are incompetent or learning a skill you will perform worse in company than alone.
- Social loafing leads to a reduction of individual effort when working as part of a group or team and many factors have been shown to affect the extent of social loafing.
- Teams are more likely to win at home but not always in pressure games when the home supporters have high expectations.

Group processes

Within psychology, group processes or dynamics is another major area of research. Given the significance of the team in sport, it is little wonder that attention has turned to an understanding of team dynamics, and in particular, team cohesion, team maturity and leadership.

Membership continuity and team development

The age of a team and how long it has played together, will also be significant, as teams take time to develop and mature. Stage models of group development, such as Tuckman's, describe group development in terms of key stages.

- The **forming stage**: A group gets together and an air of formality is common.
- The **storming stage**: There may be heightened tension associated with role differentiation and competition for status and influence.
- The **norming stage**: Norms, rules and standards of behaviour begin to stabilise.
- The **performing stage**: The group will have matured to a point where it is able to work together as a unit.

Clearly these stages take time, and when new players are introduced, the team has to readjust, investing yet more time.

Research using data derived from sports such as soccer, baseball, basketball and gymnastics demonstrates that maturity is important. Player turnover rates and performance are negatively related. There are also large differences between sports in terms of the time taken to reach maturity and then the period for which good teams stay at the top. The effective life of successful teams is likely to depend on many factors including the age of players, the type of sport and various facets of group dynamics including cohesiveness and role differentiation.

Team cohesion and team spirit

Research has repeatedly shown that what makes an effective team is far removed from what 'common sense' tells us should be the case. We are conditioned to respect group decisions, to assume that two heads will be better than one, and that within sport, the team which mixes socially together will be the team which plays and wins together. A commonly-held belief amongst coaches and players alike is that a tight, cohesive sports team will be a successful team. As a consequence of these and similar influences, many practising sport psychologist still believe that their primary task remains to engender good team spirit. In reality, the answer is not so simple, and there is a good deal of research which has begun to help us unravel the complexities of the relationship between team cohesion and performance. This research reveals a number of significant points, namely that:

- many factors interact to determine group cohesion.
- cohesion does not always predict team success; more often success predicts cohesion.
- the concept of cohesion is not easily analysed.
- measurement of cohesion presents major difficulties.

Team cohesion depends on numerous factors including group size, propinquity (physical proximity) between members, the costs incurred in joining the group, leadership styles, team maturity, competition, success and similarity. Some argue that similarity encourages cohesiveness, while others maintain that it inhibits healthy group development. As yet, the issue has to be satisfactorily resolved.

The Canadian sport psychologist Albert Carron has made the important distinction between task cohesion (or group integration) which refers to how well the group or team operates as a working unit, and social cohesion (or individual attraction) which refers to how well members like each other and the extent of team identity. Most research has considered the relationship between these types of cohesion and performance.

Research shows that successful performance does depend on task cohesion but that social cohesion is far less important. Overall, the relationship between cohesion and performance hinges on the type of sport being considered. On the one hand, studies of team sports, including basketball, American football, soccer, volleyball and baseball, have concluded that the success of teams can depend more on cohesion than the level of skill of individual members. However, other research has shown that conflict and rivalry within a team can be a spur to success, or can drive individual team members to great things. One example of this was the West German rowing eight in the 1960s, who were on the point of breaking up because of internal disputes and yet went on to win the Olympic gold in 1968. Formula One motor racing is littered with stories of team conflicts and rivalries but these rarely have an effect on results, unless rivalry spills on to the track itself.

The relationship between cohesion and performance, and the direction of causality remains uncertain. Does cohesion engender success or does success engender cohesion? A recent meta-analysis (a statistical review of existing studies) by Mullen and Cooper (1993) concluded that a cohesion–effectiveness relationship probably does exist. However, the effect derives most significantly from task commitment or cohesion, and not from social or interpersonal cohesion. Also, according to the researchers, the stronger direction of effect seems to be from performance to cohesiveness, and not from cohesiveness to performance. This is not to argue that cohesion cannot influence performance, but that the performance to cohesion link is the stronger.

Figure 7.11 Pulling together: task cohesion at work

The type of sport which is being played is highly significant. It is important to know how to distinguish between sports. The more that the sport requires team members to rely on each other and are interdependent (interactive sports), the more significant cohesion is likely to be. In sports where athletes may represent the same team but individual performance does not depend on team work (coacting sports), the research shows team cohesion is less important in determining outcome. Unfortunately the picture is yet more cloudy because some sports are both highly interactive and coactive (for example, rowing, tug-of-war). Others are highly interactive but do not involve coaction (for example, volleyball). Others may be low on both dimensions (for example, fell running, chess) and yet others may be coactive but not interactive (for example, archery, bowls). As a general conclusion, the more that players are interdependent on each other, and the team's performance depends on coordinated action, then the more important cohesion will be.

Other research has shown that cohesion may actually have an adverse impact on performance. Work on conformity in small groups shows that the tighter or more cohesive the group, the less likely it is that people will be able to express their individuality. In team sports, one effect may be that players will all perform to the same standard and thus minimise competition within the group. On the one hand, this may encourage high levels of cooperation among players, a strong identification with the team, and heightened competition with other teams. On the other hand, this cohesion may mean that players stick together so closely that the atmosphere becomes too comfortable, for example, no-one competes in training. In this case, team spirit or cohesion will not help performance, and conflict may actually have to be introduced by the coach or captain to motivate players.

Leadership

Leading groups or teams in sport is not fundamentally different from leading groups in other contexts. It is not surprising therefore that many of the models which are used elsewhere reappear in sport psychology. The question which often recurs is 'What makes a good leader, a good captain or a good coach?' To answer this question is simply to measure what good leaders in sport actually do. Sport-specific leadership scales have been developed, including the Coach Behaviour Description Questionnaire (CBDQ) and the Leadership Scale for Sports (LSS). The CBDQ is a 20-item scale which includes eight categories, which deal with competitive training, initiation, interpersonal team operations, social behaviour, representation behaviour, organised communication, recognition and general excitement.

The LSS is a 40-item scale, made up of five sub-scales namely, training and instruction, autocratic behaviour, democratic behaviour, social support and positive feedback. The LSS can be administered in one of two forms. The first considers the way in which the athlete perceives his or her coach ('My coach . . .'), the second deals with the athlete's preferred behaviour ('I prefer my coach to . . .'). Differences between scores derived from both question types (known as the discrepancy score) indicate the mismatch between experience and preference, and then relate this to satisfaction. On several occasions, levels of satisfaction with the coach have been found to correlate negatively with discrepancy scores, and particularly those from two sub-scales, positive feedback and training and instruction. The coaches who were regarded least highly were those who did not provide feedback and who did not offer specific technical advice. Also, this research has shown that men prefer autocratic coaching styles whereas women prefer democratic and participative styles.

A further scale, the Coaching Behaviour Assessment System (CBAS) has also been developed to consider the behaviour of coaches and to categorise that behaviour. This scale has now been incorporated as part of a sport-specific, interactional model of leadership behaviour known as the mediational model. This model considers the relationship between the coach, the player and the situation in determining appropriate coaching behaviour. Using this model it has been found that children with low self-esteem most needed coaches who valued their contribution and provided positive feedback for successful work.

Contingency models of leadership

It is important to know why certain leadership styles work while others do not. Overall, leadership research has long since abandoned the search for a unique leadership formula, that is, the set of traits or characteristics which define leaders sometimes known as the Great Man approach. The trait approach has been replaced with a number of contingency models which consider the match between style and circumstance when considering leadership effectiveness. Four of these models are presented here.

Fiedler's contingency theory

Fiedler's contingency theory, developed for business managers, argues that different individuals will be more or less effective as leaders in different situations. First, individuals are categorised by their score on the Least Preferred Co-worker scale (or LPC). This scale measures what the individual thinks of the person he or she least liked working with. Low LPC people have a low opinion of their least preferred co-worker; high LPC people have a high opinion of them. Situations in which the person must lead are then categorised in relation to three factors (task structure, leader-member relations and position power of the leader). These are factors which define the degree of control which the leader has in a given situation.

In situations of either high control (clear task structure, good leader-member relations, strong position power) or low control (unclear task structure, poor leader-member relations, weak position power), low LPC people have been found to be most effective as leaders. However, in situations where there is a medium degree of control, high LPC people are more effective as leaders.

Of all the criticisms levelled against Fiedler's work, the most important is that our LPC score is seen as permanent, almost as if it is a personality trait, and therefore we cannot change to meet changing needs. According to Fiedler, we are what we are, either low, moderate or high LPC people. Hence when leading, we are best advised to change situations to suit who we are, rather than trying to change our leadership style.

Three alternative contingency approaches have had a far more significant impact in sport psychology. This is probably because the message they give is more optimistic, namely that the responsibility is on the coach or captain to try to change or adapt his or her style to changing circumstances.

Vroom and Yetton's normative theory

According to Vroom and Yetton's normative theory, one of the primary leadership functions is decision-making. When making decisions, a leader or manager must weigh up two considerations – the quality of the decision and the acceptance of the decision by the rest of the group. On some occasions decision quality is important irrespective of its acceptance by the group; on other occasions acceptance is of most concern. Depending on which is true, then the coach should use one of three decision-making styles, these styles being either autocratic, delegative or participative. Autocratic implies that the decision is reached by the coach with little consultation, delegative assumes that the coach delegates responsibility to others, and a participative style is one where the team or group as a whole makes the decision.

Hershey and Blanchard's situational leadership theory

Hershey and Blanchard's situational leadership theory focuses attention on the characteristics of followers and, most especially, on their level of maturity. When subordinates are inexperienced, the leader must be directive. As they become more experienced then the leader must show more concern for emotional support When they are fully mature, the leader ought to learn how to back off, giving space for personal growth by being neither directive nor over concerned about offering social support. The overriding message for sport which the theory conveys is that coaches and captains must remain responsive to the changing needs of their athletes. For example, young, immature athletes need considerable social support early in their careers but this need decreases as time goes by. In contrast, early in a sporting career too much emphasis on skills training may be demotivating. The time for this technical advice is in mid-career, before once more backing off as the mature athlete learns to become self-sufficient.

Path-goal theory

A final contingency model which appears in sport psychology is known as the path-goal theory. This theory deals with how leaders can influence motivation and perceptions by using one of a number of leadership styles. These are directive, supportive, achievement-oriented or participative. The style is chosen which best reflects environmental demands. Environmental demands include the task, the organisational structure and interpersonal relationships. The characteristics of followers are also thought to be important here, including their ability, locus of control and authoritarianism score. The leader is expected to maximise effort by showing how rewards can be reached, by clearing obstacles in the path and by providing positive feedback for work well done.

From the wide range of available contingency models on offer, the common conclusion to emerge is that in sport, as elsewhere, there is simply no magic formula for predicting who will be a successful leader. There is also no single leadership, management or coaching style which will ever be successful across a range of situations. Instead, the best advice which can be offered is that sports coaches, managers or captains must develop the ability to assess changing situations. They must then employ a leadership style which is appropriate to the needs of their followers and the demands of the situation.

Chelladurai's multi-dimensional model of leadership

While these approaches developed outside of sport, researchers have sought to develop sport-specific theories and models of leadership which are able to accommodate ideas and concepts from a great many sources. One of these is Chelladurai's multi-dimensional model of leadership, and is shown in figure 7.12.

The effectiveness of the leader is determined by two principal outcomes: how well athlete's perform, and how satisfied they are with the process. The three interacting aspects of the leader's behaviour which can produce these outcomes are:

- the behaviour which is required of a leader in these circumstances
- the actual behaviour displayed by the leader
- the behaviour which is preferred by the athletes themselves.

In turn, each of these are influenced by other factors. The behaviour required of the coach in any situation will depend on the sport itself, the goals of the organisation and indeed the whole environment within which the sport exists. The leader's behaviour will depend on ability, knowledge and interpersonal skills, while his or her preferred behaviour reflects both characteristics of the members and the situation.

Antecedents   Leader behaviour   Consequences

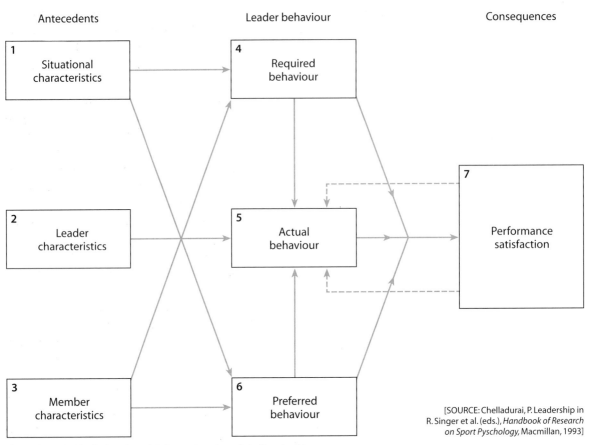

Figure 7.12   Chelladurai's multi-dimensional model of leadership

[SOURCE: Chelladurai, P. Leadership in R. Singer et al. (eds.), *Handbook of Research on Sport Pyschology*, Macmillan, 1993]

SUMMARY

- Groups develop over four stages: forming, storming, norming and performing.
- Many factors determine group cohesion.
- Cohesion does not always predict team success, more often success predicts cohesion.
- A number of models of leadership have been applied to sport, including Fiedler's contingency model, Vroom and Yetton's normative theory and Hersey and Blanchard's situational theory.
- Chelladurai's multi-dimensional model of leadership is a sport-specific model which emphasises the interaction of antecedents and consequences on leader behaviours.

Violence and aggression in sport

While many people have written about and speculated on violence in sport, there has been relatively little systematic research on aggression in sport and exercise settings. One problem which may explain this concerns definition, that is, how we define 'aggression'. Most people would agree that it is difficult to arrive at a satisfactory definition of aggression. For example, aggression can be a personality trait, a learned habit, or a biological process. Most psychological definitions agree however that aggression includes both intention (motivation to harm, whether physically, mentally or emotionally) and outcome (behaviour rather than emotion or cognition). A widely accepted definition would be that *aggression is the intention to hurt someone who is motivated to avoid such treatment.*

In sport this has normally meant concentrating attention on behaviours which deliberately and illegally cause physical injury to another person. The psycho-biologist Moyer (1976) originally made a distinction between two forms of aggression – instrumental or rule-governed aggression, and reactive or hostile aggression. The former is essential in competitive sport, but it is the latter, reactive aggression, which normally forms the focus of attention.

A number of theories are still in competition as to why we are aggressive. According to the social learning approach, we learn our aggressiveness by imitating others, and particularly from significant others in our lives. A famous experiment to support this theory was carried out by Albert Bandura using a group of children who watched adults playing with toys before they were allowed to play themselves. In one condition the adults played quietly with the toys, including a large inflatable bobo doll. In another condition, the adults played aggressively with the toys, punching and kicking the bobo doll around the room in the process. When the children played, those who had watched the aggressive adults likewise behaved aggressively. Those who had watched the more restrained adults imitated their behaviour.

According to Dollard and Miller's drive theory, aggression is nothing more than a consequence of frustration. The more we are prevented from reaching attractive goals, the more physiologically aroused we become and the more likely we are to act aggressively, essentially to clear the path to those goals.

Other psychologists present more psychobiological explanations. For example, Freudians argue that humans are naturally aggressive. They state that unless we have socially acceptable ways for venting our aggression (as in sport), then this aggression will show itself in other ways which may be more dangerous. Sport therefore represents a cultivation or refinement of the aggressive and destructive instincts. It acts as a form of catharsis, that is, a safety valve for satisfying that instinct.

The majority of researchers appear to loosely adopt either the frustration–aggression hypothesis or a social learning perspective. Psychoanalysis, with its emphasis on instinctive drives, is presented as a counterpoint. While the idea of catharsis may be appealing as common sense, there is little evidence to support the idea that playing sport makes us less aggressive, either in the short or the long term. Instead, those who play competitive sport are also likely to be competitive and aggressive in other fields, including work.

Working from a social learning or drive perspective, a great many variables have been shown to be associated with an increase in reactive aggression amongst competitors. These include whether a

Figure 7.13 Violence on the terraces

team or competitor is losing, playing away from home, the distance from home, the type of sport, current values and norms in that particular sport, and the importance of the game to the individual. Most research has focused on contact sports which already have some association with violence. High on this list are ice hockey and soccer, and the most common dependent variable which is measured is the number of fouls or rule infringements.

A further area of research on aggression in sport looks at spectators or fans and the factors which influence violence on the terraces. Rather than showing that hooliganism and fan violence is a recent phenomenon, sport sociologists and psychologists have shown a long history of spectator violence in Europe and in Britain, in relation to soccer. However, North America has not been immune from what is known as 'the British disease'. North America's sports crowd disorders have in fact been downplayed. For example, a study by White (1989) considered the incidence of murders in American cities which had American football teams through to the National Football League playoff games. He found that in those cities where the team lost a play-off, there was a subsequent increase in reported murders in the subsequent six days but the crime rate remained unchanged if the team was successful.

Other spectator research has been generated in response to particular events, or even major disasters. Examples include the work associated with the 1986 Popplewell Inquiry into Crowd Safety and Control at Sports Grounds in the UK. This inquiry was set up following the tragic events in early 1985, including the West Stand fire at Bradford City Football Club and the Heysel stadium disaster in Brussels which led to 39 fatalities and which was a direct result of fan violence. In their book *Football in its place*, Canter, Comber and Uzzell (1989) refer to 'environmental psychology' in order to explore many themes which they regard as relevant to the Popplewell Inquiry. These include stadia design, spectators' attitudes and experiences, soccer club cultures, crowd and emergency behaviour and violence in sport. This sort of research has been very influential in determining how sports such as soccer have reacted to the lessons of Bradford and Heysel, including the introduction of all-seater stadia and the removal or adaptation of fences. However, it still remains to be seen whether these measures will have a major impact on the problems associated with the soccer culture over the coming years.

To understand fan violence it is necessary to incorporate many factors into discussion. Recently, Simons and Taylor (1992) developed a model which considers:

- factors which predetermine violence, including socio-economic conditions, politics and geography, media influences and community norms.

- critical factors such as social and personal identification with certain teams, group solidarity, de-individuation, dehumanisation of the opposition and leadership.
- events on the field which may spark trouble, including the type of sport, modeling, the score and competitive events.
- contributory factors off the field including alcohol, crowd density, frustration and role modelling.

It is only when a special set of these factors come together that the spark of violence ignites. It is important to consider all these dimensions in combination and not in isolation, as research did in the past.

SUMMARY

- An accepted definition of aggression is that aggression is the intention to hurt someone who is motivated to avoid such treatment.
- Theories of aggression include drive theory, the frustration-aggression hypothesis and social learning views.
- It is often suggested that sport can act as a catharsis or safety valve for releasing aggression but there is very little evidence to support this view.
- Crowd violence can only be understood by taking a very broad perspective which examines socio-economic conditions, politics and geography, media influences and community norms.

Questions

1 Name and describe two different personality inventories. Is it possible to predict athletic success based on personality testing?
2 Discuss the terms arousal, anxiety and stress and say how the concepts are similar or dissimilar.
3 Outline the difference between state anxiety and trait anxiety. Describe the measurement techniques appropriate to each.
4 What is achievement motivation? Outline the McClelland-Atkinson model and explain its predictions for sporting situations.
5 What is causal attribution? Outline the types of attributions people give for situations in which the outcome is consistent with previous performance? Inconsistent?
6 Does viewing acts of aggression in sport result in catharsis or learned aggression? Expand and explain.
7 What is social facilitation and what is its main effect on sporting performance of beginners? Of skilled performers?
8 Outline and discuss Chelladurai's (1978) multi-dimensional model of leadership.

References

Cox R H *Sport Psychology: Concepts and Applications* C. Brown (1993)

Horn T S (ed.) *Advances in Sport Psychology* Human Kinetics (1992)

Kremer J, Scully D *Psychology in Sport* Taylor and Francis (1994)

Singer R N, Murphey M, Tennant L K (eds.) *Handbook of Research on Sport Psychology* Macmillan (1993)

Willis J D, Campbell L F *Exercise Psychology* Human Kinetics (1992)

8 HISTORY OF SPORT

Objectives

To understand

- the major events in British sporting history
- how and why sport has changed over the centuries
- how the social, economic and political conditions of the time have affected sports development
- the different ways in which the state has been involved with sport
- how the different sociological approaches interpret the history of sport in different ways

Theoretical approaches

Studying the history of sport is not quite as simple as it sometimes appears. Certain facts cannot be disputed, for example, the Cruelty to Animals Act was passed in 1835, the All-England Women's Hockey Association was formed in 1895, and the last Gentlemen versus Players cricket match was played in 1962. However, the interpretation of these events is another matter.

- Why did these events take place at the time that they did?
- Which factors in society – economic, social, political – were especially important in producing the conditions for the event to take place?
- To what extent did individuals and groups of people take responsibility for the events within the overall social framework of the time?

The answers to these questions will depend on your own view of how society works and changes. Thus, sports history cannot be studied in isolation or divorced from what was happening in the world at the time. Sporting happenings and changes must always be considered alongside the mix of economic, social and political relationships in place during the particular period of time.

Within sociology there are a number of theoretical approaches to the study of society which attempt to answer fundamental questions such as: How is society constructed? How does society function? What causes social change? What is the relationship of the individual to society?

There are four main approaches which all give different answers to these and other questions about society. They are Functionalism,

Figure 8.1 Early days of hockey in the 1890s

Figure 8.2 Playground games. Walsgrave Colliery School, Coventry in 1952

Marxism, Social Action and Interactionism. Since each has a different view of society, each approach will have a different view of the place of sport in society and hence of the changes that have taken place over the centuries.

The first three approaches are all structural in nature, that is, they are firstly concerned with how society affects individual and group behaviour, rather than how individuals and groups create society. A structural sociologist would be interested in, for example, how class and family background of a sportsperson affect his or her chance of success in the sport. For Functionalism, agreement between people on moral values has a central role in maintaining social order. In contrast, Marxism and Social Action both stress the conflict rather than agreement seen in society. All structuralist theories also take a scientific view of society and try to find scientific explanations of social behaviour, for example, by gathering data through surveys. Interpretative sociology, in comparison to structuralism, is basically concerned with how individuals and groups create, find meaning in, and experience society. They are not as interested in how society affects groups and individuals and they reject the scientific approach to research. They would be interested in, for example, what it feels like to be a housewife bringing up three small children and having no access to sport. These sociological theories of sport are discussed in detail in chapter 10.

Introduction

Play, in its various forms, has always been a part of the life of people living in social groups. There is evidence of play in the ancient civilisations. The so-called 'primitive' societies which survive today around the world often have elaborate and distinctive forms of play.

The last century in Britain has seen some aspects of formal play and recreation develop into an international circus of high finance and commercialisation. At the same time, opportunities for the ordinary citizen to take part in sporting activities have expanded at an unprecedented rate. Critical as this development has been to modern sport, there were, of course, important but gradual changes in play and recreation over the preceding centuries. The steady evolution of sports, games and pastimes in the centuries before the Victorian era is a fascinating study, since a wide range of activities existed throughout the country. However, the problem of finding evidence and interpreting it is difficult in comparison with the study of sport over the last century, which is relatively well-documented and easily accessible.

When looking at the history of play, games and recreational activities, it is necessary to consider the social, economic and political conditions of the time. It is also important to look at the various cultural influences at work throughout society. Central to the development of leisure-time activities, was the steady improvement in the quality of life for the mass of people. Other major influences were the values given to play by people in general and most importantly, the way play was regarded by those in power, by both the church and the state.

Traditional play and games 1200 – 1837

Games played in medieval times (1200-1485) were very different from those of today because life itself was so different. Games were simple enough to be passed on through the generations by imitation and word of mouth. In order to survive, the vast majority of the population had to work very hard and long each day. There was little time or opportunity for leisure for most of the year. The health of most people was unlikely to have been able to support regular demanding exercise for anything else but the essential daily work.

The only exceptions to the diet of work and more work were the many annual festivals associated with agriculture and the church. Shrove Tuesday was the start of the medieval sporting year with such activities as football, fighting, wrestling, tug-of-war, animal baiting, skittles and bowls. In the summer there were running, jumping and throwing contests, while the important Whitsuntide celebrations also included dancing and country games, chasing and simple ball games.

Gradually sports broke free from particular holy days and were played at other times. Most importantly, they began to be played for their own sake. Betting on the result also started.

For the medieval lords, the horse was central to sporting activity. The most common, and also the earliest, sport for the privileged was hunting. That racing on horseback took place is quite certain, but it was not organised in any way. Tournaments were highly organised events with elaborate rules and codes of conduct. The knights in teams or individually, charged at each other on horseback in a specially designated area, the tilt yard. Various forms of handball emerged in areas which had substantial buildings, like palaces, churches and castles, and could provide walls.

Sporting events were beginning to attract spectators in large numbers and with the crowds sometimes came disorder. For the ruling authorities, both the government and the church, there was a continuing dilemma. They needed to keep the population at large happy and content in order to answer the call to arms, while at the same time avoiding the slide into lawlessness and civil disorder that popular play appeared to encourage.

In the later Middle Ages, sport began to emerge and exist on its own. No longer fixed to holy days, it developed a greater variety of forms. The Church was worried about the influence of sporting pastimes on the population as a whole.

The English archers, with their longbows, were highly successful at the Battle of Crecy in 1346. After the battle, the government decided that practice and training using the longbow should override all other considerations in the use of leisure time. Many people resented this interference with their traditional pursuits, while others took readily to the new activities. Games and sports were forbidden, not because of the fear for public order, nor for the enjoyment gained, nor for the failure to attend church, but solely to promote archery and provide a skilled citizen army of archers. However, the government of the time found it difficult to effectively control the play of the population at large.

In Tudor times (1485 to 1603), the Renaissance gentleman needed military strengths combined with a knowledge of the arts and letters. He was also expected to be skilled in the acceptable games and recreations of the time, including hunting, horsemanship, wrestling, swordplay, jousting, real tennis and dancing, but certainly not football! Henry VIII was an all-round sportsman who built his own tennis court at Hampton Court Palace.

Figure 8.3 Hunting in medieval times

The population at large kept mainly to their own traditional sporting games and pastimes. Gambling became ever more popular and attached itself to a wide variety of activities. Archery and bowls were activities played across social groups, although it is less certain that the different groups played together. Play still centred on the traditional local festivals and fair days, as well as the national celebrations at Christmas, Easter and Whitsun. Games were local or regional in nature.

While football continued to be mainly a violent and uncontrolled mauling mob of men, there were signs of some organisation in the game and even the occasional involvement of the nobility. However, in general, mob-football continued its own traditional form unchecked. It gave vent to inter-village rivalry and allowed the discharge of vast amounts of energy. In towns it was far less welcome as damage to property became of increasing concern.

Overall, the Elizabethan era was a period when sport and games flourished, in stark contrast to the Stuart Period (1603 to 1714) which followed. The development and rise of Puritanism, in the second half of the sixteenth century, caused the whole subject of recreation to be carefully examined. For the Puritans, a sober, quiet and hard-working family life was the only way to salvation. Play with all its spontaneous enjoyment was thought to provide too many opportunities for the devil! The traditional folk festivals, with their pagan origins, were subject to fierce attack. Previously, Sundays and saints' days were accepted as days for recreation after church had been attended. For the Puritans, Sunday was the Lord's day and there was no place for play at all. The successful implementation of their views completely changed traditional play patterns in some parts of the country. Urban authorities were concerned with the lawlessness associated with many games and recreation generally. The government approved of tighter controls on the ordinary people, for reasons of good social order. A quiet Sunday rest day for the working population and the removal of disruptive feast days throughout the calendar appealed to the developing manufacturing class. One positive effect on sport, not to be overlooked, was the Puritans' dislike of cruel animal sports. They campaigned for their abolition and were successful in closing the London bear pits permanently.

In 1617, James I issued a declaration known as the 'Book of Sports'. The declaration claimed that the restriction of play on Sundays was harmful to the nation. As long as there was church attendance first, activities such as dancing, archery, leaping, vaulting, morris dancing and other harmless recreations were allowed.

Puritans certainly left an indelible mark on the development of sport. The restoration of the monarchy in 1660 reduced the effect of Puritan influence on play. However, play in the future was forced to try to move away from its traditional association with drinking, revelry and lawlessness in order to become more acceptable throughout society. Above all in questioning the whole idea of recreation, Puritans enabled the subject to be debated and indeed defended.

In the period following the Restoration, there were opportunities for a revival of the old ways of playing and new forms to develop. However, some of the Puritan influences, for example, a more regular working week and a quieter Sunday, were to remain. Nevertheless, there was greater tolerance in general to recreation. Saints' days were again celebrated and parish feasts revived. The attacks on such disorderly sporting pastimes as football and May games faded.

The major limitations on recreation and sport were now class-based. The new Game Laws of 1671 protected the rights of landowners and prevented ordinary people lawfully from taking game from their land. The first regular horse racing took place at Newmarket at this time. The contests were initially betting races for two horses organised by their owners.

In the late seventeenth century, leisure began to be seen increasingly as a source of income. Crowds and, in particular, paying spectators grew considerably. Business people saw an opportunity for profit in providing food and drink, especially beer, for the spectators. The number of players receiving payment also expanded.

Although confined to south-east England, cricket made progress and agreement on the general form of play developed, allowing competition over a wider area. In stark contrast, football remained rooted in its own particular area. Games continued to be mainly a competition between huge groups of men rampaging across vast areas of the countryside.

In the Hanoverian period (1714 to 1790), sport developed without either specific encouragement or hindrance from the state at national level. The lasting effects of Puritanism remained with a regular working pattern and a sober Sunday being the most important. The Church's interest in and influence on play faded, with many country parsons accepting the traditional forms of play. The creeping influence of industrialisation made a regular pattern of work very important. The authorities continued to be wary of major sporting events which brought with them possibilities for social disorder, such as large crowds, much gambling and a host of activities which often ran close to the law. Nevertheless, no major restrictive laws were passed and people of all classes enjoyed their leisure largely unrestricted.

Patronage by the aristocracy continued to support a number of major sports. In particular, cricket benefited from the nobility who set up the wagers, provided the grounds and equipment and ensured that professional players were available. The rise of prize fighting was also due to the backing of wealthy patrons, although unlike cricket, they did not take part themselves. Horse racing was often supported by the town council on whose land the racing took place. They hoped that by building grandstands and improving the general amenities that they could continue to attract large numbers of spectators with all the commercial advantages which followed. The sponsoring of races by Royalty did much to promote racing at some courses.

Financial rewards for the participants continued to grow throughout the century. Along with the development of the sport itself came a whole commercial infrastructure. The need for order and regulation in competition, and the associated gambling, became

Figure 8.4 Two pugilists from the 1750s

essential as sport became more complex and spread across the nation. By the middle of the century, horse racing rules were firmly established, based on those set up at Newmarket by Charles II towards the end of the previous century. The *Racing Calendar* was published regularly from the 1740s. Racing flourished throughout the land and was highly organised with well developed rules and a body, the Jockey Club, founded in 1752, accepted as the arbitrator of disputes.

Cricket made great strides during the century, thanks to wealthy patronage. It too acquired written rules which were revised and agreed upon in 1774 and which were enforced by umpires. It was played on particular grounds in front of paying spectators and had professional players taking part.

In mid-century, prize fighting enjoyed a brief period of legality and support from the nobility. Prize fighting continued to rely mainly on Jack Broughton's original rules of 1743, which were more specifically concerned with control of the betting than the welfare of the fighters. Later, the sport fell into disrepute and went underground.

The period from 1790 to 1837 was a time of changing circumstances for sport. A number of factors contributed. The movement of people from the country to the town started in earnest as industry gradually pulled people away from working on the land. Work patterns in the new urban areas greatly reduced free time. The churches once again emphasised the importance of morality and seriousness in life, and found themselves at odds with popular recreation. Such events as cockfighting, horse racing and prize fighting brought opposition from all quarters. The church saw them all as unacceptable opportunities for the devil's work, property owners of all types feared the destruction of their property in the associated disorder, and the new industrial employers were concerned at the loss of regular patterns of work. In addition, the open land where traditional play often took place was in danger of being enclosed. Old styles of play and recreation needed new forms and new venues in order to have any future. However, changes were not always successful in making play acceptable to the authorities. This led to the questioning of the whole notion of leisure and recreation. Precisely how and where people should enjoy their free time became an issue again.

In the recent past the Church had been the centre for local recreation. The church calendar supplied the feast days, the walls of the building and its grounds were used as a playground and

Figure 8.5 Bullbaiting, 1820

Figure 8.6 The last days of street football. Shrove Tuesday at Kingston-upon Thames, 1846

the parson had been content to let it all happen. This relaxed situation was first attacked by George III's proclamation, in 1787, 'For the Encouragement of Piety and Virtue, and for the Preventing or Punishing of Vice'. In practice, this resulted in a clamp down on Sunday play. There was also pressure from other churchmen to ban the old festivals, race meetings, prize fights and animal baiting.

With the increasing unpopularity of the traditional leisure pursuits, the upper class distanced themselves more and more from them. Patronage of pedestrianism and prize fighting faded and the upper class retreated into the country sports of hunting, shooting and fishing.

Changes brought by the Industrial Revolution were dramatic. By 1800, only 35% of workers were left working directly in agriculture. Many towns, especially in the Midlands and the North, doubled in size in the early nineteenth century. Sport needed to adapt to the new urban environment. The baiting of animals was easy to organise in towns and continued to attract crowds up until the 1835 Cruelty to Animals Act.

The factory system, with twelve or more hours a day, six days a week left, people with little energy or time for leisure. Nevertheless, pedestrian contests, prize fights and race meeting in the industrial towns were popular, sometimes emptying the factories. Increasingly, the ordinary people turned to the inn for their recreation, where those innkeepers with fields were able to offer an even wider variety of entertainment with the alcohol.

The ordinary people took part in whatever recreation was available, whether officially allowed or not. The middle and upper classes found it hard to understand and accept what was happening and focused on popular leisure as a problem. Traditional activities, with their rowdiness and lawlessness, were thought unsuitable and it was hoped that the masses could be directed into more wholesome family-centred recreation. The idea of 'rational recreation' was offered as an alternative, to include sedate walks, country dancing, gymnastic exercises and more carefully regulated traditional sports.

However, the solution to the problem of leisure was not found by the imposition of activities thought to be right and proper on the masses by their betters. It was achieved by the changing and modernising of the old traditional activities into sports and games which were acceptable across a wide social spectrum.

Cricket, the traditional English game, led the way. Gambling, drinking and rowdiness were still a problem in the early part of the nineteenth century. However, gambling was banned from Lords in the

1820s. Crowds increased without greater disorder and annual fixture lists developed.

Racing, strongly supported by the nobility, was able to over-ride the objections many still had to race meetings. They were often seen as opportunities for violence and gambling which also attracted in their wake a host of undesirables. The Jockey Club continued to develop as the sport's governing body, in 1833 agreeing to intervene in problems arising at any meeting where its own rules were followed.

While cricket and horse racing moved reasonably smoothly into the modern sporting world, other sports fared differently. Pedestrianism became corrupt, lost the support of its upper class patrons, fell into disrepute and disappeared. Prize fighting suffered a similar fate. It had the additional burden of being declared illegal and with better law enforcement and declining support, its disappearance was certain.

The contribution of the Oxford and Cambridge Universities boat

SUMMARY

Medieval period (1200 – 1485)
- People had little time or energy for recreational activities.
- Leisure time activities were originally confined to feast days.
- Games were local in nature, each village having its own particular activities for feast days.
- From time to time the government banned traditional activities in favour of archery training.

Tudor and Stuart period (1485-1714)
- Traditional folk games and activities flourished in Tudor times.
- Puritanism greatly reduced the opportunities to play and types of activity allowed.
- After the restoration in 1660, traditional activities were revived.
- Sport moved away from its former links with merry making and lawlessness.

Hanoverian period (1714 – 1790)
- Play and sport were largely ignored by the government.
- People of all classes enjoyed their leisure to the full.
- Increasing industrialisation demanded regular working patterns.
- There was some pressure for Sunday to be a day of rest.
- Large gatherings for sport often meant social disorder.
- Regular, organised, rule-governed sport on a national scale emerged.

Changing times (1790 – 1837)
- Traditional sport was under attack from all sides.
- Factory owners wanted a regular working week.
- Property owners feared the damage caused by large crowds.
- Churches criticised idleness, drunkenness and slack morality.
- Commercialisation of sport developed, especially in horse racing, cricket and prize fighting.

race to the new acceptable form of sport was very great. Although the first race in 1829 aroused little interest, crowds grew gradually. They were attracted by a new moral sports activity – two matched sides, competing for the honour of winning only, without gambling and in the spirit of fair play. These ideals were to govern the development of sport for the rest of the century and lay the foundations for sport today.

Questions

1 Medieval recreation was very different from that of today. Explain how and when people played in medieval times.
2 The Puritans had a lasting influence on sport in Britain. Explain the effect they had on the traditional pattern of play at the time and how their influence remains today.
3 Patronage was the vital ingredient in the growth of a number of sports in the eighteenth century. Explain what was involved, the sports which were promoted, and the importance of patronage in sports development.
4 Industrialisation moved people from the land into the cities. Explain how this affected people's recreation in the new urban areas and what changes occurred in the traditional patterns of play.

Fair play and Victorian sport: 1837 – 1901

During the Victorian era, sport gradually became associated with morality. In doing so it was necessary for all the traditional associations with revelry, debauchery and lawlessness to be completely removed. Sport had to be redefined in moral terms. Competition had to take place fairly within given rules which were acceptable to all those involved. Fairness was achieved by upholding the rules, making conditions the same for all competitors and ensuring equal numbers in the team games. Idealism governed the purpose of sport. It was to be played for its own sake and without financial reward. Losing was an integral part of the activity, as long as the competition was fair and honest. It was accepted that sport was not played purely for pleasure, but was important for character-building, and for developing qualities of the individual in acceptable directions. In doing so, it contributed to the health and vitality of the whole nation.

This new vision of sport arose from the middle classes. They carried great influence in Victorian times. They wanted more leisure and recreation, as long as the activities fitted in with their own established values. Many sports and their governing bodies were sensitive to the changing mood of society. They reorganised and regulated their sports with the new views in mind. The development of sporting activities acceptable throughout society began. Public schools played a major role in the spread of the new sporting ideas and the new national governing bodies organised and controlled the changes.

Technology and travel

The arrival of faster and easier travel and communication helped national sport grow. New technological developments allowed the actual playing of games to move ahead in terms of skill and technique, through new and improved equipment, clothing and facilities. Ultimately, the development of mass sport was dependent on the availability of time to play. The movement towards Saturday afternoon free from work started in the 1840s. By the 1870s, most of the industry had followed suit, allowing the mass of the population to become involved in sport either as spectators or players. These developments were almost exclusively for the male population alone. Mass participation in sport by women was still many decades away. In the early part of the century, the new methods of production, which were central to the industrial revolution, had reduced both the leisure time of the factory worker and the playing space available. The introduction of steam power for the factories meant steam power for transport which in turn benefited sport greatly. The arrival of the railways quickly changed horse racing for the better. It was soon possible to move spectators and horses about the country quickly and easily.

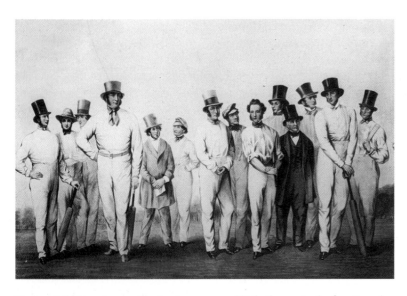

Figure 8.7 The eleven of England 1847. Cricketers were soon touring the country by train to promote their sport. Cricket had always been popular throughout the country, but matches were usually played on a regional basis. In 1846, William Clarke formed the first 'All England XI' and they toured widely.

With the arrival of national sports there was a need for nationally-accepted rules and procedures for play. Ease of travel meant that standards of play soon became nationally accepted. Electric telegraph lines sprang up alongside the railway track. They made local news available quickly to the centres of population, where often a fight, match or race result was eagerly awaited. Time-keeping in all sports was improved with the development of reliable stopwatches. This allowed shorter races to be more accurately recorded and easier comparison made between runners.

Technological advances in materials changed many sporting activities. The use of rubber produced more reliable balls. The use of metal in equipment such as golf clubs, changed the sport. More advanced machinery to cut grass and maintain fields led to improved playing surfaces. Metal turnstiles and the use of concrete by the end of the century improved facilities and allowed more accurate recording of spectator numbers.

Although the study of medicine had made great progress and concern existed about public health and hygiene, there was little official interest in sporting fitness. For most sportsmen, training was based on traditional methods with the occasional change due to personal fads. As competition developed nationally, interest in training and fitness increased, along with the development of skill and techniques, which together improved the standard of play.

Changing sports

The nineteenth century saw the rise of the middle classes in Britain in terms of numbers, economic power and social influence. In order for sport to gain their support, it had to be acceptable under their moral code. This meant it had to be a healthy physical activity, free from associations with drinking, gambling, cruelty and immorality of any kind. By the middle of the century, the middle classes had become interested in play, but only if it was quite distinct from the traditional sporting activities. Their choice was limited at first. Prize fighting was

inappropriate with its violence, rowdy crowds and gambling. Horse racing had always been under the control and patronage of the nobility and betting was inextricably involved. Cricket, although originally developed by the upper classes, had always had support from other classes. It became a game dominated by the middle classes and their morality. The phrase 'it's not cricket' became part of ordinary language. Gambling had to be removed, crowds were to be better controlled, and stricter rules for the game introduced. Cricket

Figure 8.8 Henley regatta, 1895

abandoned the earlier practice of playing until a result was achieved and also regulated daily playing hours. These changes were reflected in the attitude of the spectators. No longer were crowds just interested in victory for their team or player; the manner of winning became important. Sport moved from being purely an interesting spectacle to being a competitive activity, where performances could be assessed and compared with others. In cricket, the increasing importance of evenly balanced county matches from the middle of the century caused the decline of the professional touring sides.

The prize ring could not make these changes. However, the rise of boxing 'the noble art of self defence' was helped by the Queensbury Rules in 1865. Rounds of fixed duration were introduced and gloves were increasingly worn in order to prevent serious injury. Racing, although never free from gambling, responded with a limited clean-up in the 1840s. This included a new starting system, the numbering of horses and more careful weighing-in and weighing-out. Racing became more regular, more frequent and, through the influence of the railways, more structured in its operation.

Figure 8.9 Football at Rugby, 1870

Victorian sport was often more class-orientated than earlier sport. Rowing regattas previously open to amateurs, professionals and women, gradually became more exclusive. Eventually they were limited to amateurs only. Fishing also resorted to class distinctions with coarse fishing for the masses and fish such as trout and salmon reserved for those who owned the land or could pay to fish there. A similar change occurred with hunting, where the traditional local worker's hunts gradually disappeared, leaving only the hunts of the gentry with the access to wide expanses of land.

Towards the end of the nineteenth century, the arrival of Saturday afternoons for leisure-time activities again allowed the mass of people to enjoy play without conflict. In the past, the authorities had at times persecuted play or at best ignored it. Now for the first time play in general could find approval from those in power.

Football had a key role to play in the development of sport for the masses. It was middle class influence which led to the transformation of football from its traditional origins to the one great working class sport of the century which followed. It did have the advantage of always having been free from gambling, but its past association with lawlessness and violence appeared to rule it out. In many areas it had been in decline or had disappeared. Only its rebirth in an orderly form with limited numbers made it attractive again. There is no doubt that the survival of the game over the centuries showed the deep desire of the ordinary people for a football-type activity. Its return was greatly assisted by the creation of work-free Saturday afternoons and its adoption as the major winter game by the growing number of public schools.

Originally the public schools all developed their own particular version of the game, some based on the dribbling game, such as Harrow, others using the handling code, like Rugby. The need for standardisation became apparent when their former pupils wanted to continue playing at university. In the early 1840s a set of rules was used for a game in Cambridge between men from Eton, Shrewsbury and Winchester. By the early 1860s many clubs had been formed and Thring, headmaster of Uppingham School, drew up a list of ten basic rules for football in 1862. Cambridge University then produced a version of its rules in 1863, based on Thring's original rules. Later that year a meeting was held in London, which led to the foundation of the Football Association. The clubs agreed on rules which made wide

Rational recreation (e.g. football)	Popular recreation (e.g. mob football)
New Victorian ethic	Traditional values
For an elite group	Available to all
Highly organised	Loose organisation
Regular	Occasional
Fixture list	Special occasions
Rule governed	A few simple rules
Universal rules	Local rules
Equal numbers	No limit on numbers
Fairplay ethic	Win at all costs
Purposeful	Pleasurable
Recognised skills	Few specific skills
Respectable	Unruly
Encouraged by schools and government – character building, forming law-abiding citizens	Discouraged by schools and government – uncontrolled behavior, violence and damage

variation in play possible, although running with the ball was prohibited. Clubs who wished to continue with that style founded the Rugby Football Union in 1871. Rugby's expansion nation-wide took place more slowly, although the first international, England versus Scotland, was played in 1871 and the Oxford versus Cambridge match a year later.

Although founded in London, football flourished in the industrial towns of the North and Midlands. From the mid-1840s, factories had closed on Saturday afternoon. This was also, with Wednesday afternoon, the time when public school-boys were used to playing football. When the Football League was founded in 1888 – 89, the vast majority of the teams were from the Lancashire and greater Birmingham area. The game developed very quickly in England with county associations and cups. The first international match between England and Scotland took place in 1870, and by 1885, all the home countries were playing against each other.

The speed with which rugby in the south Wales valleys and soccer in the northern textile towns set up networks of local clubs was remarkable. It was not achieved merely by developments at national level nor the direct influence of the public schools. The rise of team games for working class men came through the efforts of the young men themselves to form clubs at the workplace, in the pub, or at the church. In the urban environment, team games offered more than just physical exercise, of which most men had had enough during their normal day's work. They offered companionship, identity and enjoyment, the very things that had been lost from their lives in the mass movement from the rural areas to the city. Quite often the working men's clubs became the focus of male social and sporting life in the community.

In the second half of the century, concern developed over the way the lower classes, and in particular young working class men, amused themselves during their leisure time. A group of reformers argued that sports was important, alongside provision of parks, museums, libraries and baths, in creating a healthy, moral and orderly workforce. This rational recreation movement tried to guide popular recreation into acceptable activities, but with only limited success. The men who led this movement were often former public school boys who, having experienced games in their schooldays, thought that it would be possible to transfer them and all the things they stood for, directly to the lower classes. The Boys' Brigade and the YMCA used sport to increase their membership and to improve the social discipline of the young. A number of teams which founded the Football League had their origins in the church and youth movements.

Public schools and the gentleman amateur

Victorian society was dominated by its class structure. The educational system not only reflected this structure, but reinforced it in many areas. One of these areas was the type of sport and physical activity encouraged by the different classes.

The public schools served the middle classes, producing men to guide the affairs of government and industry in Britain and in the expanding empire. The qualities of courage, loyalty, discipline, commitment and leadership were highly valued. The schools' philosophy was that both character development and morality could be achieved through sport and especially team games. It was in sport that the boys learned how to conform to the established way of doing things within their social group. Doctor Arnold of Rugby is usually thought of as the architect of the games cult in public schools although in fact the development had started before his reforms.

The cult of athleticism, sometimes called 'Muscular Christianity', developed in the second half of the century. It stressed order, restraint, manliness and character. Earlier the schools often had a poor reputation with the local people, since pupils rampaged at will over the countryside in pursuit of all manner of prey. At this time the boys themselves were responsible for their own sport without interference from masters at the school. This wild behaviour was gradually reduced as the more acceptable sports were developed and gained higher status with the involvement of the masters. Many of the schools already had rowing, cricket and their own particular form of football matches firmly established amongst themselves. From being used as a source of morality and discipline, games gradually developed into an end in themselves and dominated the whole system of elite education.

In the 1830s and 1840s an important part in this change was played by the first graduates from Oxford and Cambridge who had some experience of organised sport. Thereafter the schools provided a continuous flow of sportsmen to universities, and back to school as teachers. The new young sportsmen were convinced of the value of their experiences of competitive organised sport in school and happily developed the tradition. After the first boat race between Oxford and Cambridge in 1829, sport between the universities only developed very slowly until the 1860s. However, by the 1890s the sports included athletics, golf, football. rugby, cross-country, tennis, boxing, hockey and swimming.

Children from the working class did not have access to the games culture of the middle and upper class. Inequalities in life were reflected in sport. The distinctive sporting experiences of children were reinforced in adulthood. To these were added the distinction of amateurs and professionals. Far from dealing with financial reward, sport was a form of social control. The amateur code was often used in practice to exclude the working class players from high level competition. Amateurs were those who, because of their social position and

Thomas Hughes in his book *Tom Brown's Schooldays* vividly contrasts the pagan attractions of the old style of play at schools with the new manly, sporting games. In one passage the young master talks of the value of cricket for developing both team spirit and co-operation: *'The discipline and reliance on one another, which it teaches are so valuable … it merges the individual into the eleven; he doesn't play that he may win but that his side may win.'*

Figure 8.10 'Tom saves the day' from *Tom Brown's Schooldays*

financial situation, did not need to seek payment for their sporting activities. However, this did not stop them being rewarded in a variety of ways. W G Grace received all manner of financial rewards for his cricketing performances, although as a doctor he could not be described as anything but a 'gentleman amateur'. Amateurs were gentlemen of the upper and middle classes who played sports in a special way. Fair play meant not only following the rules of the sport but respecting the spirit of the game. 'Not playing the game' as a sporting expression, referred to the manner in which the game was played, rather than the rules of play. This code was not thought to require enforcement and hence some football teams refused to have anything to do with penalty kicks, since they maintained that no player of theirs would deliberately foul an opponent!

Cricket mirrored society's divisions with its gentlemen amateurs and professional players. However, in cricket, there was a long tradition of professionalism and also a code of conduct which carefully distinguished between gentlemen and players. This allowed them to play together in the same team as long as a professional player did not captain the team if an amateur player was available. These distinctions between amateurs and professionals were not abolished until the 1960s. Nevertheless, the gentlemen of the MCC and county committees have always been firmly in control of cricket.

Rowing maintained the exclusive nature of its activity by ensuring that gentlemen never raced against those who rowed for a living on the river. Indeed, the Amateur Rowing Association, formed in 1882 went further and excluded all those involved in manual labour as a living. This ruling was unsuccessfully challenged by the National Amateur Rowing Association, set up in 1890, who wanted to include all but professional oarsmen. The Amateur Athletic Association in 1865 also excluded 'any tradesman, mechanic, artisan or labourer', although the rule was changed within a few years to exclude only those competing for money. In golf, amateurs did originally play against those professionals involved in the game itself, although this too was changed, preventing those who accepted money from competing in amateur competition.

The majority of sports which were played just for the pleasure of the players found the amateur and professional distinction a help in maintaining class divisions. However, the sports which had begun to rely on the support of spectators faced a dilemma. The administrators, usually originating from the public schools, had little sympathy for professionalism. They were concerned that if soccer was commercialised then the winning would be more important than the taking part. They feared this would lead to the fixing of matches and corrup-

Figure 8.11   Hurdling at the Oxford vs Cambridge sports meeting, 1871

tion, a take-over of the game by professionals and above all, the loss of the traditional values which were central to games playing. It soon became obvious that the best players could not take time off work indefinitely without financial support. With the formation of the Football League in 1885, the FA accepted professionals within their organisation, if somewhat reluctantly.

For rugby the outcome was quite different, with the sport having split in two. The southern clubs were certain that players should not be paid, while the more commercially minded northern clubs accepted professionalism. Effectively the South was excluding manual workers, who needed to take time off work to train and travel, from the better teams. The results of this rift were seen in many outbreaks of bad feeling between the two codes. The division went deeper still. It underlined the South's wholehearted acceptance of athletiscm with the superiority of the gentleman amateur, contrasting sharply with the desire for play for the whole community in the Midlands and North. In 1895, the larger Northern clubs formed their own Northern Rugby Football Union after failing to win broken-time payments for players. Rugby Union maintained its amateur ideals until very recently. It found them increasingly difficult to defend when international matches generate vast income and players at the top level are professional in terms of their commitment and time given up to the sport. In 1995 rugby union embraced professionalism.

Victorian women and sport

For the mass of children outside the public school system, both their education and their experience of sport was quite different from the privileged elite. Before the 1870 Education Act, the provision for education itself was poor and haphazard, and that for physical activity was similar. Following the Act, drill became part of the curriculum, largely for military and disciplinary purposes. However in 1878, the London Board introduced therapeutic Swedish gymnastics into girls' education. By 1895 instruction in Swedish or other drill or suitable physical exercises was brought into the payment by results system. Working class women were almost entirely left outside the masculine sports culture of the nineteenth century, apart from their experience of drill in school

The public schools had encouraged a new idea of 'manliness'. This was the harmonious development of the young man's body and character together. The culture of games, health and fair play was not offered to girls from the middle and upper classes who were educated at home or in exclusive girls' schools. There was conflict between vigorous physical activity and the view of the Victorian woman of

Figure 8.12 Children doing drill in a Victorian school

leisure as being vulnerable, emotional and weak. The physical demands of the playing field were thought to prepare men for their future careers, while women had no such prospects and therefore needed no such preparation. The development of women's sport based around the social activities of private clubs, only served to reinforce the place of middle-class women in society. Physical activity was acceptable as long as it was kept within strict social limits, play was ladylike and vigorous competition was avoided.

One important influence on the private schools was the new games mistress, trained initially at a private college of physical education founded in 1895 in Dartford. This college was run by Madame Bergman-Osterberg who had a great influence on the development of women's physical education. Her pupils founded three further colleges of physical education at Anstey, Bedford and Dumferline. Madame Bergman-Osterberg developed a separate tradition in sport, combining team games with Swedish gymnastics. She emphasised separate development for women, rejecting both the drill sergeant and other male physical trainers.

Gradually men came to accept women in some sports like tennis and golf, but certainly not in cricket, football nor even athletics. Hockey was able to establish itself as a suitable activity with the All England Women's Hockey Association formed in 1895. Predictably the hockey players, like cyclists and tennis players, ran into problems with clothing and competitiveness.

SUMMARY

- Sport developed in the context of industrial capitalism and class inequality.
- Sport became linked to a moral code defined by the middle classes:
  - it was accepted that sport developed character and morality
  - competition had to be fair and rule-governed with similar conditions for all players
  - sport was to be played, not for reward, but for its own sake.
- Nationwide sport developed through the influence of technology, the public schools and the national governing bodies.
- For the masses, Saturday afternoon free from work was the turning point, enabling them to play and spectate.
- Amateur and professional sport became increasingly separated.
- Working class sport in school was limited largely to drill and therapeutic gymnastics.

Questions

1 In the Victorian period sport became highly organised. Describe what happened and account for the changes.

2 The public schools played an important part in the development of organised sport nationwide. Explain their importance.

3 The control of sport in the last century was very much in the hands of the gentlemen amateurs. Explain why this was so and suggest how their influence continued into this century.

4 In some sports, professionals had existed from the early days. However, in others, professionalism was a problem to be dealt with in the second half of the nineteenth century. Explain how and why sports dealt with the issue in different ways.

5 The contrast between physical education offered in public schools and state schools in Victorian times was very great. Describe the difference in provision for the different social groups at the time and comment on the differing provision for boys and girls.

6 Explain how improved communications and travel helped the development of sport nationally during the nineteenth century.

Edwardian sport: 1901 – 1918

In the Edwardian period, the upper and middle classes separated their sport even further from the working classes. This merely reflected a society in which profits soared but real wages declined after having increased greatly in the last quarter of the century. Surveys showed a great deal of poverty while fierce campaigns for rights were fought by trade unionists and suffragettes. Nevertheless, organised sporting involvement expanded rapidly across all social groups. During this period sport became firmly established as a form of mass entertainment. A number of factors, also common to the late Victorian period, enabled this progress to be made, including a heavy concentration of population in urban areas, increased leisure time for much of the working class, better transport, a national press, technological developments and improved communications. The direction of the changes was strongly influenced by particular groups. These included middle class groups with sporting interests, the demands of working class people for more participation, women's desire for greater involvement and the opportunities seen by businessmen in the leisure industry. Many church and youth movements continued to use sport as a means of attracting young men to their organisations.

Socially-exclusive clubs for tennis and golf were very popular with the middle classes. Few public facilities for these games existed in England, although in Scotland golf had always been a game for all social classes. Cycling was originally limited only to those who could afford the expense of a cycle, thus excluding the ordinary working people. However, by the turn of the century it was a popular leisure activity and available to a wide social range. It was popular with spectators too, but in the early years of the century it declined for reasons similar to the demise of pedestrianism – fixed races and the greed of both competitors and organisers. Other contributing factors were the ready acceptance of professionalism, the close links of the sport with the cycle manufacturers and hence the problems of defining amateurism for the sport.

In 1893 the Prince of Wales' horse won the Derby and thus gave the seal of approval to the sport. Gradually the sport had become more orderly with the Jockey Club's tight rules for the licensing of new meetings. Gambling was made more honest, second-rate courses were closed and as open access gave way to paid admission, the course owners were able to exercise more control over the events in general. The suicide of the suffragette, Emily Davison, under the King's horse in the 1913 Derby showed the ever present link between sport and politics.

Athletics remained a minor sport, despite the 1908 Olympics being held in London. The Games are best remembered for the pictures of the exhausted marathon runner, Dorando Pietri, being helped across the line for which he was later disqualified. Generally the Games were ignored by Londoners, crowds only attending in large numbers when the royal family made an appearance. There were many irregularities during the Games, including the questioning of the amateur status of some cyclists and tennis players. Following a number of disputes, it was decided that in future, officials would no longer be provided by the home country.

The participation of women in the Olympics before 1914 was largely limited to figure skating and swimming events. De Coubertin in 1902 had said that athletics for women was 'against the laws of nature', a view which he maintained throughout his life.

Figure 8.13 The Prince of Wales' horse, Persimmon, wins the 1896 Derby

The Edwardian period continued the social prejudice of the Victorian era, with women expected to be mainly decorative rather than active in sporting situations. Middle class women made some progress, playing croquet, tennis, golf and even cycling. However, working class women were still almost totally excluded from the sporting world, both as participants and spectators. This was in direct contrast to the enthusiastic involvement of working class men.

During the second half of the Victorian period, cricket had become accepted as the national game. At one stage it was dominated by the professional touring sides, but gradually the county clubs took over. With increasing gate money and membership they prospered, even enabling the professional players to gain some job security and better pay. From the start, the county championships had problems in awarding points for matches, especially draws, nevertheless it has

Figure 8.14 Dorando Pietri finishing the Olympic marathon, London 1908

survived until today. The county cricket scene had strong competition in two major forms. In the Midlands and North, talent and support for the game was very strong. In addition to county cricket, regular league cricket was organised together with 'money matches'. Elsewhere the attraction for the top cricketers was country house cricket. The aristocracy organised pleasant social weekends of cricket at their great houses, which cricketers, quite understandably, found hard to turn down. Within the game itself, there were those who wanted to see it played artistically for its own sake, while others took a more pragmatic approach, developing their technique in order to win leagues and championships.

During this period, football, in one form or another, provided the masses with their major sporting entertainment. Soccer was most popular in England and Scotland, rugby in Wales, while in Ireland there was a mixture of both, together with its own unique form of football. The English football league was dominated by clubs from the large centres of population in the North and West Midlands. The first southern club to be included, Woolwich Arsenal, took its place in the newly-formed second division in 1901. There was concern in the South, particularly amongst many people who had helped develop the game, that it was in danger of being taken over by northern professionals. The working class domination of soccer changed the nature of the game away from the tradition of athleticism. This was seen in the strong partisan support, the importance of winning and the financial rewards given for winning. The response of the public school administrators was to establish a team of outstanding amateurs called 'the Corinthians' who for many years competed with great success against professional sides. The rejection of professionalism had earlier led to the formation of amateur-only leagues, an amateur cup and amateur international fixtures.

The professionals in the football league had a maximum wage set in 1904 at four pounds a week. This tied the player to the club, but at the same time encouraged illegal undercover payments. For the fans, the financial arrangements for players and clubs were of little interest. They flocked in their thousands to the games and passions often ran high. Inevitably there were crowd problems, usually linked to events on the pitch or deep religious differences. Although stadiums continued to be built on a large scale, facilities for spectators remained primitive.

At this time football spread across Europe and the International Football Federation (FIFA) was formed in 1904, although it was largely ignored by the home countries. However, they joined later with England, Scotland, Wales and Ireland all being accepted individually, a situation which still exists today. In contrast, rugby entered more enthusiastically into the international world, with France included in the home countries championship for the 1905 – 06 season. A tour of Australia took place as early as 1880 and there were also regular matches against teams from New Zealand and South Africa by 1914. Commercialisation of sport continued to develop rapidly. Spectators were spending significant amounts of money to watch sport. In the 1908 – 09 season, six million people watched First Division football matches in England, an average of approximately 16 000 people per game. Crowds at horse racing were often of similar size, perhaps rising to as much as 80 000 at the bank holiday events. Cricket and rugby league also began to attract large attendances. At the same time there were increased opportunities for professional players. By 1910 there were 200 first class professional cricket players, not including league professionals, 400 jockeys and apprentices and 6800 registered paid footballers.

Although little changed in the public schools with regard to the place of sport, there was some progress in the state schools. The 1870 Education Act permitted elementary schoolchildren to be instructed in drill. In 1895, instruction in Swedish or other drill or suitable physical exercises had been brought into the payment by results scheme. This development of alternatives to military drill received a temporary set back with the wholesale rejection of recruits for the Boer War (1899 – 1902). Schools were thought to have failed and there was a demand to return to military training. As a result, in 1902, the Model Course was issued. The course aimed to increase the pupil's fitness for military service and to prepare him for combat. This aroused strong protests, especially from women teachers, and after much public debate the Swedish system was readopted in the first Board of Education syllabus in 1904, with military drill fading for good.

Three significant events then occurred. In 1908, the medical department of the Board of Education was established and given oversight of physical education. This gave greater attention to the physical welfare of school children. A year later a new Syllabus of Physical Training was produced, based on the Swedish system and containing some games and recreative activities. In the same year, 1909, the subject was finally established when physical training was

Figure 8.15   C. B. Fry.

One of the great sportsmen of the era, or indeed of any era, was C B Fry. He was the true all-round sporting gentleman amateur. He played football for England and appeared in the FA cup final for Southampton, while holding the English high jump record for twenty one years. He was an outstanding cricketer, playing regularly for England and topping the first class batting averages for six years. Apart from these sporting achievements, he was a scholar, writer and later a diplomat.

made a compulsory and examinable subject in teacher training colleges. The underlying change was from discipline to therapy. In future, exercises were to be undertaken for their effect on the physique in particular and health in general.

SUMMARY

- Organised sporting involvement expanded rapidly across all classes.
- Increasingly, the different classes played their sport separately.
- Public school athleticism still dominated sport.
- Male working class influence increased, notably in football in England and rugby in Wales. However, working class women were largely excluded from sporting involvement.
- Commercialisation of sport continued with large numbers of spectators and increased numbers of professionals in major sports.
- Sport was increasingly a matter of national concern

Questions

1 In the Edwardian period sport became increasingly class orientated. Give examples of various sports to show this trend and explain what happened.

2 The ideals of public schools' athleticism were often in conflict with the development of football as the great spectator sport of the masses. Explain why it was so at this time.

3 There were a number of important developments in physical education in the period from the turn of the century until the First World War. Explain what happened and the relevance for the future of physical education.

Inter-war sporting progress: 1918 – 1939

Following the end of the First World War, there were great expectations of a more equal and open society. However, by the time of the General Strike in 1926, many people were convinced that little had changed in society. There had been a reduction of working hours from 54 to 48 in the first two years of peace, but little more. Men still worked on Saturday mornings throughout the inter-war period, although gradually the idea of the weekend permeated down through the social classes. During the war, the restrictions on Sunday sport had been relaxed but the move had not been maintained. Women had contributed considerably to the war effort, both in the factories and on the land, and there had been some relaxation of their traditional social restrictions. Women certainly emerged from the war more independent and confident. However, for working class wives, life was a continuous struggle against poverty and domestic chores. Women in general continued to have only limited access to sport, and spectator sport remained a male preserve.

Nevertheless, the period between the two world wars saw steady growth in the traditional games and an increase in the variety of sport played by all classes. This came about because of the overall economic growth, the rise in real wages, increased consumer spending and better social conditions. Although in general there was an increased demand for sport, there was an uneven development across the classes and sexes. Many sports remained expensive, exclusive and class-ridden. For women there was greater involvement but it tended to seep down through the social classes, affecting the working class least of all. Although the Victorians had provided many public facilities, this provision had slowed to a trickle and lagged far behind public demand. This problem did not affect the upper and middle classes very much at all, as their facilities were usually private. The combination of the costs of participation and the shortage of public provision effectively prevented the participation of the working class in a whole range of sports. Sport, in general, was still in the hands of the amateur gentlemen. The controlling bodies were run by part-time amateur administrators and many international bodies were dominated by the same men. Amateurism was rigidly enforced in major sports like rugby and tennis, with strict divisions between amateur and professional players in such sports as cricket and football.

During this period, sport alongside the radio, cinema and the dance hall became part of a commercialised mass entertainment industry. Football and cricket enjoyed very large attendances and interest in athletics boomed. Horse racing, boxing and swimming continued to thrive and new, highly-commercialised sports like speedway, greyhound and motor cycle racing became popular. Ice hockey also made an impact with the building of many ice rinks throughout the country.

Horse racing in the early 1920s suffered a lot from gangs who attended meetings. The situation was improved after the formation of the Bookmakers' Protection Association in 1921. The totalisator was introduced under the Betting Act of 1926 to regulate on-course betting. Later, in the 1930s, the Racecourse Betting Control Board was established which, together with the totalisator, guaranteed fair returns to gamblers.

In 1929 in Manchester, the first electric hare was used for greyhound racing and its popularity took off. A year later, sixty companies were running greyhound racing and it continued to expand quickly, to 187 tracks in 1932. Many tracks sprang up in stadiums around football pitches. Alternatively, since the activity was relatively easy to provide for in terms of facilities, a purpose-built cheap stadium could be constructed quite quickly. Meetings were usually held in the evenings, often five a week, in order to attract men after work. The inability of many to resist such a temptation has remained in the language in the expression 'going to the dogs'.

Speedway racing, first introduced in the 1920s, also achieved great popularity at this time and was sometimes found in football stadiums. However, its demand for space was much greater than for greyhound racing and many stadiums were too small to accommodate it.

Figure 8.16 Greyhound racing became popular in the 1920s

While speedway and greyhound racing were working class pursuits, activities such as polo, yachting, sailing, motor racing and skiing, all developed through wealthy participants. There was also great interest in sports which required machines. The great motor cars like Bentleys and Alfa Romeos were found on the racing tracks all over Europe. The fame of the tourist trophy motor cycle races on the Isle of Man spread far and wide, while the exploits of the early aviators made national heroes of such people as Amy Johnson and Amelia Earhart.

During this period many sports became increasingly class-orientated. Those which required expensive equipment, clothing, animals, vehicles or facilities, were obviously limited to people who could afford to participate. Others were able to maintain their exclusive class nature because of the lack of public facilities, for example tennis, hockey, rowing and golf (outside Scotland). Apart from the Boat Race and Wimbledon crowds, these sports had relatively little spectator appeal and income was therefore limited. Rather than expand to accommodate more members, they often chose to maintain their exclusiveness. As a result, class divisions within sport were reinforced rather than weakened. This could also be seen in the decision of many public schools to change from football to rugby as their winter game, as rugby was thought to be a more suitable game for young gentlemen! Although tennis at the top level had become a spectator sport, it was dominated by the middle class in their clubs, while the general public was only gradually provided with tarmac courts by the local councils.

One sport with very limited participation but considerable public interest was channel swimming. In 1926, Gertrude Ederle swam the channel two hours faster than the best male swimmer. The popularity of swimming was due to the fact that it was often part of the developing physical education in schools, thanks to the Victorian public baths builders. This was not the only sport in which women made their mark. At Wimbledon, Suzanne Lenglen, the champion of France, set new standards of play and dress. Up to this time, long and heavy skirts and dresses had made active tennis for women almost impossible. Lenglen played in light, shorter skirts which scandalised society at the time. In golf too, women's participation expanded and was accepted, but only as long as the lady golfer knew her place. The golf clubs usually only allowed their ladies to play in off-peak periods and frequently restricted their use of the clubhouse. The Ladies' Golf

Union accepted these conditions and in 1933, even apologised because a member was wearing trousers and a sweater to play in a competition. Nevertheless, women made significant progress after the first World War with shorter games skirts and the general acceptance of shorts and trousers. The fact that far more of a woman's body could now be seen in public was a profound change and one that sport helped bring about. However, women were still restricted to a narrow range of sports which men considered suitable for them.

Women's progress in athletics was slow, with the Women's AAA, founded in 1922. Participants were only allowed in the Olympics athletics at Amsterdam in 1928. They were not allowed to race in events greater than 800 metres as these were thought to be too strenuous for them. Unfortunately a number of the runners in the women's 800-metres race finished the race in a distressed condition which appeared to confirm male opinion. In line with the male public schools and for similar social reasons, girls' independent schools helped the development of their own particular sports, notably hockey and cricket.

Both men and women were attracted to the outdoor activities boom of the thirties which included cycling, walking, camping and rambling. In contrast to the development of games, these activities were non-competitive, often individually-organised and involved both sexes sharing physical recreation. The popularity of such activities was reflected in the growth in membership of the Youth Hostels Association from 6000 in 1934 to 83 000 in 1939. These activities became popular as the desire for healthy activities grew among the public, supported by the government's National Fitness Campaign. The Women's League of Health and Beauty formed in 1929, increased in membership from 20 000 in 1933 to 166 000 in 1939.

The failure of British teams in the world of international sport became increasingly common. While it was natural that Britain's earlier supremacy should fade as other countries started catching up, it did provoke public comment and attention moved to facilities, or rather the lack of them. In 1929 the London County Council had requests from over a thousand football clubs for use of only 350 pitches. The need for more facilities led to the foundation of the National Playing Fields Association in 1925 and the Central Council of Recreative Physical Training in 1935. The Council was formed as an umbrella organisation for all the voluntary bodies and agencies concerned with sport and physical recreation. It was later to become the most important factor in state intervention in sport. It worked closely with the Board of Education and following its work on post-school physical recreation in 1936, the National Fitness Council was

Figure 8.17 Suzanne Lenglen in action at Wimbledon, 1924

formed in 1937. The Physical Training and Recreation Act of 1937 provided public money to both local authorities and voluntary organisations to help provide more gymnasiums, swimming pools and playing fields.

The aim of the Council was 'to help improve the physical and mental health of the community through physical recreation, by developing existing facilities for recreative activity of all kinds and also by making provision for thousands not yet associated with any organisation'. This aim could be seen as using sport as a form of social control, with the working class as the main target. This view has its origins in the rational recreation tradition which saw sport as bringing society together and improving national efficiency. During the inter-war period there was relatively little central government interference in sport and recreation, apart from the developments in state school physical education. It was a period when government money was tightly controlled. Such improvements as there were came largely from local authority initiatives, which varied greatly across the country.

Although cricket was still the national game, it was football which became Britain's major sporting activity. Attendances soared with the average first division gate rising from 23 115 in 1913 – 14 season to 30 659 in 1938 – 39. By the 1937 – 38 season, the four first divisions in the English League attracted a total of 31.43 million fans, paying £1.57 million. The healthy position of football at the end of the 1930s allowed the authorities to ignore the primitive conditions provided for the spectators, to largely reject international competition and to refuse to consider floodlighting and Sunday football. English football remained proud and insular. England was not a member of FIFA and did not take part in the new World Cup. For the players the maximum wage and the retain-and-transfer system restricted their prospects considerably. Although football depended on, and belonged to working class men, both the players and the spectators in practice had little control over the game.

Sport had close links with the press, broadcasting and the cinema. Even in the 1930s there were complaints that sports journalists were irresponsible in the way they encouraged sensationalism in their sports reporting! BBC live coverage of sporting events on the radio started in 1927, with Saturday afternoon sporting programmes by the middle of the 1930s. Broadcasting coverage of all major events to almost all homes in the country, showed the existence of a national sporting calendar by the end of the 1930s. The press and radio played a very important role in the development of spectator sport, and through their influence, the first truly national sports stars arrived to public acclaim.

Following the end of the First World War there was a real danger that physical education in public elementary schools might slip back into military training. However, Fisher's Education Act of 1918, showed a wider view of the subject than had appeared before. It allowed local authorities to increase the provision for sport through more playing fields, swimming pools, camping centres and equipment. The 1919 syllabus which followed maintained the therapeutic nature of the subject, saying *'the object of physical education and training is to help in the production and maintenance of health in body and mind'*. This was very different from the character training reasoning for games in the public schools. It relied mainly on the Swedish system and therapeutic exercises, although there were suggestions on games. The Haddow Report of 1926, amongst other things, reorganised school life with a break at eleven years. The 1933 syllabus referred to the different needs of junior and senior children. The original exercises had been overhauled, fresh exercises included and revised methods of teaching introduced. There was a move away from the rigid class lessons towards group work. Many simple games were described which were intended to lead later to the major games. The emphasis was on the production of a healthy efficient body.

There was still no college in England to train male physical education specialists until the opening of the Carnegie Physical Training College in 1933. Others followed at Loughborough College and Goldsmiths' College, all offering one-year courses to qualified male teachers. Gradually there were moves away from therapeutic exercises towards recreative physical training. In 1936, the Board of Education advised elementary schools to organise daily physical activity including exercises, swimming and games, or dance. Local education authorities were reminded of their power to provide adequate facilities and similar provision was demanded in secondary schools. In public schools, experiments continued with the appointment of gymnastic teachers, but in the main, games continued to rule.

Thus by the outbreak of war, physical education had consolidated its position in the state education system and had a regular supply of trained teachers of both sexes. The elementary and public schools were still far apart in their concept of physical education, using different methods to produce different products. In the elementary schools, control was largely in the hands of the Board of Education, with its prescribed syllabuses, and the local education authorities who supplied the facilities.

The demand for sport and its commercialisation led to the development of a thriving sports industry. Between 1912 and 1935,

Figure 8.18 Cameras in use at Crystal Palace, 1937

the gross output of the industry almost doubled. Names such as Dunlop, Slazenger and Spalding became prominent as important employers and manufacturers of sporting equipment.

Gambling by the mid-1930s was a major industry with an annual turnover of perhaps £400 million. This included horse and greyhound racing and the increasingly popular football pools. A massive growth of expenditure on the pools enabled the industry to develop rapidly and it was soon employing thousands of workers. There was concern at the time that too many sporting activities were still linked to gambling and others only required a minimum of physical activity.

During the inter-war years, participation in sport at an amateur level for all classes, purely for recreational purposes, became more and more popular. However, the most important factor in sporting development at this time was the commercialisation of sport. Sports promoters throughout the country were building the facilities and providing the opportunities to satisfy the increasing demand. Sport was becoming big business. Sport in this period had developed against a background of economic rebuilding. The new opportunities available, however, could not be exploited by all, with the unemployed and women being particularly disadvantaged. Nevertheless, the working class were not just passive receivers of commercial sport. They were able to bring to commercialised sport, as they had brought to their own recreational sporting interests, their own distinctive culture and values.

SUMMARY

- Steady growth in sports participation continued for all classes of society, although working class women were least involved.
- Most sports were still class orientated.
- Football (in all its versions) continued to increase in popularity and by the 1930s, was the most popular sporting activity.
- Lack of facilities became an issue, particularly when national teams failed.
- There was little government involvement in sport, apart from physical education in schools.
- School physical education moved from therapeutic exercises to recreative physical training.
- Commercialisation of sport expanded rapidly, especially the provision for spectator sport.
- Sport, as a part of a national culture, now extended to the majority of the population.

Questions

1 Although women continued to be restricted to participation in a limited number of sports, significant progress was made in a number of different ways. Explain these developments in the inter-war period.

2 Government involvement in the development of physical education ensured that the subject became firmly established in the state education system. Explain how the subject was directed away from military drill into other systems.

3 In between the world wars, some new commercialised forms of sport developed alongside the established ones. Discuss these developments in particular, and the general move towards a mass entertainment industry.

4 Explain why there was an expansion of sporting opportunities for all sections of society between the wars. Consider why it did not apply equally across all social classes and for both men and women.

Modern British sport since 1945

In the late nineteenth century, sport was first established on a regular basis, with national organisations, wide public interest and commercial awareness. A century later sport has become international, highly commercialised, instantly available and universally accessible. While Britain was at the forefront of the first sporting revolution, it has been relegated to an increasingly marginal position today. Sport within Britain now plays an important part in the life of many people; it is of increasing value to the economy and has become a major aspect of the culture.

The post-war period has seen the standard of living greatly improve. The mass of people have had more money available to spend on leisure time activities. This has also allowed sports, which require a large financial outlay to become more widely available to all sections of the population. Basic working hours have been progressively reduced and this has given increased time for leisure. More recently, the rise in unemployment, short-time working and early retirement have all led to a greater amount of leisure time. Work has become less demanding physically, as has life in general. Labour-saving devices in the home and workplace, together with the acquisition of cars, have saved people time and opened up opportunities for a wider use of leisure time. Im-provements in medical care, diet and sanitation have raised the general health of the population. At the same time, the medical importance of a healthy life style and the popularity of the fitness image have encouraged people to take part actively in physical recreation. Facilities for sport and physical recreation have greatly improved,

Figure 8.19 Some sports require great expense

largely through the efforts of the Sports Council and the local authorities. Today, opportunities for taking part in sport are widely available and participation levels have risen in general.

Sport has become increasingly commercialised as its popularity has increased and opportunities for profit have emerged. As the rewards for success have grown, so have the temptations for drug abuse, violence, commercial manipulation and greed. The influence of the media, especially television, has enabled sport of all kinds to be brought into every home. Sport today is of great national importance. Stars are created and discarded by the media with great regularity. Defeat of the national team is turned into a national disaster.

Money and professionalism

Throughout the history of sport as an organised activity, and often before, money has been involved in a variety of ways. Some of this financial involvement has been kept firmly under control. For example, the earnings of professional sportsmen were carefully regulated for a long time. Today the vast sums paid out appear only to be controlled by market forces, as is the case in the entertainment world in general. The arguments over 'broken time' payments in the last century were serious enough to lead to two quite distinct codes of rugby, each with their own particular view of financial arrangements for the game. Other financial aspects, like gambling, have varied in their significance, depending on the historical period.

The amateurs who controlled sport in the last century, only allowed market forces to enter sport in the form of professionalism amongst the players and only in a limited number of sports. There had been a long tradition of professionalism amongst jockeys and fighters. All sports made a very clear distinction between those who needed to be paid, the professionals, and those whose social position enabled them to play without direct reward, the amateurs. Although tolerated in some sports, professionalism was certainly not encouraged by the ruling bodies of sport. Rather than setting up a free market, the arrival of professionalism, for example in football, bound players to clubs and imposed a maximum wage. The Football Association decided to accept professionalism within its organisation in order to control it, while the rugby union authorities chose to reject professionalism totally and hence lost control of that part of the game.

Gambling has almost always been part of competitive games and activities. Wagers between the gentlemen who organised the early cricket matches were an essential part of the sport. Early rules for boxing were largely concerned with regulating the betting that took place rather than protecting the fighters' interests. Pedestrian races in the last century were organised mainly for the spectators to gamble on the result, while gambling and horse racing have always gone hand in hand. Gambling had always been thought to be the downfall of the lower classes, although the upper classes were thought immune from its ruinous effects. Various laws were passed from time to time to restrict gambling, usually to little effect until the mid-Victorian period, when street and public house betting were banned. Horse racing gradually became better organised and the betting more orderly in the last century. However, it was the introduction of the totalisator earlier this century which really improved the fairness of the gambling for the punters. It ensured fair and certain returns for those making bets. At this time the football pools also became very popular and were acceptable to the majority of society. There had always been concern that gambling on any sport would bring with it sharp practices of different kinds, in order to manipulate the result. Interference with horses and human performers had been common and there existed a whole variety of potions which were thought to be capable of producing the required result. However, objections to gambling gradually subsided as sports became better organised and gave better protection to the participants, both human and animal. More recently, bookmakers have been allowed back into Lords cricket ground again after all the efforts last century to exclude gambling. In 1976, bookmakers were allowed into Wimbledon. Today it is possible to bet on the result of almost any sporting activity.

After the Second World War the opportunity for a comfortable, financially secure life for the leisured classes declined. The implications for cricket were serious. First class amateur cricketers of a high calibre became hard to find as gentlemen devoted more of their time and energy to education and management of their assets. Although in 1949, 175 out of 450 county cricketers were still amateur, in 1961 the figures were down to only 72 out of 370. The difficulty of raising a strong enough team to represent the 'Gentlemen' in the annual match against the 'Players' was such that Lords decided to abandon the fixture after 1962. It was decided that all distinctions between amateurs and professionals would be scrapped in 1963 and in future all players would be simply called cricketers. At this time professional cricketers were poorly paid compared to the average manual wage and they had no one to represent them until the Cricketers' Association was founded in 1968. There have been improvements in their incomes since then, although the benefit match remains vital for the future financial security of county cricketers nearing the end of their career. Nevertheless, the financial rewards for players in general have never been great. The attractions of playing in Kerry Packer's cricket circus in Australia in the late 70s' or of coaching or taking part in rebel tours in South Africa, have been hard to resist on financial grounds for many players.

Professional footballers always had more opportunities in the sport than cricketers because the game was played more widely, for a longer period of time each season, and involved more clubs. However, sporting careers were likely to be much shorter, largely because of

Figure 8.20 Gary Lineker and Bobbie Robson with the Fairplay Award at the World Cup Rome in 1990

the differing physical demands. The maximum wage was first set in 1900 at £4 a week to prevent the development of market forces in the payment of players. Although not all clubs were in a position to pay the maximum, it is known that ambitious clubs found a variety of ways around the rule in order to get the best players. Between the wars, thanks largely to the efforts of the Professional Footballers' Association (PFA) – originally founded in 1907 – the maximum wage was gradually moved upwards and efforts were made to protect players' careers when ill or injured. In the 1950s, the declining value of the maximum wage of £20 in relation to average earnings and the failure of players to gain from the increased revenue from television, led to a surge of militancy on the part of the players. In 1960, the PFA led by Jimmy Hill, threatened strike action in order to achieve the removal of the maximum wage restriction. Freedom of contract and mobility took a little longer to achieve. George Eastham, backed by the PFA, took Newcastle United to court for 'unjustifiable restraint of trade' and won the case in 1961.

Hooliganism in football by the 1980s had become a major political issue. In 1985, at the final of the European Cup at the Heysel Stadium in Belgium, 38 spectators died as a result of rioting by Liverpool fans. Although not directly attributable to hooliganism, the tragic loss of life at the FA Cup semi-final at Hillsborough brought matters to a head. The government was determined to act and proposed imposing an identity card scheme on all spectators. This was strongly resisted by the sport for a variety of practical reasons. It was finally abandoned by the government after the Taylor Report rejected identity cards and offered other solutions to the problems. The reduction of hooliganism and the successful performance of the England team in the 1990 World Cup may have contributed to the recovery of attendances, after the all-time low in the middle eighties. The establishment of the Premier League in 1992 was originally proposed in order to reduce league fixtures. Now it might be seen merely as a way of ensuring that the top clubs take as large a share as possible of the money which comes into the game.

After football, boxing has been probably the most important working class spectator sport. The British Boxing Board of Control took over in 1929 from the gentlemen of the National Sporting Club. In the 1940s there were around a thousand registered boxers, although the number has continued to fall ever since. This century, up to the Second World War, Britain produced many world champions at different weights. The difficult social conditions in inner cities forced many young men to fight through financial necessity. Where racial minorities were oppressed in particular areas, Jewish and Catholic boxers, like Jack 'Kid' Berg and Benny Lynch, emerged to achieve world titles. In more recent times a variety of factors, including economic difficulties and immigration, have ensured a steady stream of young boxers. Today the vast sums of money available through television rights are a particularly important factor in persuading young men to take part in a potentially lethal activity. Opposition to boxing has grown gradually, helped by medical reports and the tragic deaths and disablement of a number of boxers.

Although football, cricket and boxing have the largest number of professional sportsmen, membership has increased in other sports. In tennis, in the years following the war, a number of successful amateur players turned professional each year, often following the winning of major titles like the Wimbledon Championships. However, most major competitive play was in theory amateur up to the late 1960s. The game increasingly suffered from sham amateurism until in 1968, Wimbledon and the other major tournaments were opened to professionals. Thereafter the game developed world-wide with full-time professionals touring the world to play in a wide variety of competitions and exhibition play. In recent years concern has been increasingly expressed about the young age at which players may join the professional tennis circuit. The early retirement of outstanding young female players over the years has caused the world body to raise the minimum age from 14 to 16. Tennis is one of the few sports in which female professional players play a significant part, having their own professional circuit. However, their financial rewards are always less than those offered to male players and the position of women's tennis is always subordinate to the men's game.

Figure 8.21 Andrea Jaeger retired from international tennis at a young age

In the past golf had always employed a large number of professionals, although they were rarely tournament players. They looked after the club shop, gave lessons and helped to run the club in general. Not many earned their living from the game in tournament play as until the 1950s, there were few tournaments with substantial prize money. This situation has changed completely, and today large sums of money are available at highly sponsored tournaments world wide. Like tennis, golf has produced a travelling group of top class professionals who permanently tour the world competing against each other. Events are tailored to the sponsor's requirements and winners are rewarded generously. For younger, less successful players the lifestyle is demanding, often demoralising, financially insecure and rarely glamorous. Like tennis, golf also supports professional women players though their reward, popularity and status is far below that of the men.

In the immediate post-war period interest in athletics was stimulated when the Olympic Games took place in London in 1948. However, while the rest of the world found an increasing variety of ways to circumvent the strict amateur rules of international athletics, Britain left its athletes to manage as best they could. Ever-increasing standards, meant that ways had to be found to support athletes financially. The creation of the Sports Council improved the situation

Figure 8.22 Linford Christie benefited from the trust fund arrangements

and the establishment of the Sports Aid Foundation, to support top class sportspersons financially, helped many prospective champions achieve their goals. In 1981, athletics became the first sport to set up trust funds. This enabled the athletes to safeguard their eligibility to take part in amateur competitions, while at the same time allowing them to receive financial rewards. The governing body kept control of the sport by insisting that all payments should be channelled through or authorised by them. Payments from the fund for day to day living expenses were allowed and the balance became available to the sportsperson on retirement. These arrangements enabled a group of both male and female athletes to tour the world, competing in a programme of championships and grand prix events with both appearance money and prize money for winning. Today the situation has changed and trust funds have been abolished in athletics. Payment is now made directly to athletes or their agents within new rules set by the International Amateur Athletics Association (IAAA). Although the status of women athletes is high, there are still differences in treatment, similar to those seen for women in tennis and golf.

The social changes of the sixties made it easier for women to participate in a wider variety of physical recreation and to be more accepted in sport in their own right. In the Rome Olympics, many more women took part than previously and in the Olympics that followed, women were accepted very slowly into a wider variety of events. However, even in the 1990s they are still excluded from a number of events. Concern over definitions of male and female competitors led to the introduction of sex testing for women in 1966. In the 1970s, the domination of women's athletics and swimming by East Germany brought suspicion about the use of drugs to enhance performance. Today, women take part in almost all sports although they only compete directly with men in a very few.

The words 'amateur' and 'professional' have become outdated. A large number of sports now allow participants to earn money if they are good enough. If they wish to keep their amateur status they will do this through trust funds or similar arrangements. Some sports do not distinguish at all between amateurs and professionals. The participants are referred to as players or competitors, they all compete together and the sport is known as an open sport. Today it is possible for highly paid professionals, like basketball and tennis players, to compete in the Olympic Games. The concept of amateurism has been replaced by eligibility to take part. In the case of the Olympic Games, eligibility is decided upon by the relevant international sports federations. The relaxation of the traditional definition of amateurism has benefited most sportspersons. However, there is always the danger that if competitors are contracted directly to commercial organisations without the involvement of the sports organisation, they may be exploited, to the detriment of the whole sport.

Sponsorship

Sponsorship of sporting individuals, teams, events or of the sport in general is now an integral part of the sporting scene. The commercial world is constantly looking for ways to gain publicity for its products and sport is a very attractive medium with its popular image of youth and vitality. The champions, local individuals and teams receive sponsorship. Some companies choose to become involved with achievement and coaching schemes which help encourage young people.

Corporate sponsorship has taken over in most sports, but personal sponsorship is still of some importance in particular cases. For example, successful businessmen may support football clubs, helping to finance expensive transfer deals. Most sponsorship in the late twentieth century has much more to do with profit than with sentiment. Sponsors are prepared to provide large amounts of money in return for media coverage and an attractive sporting image. There was some pre-war sponsorship, for example, the FA Cup Finalists of 1934 promoted trousers, shoe polish and Shredded Wheat! However, by modern standards there was very little sponsorship and any payments were very small amounts. In the early post-war years, Dennis Compton was famous for his cricket, and for his Brylcreem advertisement, one of the first major endorsements of a product by a sportsperson. Horse racing had always been supported by local businessmen who offered the prize for a particular race which carried their name. One of the first serious examples of modern sponsorship occurred in 1957 when Whitbreads offered £6000 prize money for the Ascot Gold Cup. In the 1960s, Gillette's sponsorship of one-day cricket helped launch a profitable and popular new form of the game.

The arrival of large-scale sponsorship for sport has removed the financial role of the paying spectator. Falling attendances at sporting events have shown that gate money is not always essential for sport's survival. Relatively few football clubs could survive purely on the money taken at the gate. In cricket, the county game in mid-week rarely draws sizeable crowds. The clubs are kept solvent through membership subscriptions, sponsorship and a share in test match profits rather than gate money. Today the really important spectator is the television viewer. For this reason, attempts have been made to change some sports, for example, to make them higher scoring or with more breaks for commercials. The financial success, or otherwise, of the sport will be determined by how popular the sport is with the armchair supporter.

BRYLCREEM

keeps your

hair right

in the

picture

For soft, lustrous hair, use Brylcreem! For handsome, healthy hair, use Brylcreem! Brylcreem makes your appearance a smart one, wherever you go, whatever you do. Massage your hair with Brylcreem every day and see how its pure oils give your hair that vital, well-cared-for look. Brylcreem controls the hair without excessive oiliness, because the oils in Brylcreem are *emulsified*. That means *clean* grooming. That means lasting hair-health. Ask for Brylcreem—in tubs 1/8 and 2/6, jars and tubes 2/6 and large economy tubs 4/6.

BRYLCREEM is *emulsified* **for clean grooming**

Figure 8.23   Dennis Compton

Thus strategies to sell sport to the general public are of vital importance. At the same time problems in the sport, for example drugs scandals, allegations of cheating or personal revelations of the star performers, are likely to damage the image of the sport with the public. In general, popular sports gain television time, and televised sport attracts sponsorship deals. The danger for sport is that the more important the sponsor becomes to the financial health of the sport, the more powerful the sponsor becomes in influencing the sport.

The increasing amount of money in sport has slowly filtered down to the sportspersons themselves. In earlier times the leading prize-fighters had won large purses from time to time, but not on a regular basis. By the end of the nineteenth century it was possible for some of the top jockeys to make £5000 a year, although footballers were only earning as little as £200 at the time.

At present the highest rewards generally go to individual sportspersons, rather than those playing in a team. Today sports such as motor racing, tennis, golf and snooker have made many players very rich. To this list should be added athletics which, although technically still an amateur sport, has found ways to enable competitors at the highest level to earn vast sums of money. The stars of sport often find that they are able to make more money from sponsorship and advertising contracts than they are actually paid for their performance. However, this life is not without its problems. For a variety of reasons, such as injury, loss of form, illness and age, the sportsperson may find it difficult to maintain his or her success. When this happens commercial opportunities quickly fade away, since companies only wish to be involved with successful sportpersons. Another recent development has been the arrival of the player's agent. He, or rarely she, is now a vital part of the star's advisory team which is likely to include a lawyer, psychologist and hairdresser. The agent is usually responsible for all the player's playing contracts, sponsorship deals and financial affairs in general. For this he, or she, is rewarded financially.

Figure 8.24 Most major sport activities are sponsored

The growing amount of money in British sport has seldom been reflected in improving or building modern sports facilities for spectators and sportspersons alike. Following the football crowd disaster at Hillsborough in 1989, the Taylor Report made numerous recommendations. Central to this report was the need to provide all-seater stadiums as soon as was practically possible, together with improved safety precautions and better police communications and medical facilities. Improvements have been made for the comfort and safety of football fans at the top clubs. In many parts of the world, large modern stadiums have been built to present a number of different sports and in some cases to allow more than one team in a particular sport to share the facility.

SUMMARY

- An improved standard of living has enabled greater participation in sport for most social groups.
- Amateur administrators only reluctantly allowed commercial forces to enter the world of sport.
- Professional sportspeople had a long battle to be given fair rewards.
- Television coverage increased in importance for sport and the sponsors.
- The definition of amateurism for competition was replaced by the concept of eligibility.

Questions

1 Explain the links between standards of living and participation in sport for the population in general.
2 Choose one sport and describe and account for the changes that have taken place within it to accommodate professional participants.
3 The concept of the amateur sportsperson at the highest level of sport has changed considerably in the post-war period. Explain what has happened and why eligibility is now a more important consideration.
4 'Today sport without sponsorship is unthinkable'. Discuss this statement .

Government involvement in sport and physical recreation

Since 1945, the state has been increasingly involved in sport and physical recreation through central and local government. In the nineties, direct state involvement ranges far and wide. The Home Office funds youth and community programmes involving sporting activity, together with physical training used for disciplinary purposes in the penal establishments. It is also responsible for the Gaming Board and the Horse-race Betting Levy Board. The Ministry of Defence manages the extensive sports facilities of the armed forces and with the Ministry of Agriculture, controls access to vast areas of the country which can be used for outdoor recreation. The Department of Health and Social Security is concerned with health and fitness aspects of sport and has general responsibility for the disabled. The Department of Trade and Industry is involved in the development of sports facilities and the leisure industry in general as sources of employment. The Department for Education and Employment has been responsible for all the recent changes in education, in particular, the national curriculum with its implications for physical education in schools. The minister with responsibility for sport is at present attached to the Department of National Heritage. Thus many different government departments have significant responsibility for sport and recreation. This fragmentation of responsibility creates problems for policy development and coordination. Other government created agencies involved in sport and recreation are the Countryside Commission, the Nature Conservancy, the National Parks Commission, the Tourist Boards, the British Inland Waterways Board, the Water Authorities and the Regional Planning Commission.

Figure 8.25 Opportunites for disabled sportspersons have expanded

To this can be added the Sports Council, which, although an independent body, is funded largely by the government. Since the Sports Council assists a large number of governing bodies and sporting organisations, the influence of government can be felt throughout sport in Britain, through its distribution of grants. In 1994, the government introduced a national lottery with some of the proceeds going to sport.

After the war there had been a huge extension of state activity into all areas of social life with the development of the Welfare State. Since physical recreation was considered valuable by society, it followed that the state should be involved in its provision. The gradual increase in state intervention started in earnest during the fifties for a number of reasons. After the end of the war, it was soon noted that there was an increasing demand from the mass of people for greater opportunities to enjoy leisure. There was added concern about the way some young people were thought to be misusing their leisure time. A number of official inquiries were launched in the late fifties to look into the problem of leisure and their subsequent recommendations influenced future policy directions. The Wolfenden Report called 'Sport and the Community' and the Albermarle Report on the Youth Service both reported in 1960.

In a world in which Britain's influence in economic, political and military spheres was seen to be in decline, success in sport was seen to be important. It was realised that without some form of assistance from the state, the chances of future British success in an increasingly competitive sporting world, were slim. The proposals that emerged from the Wolfenden Report were for an advisory sports council, an expansion of government aid for sport and the urgent development of sports facilities.

Physical education and sport

Once again a war stimulated the production of an Education Act. The Act of 1944 reshaped education in the public sector and affected physical education in a number of ways. Apart from religious education, physical education was the only subject which was included in the Act. For the first time, local education authorities were given a specific duty to provide adequate facilities for physical education and games. This enabled the content of the subject to be developed away from the narrow concept of sport into a broader field of physical recreation, including outdoor activities. More importantly, His Majesty's Inspectors of Physical Education were transferred from the school health service to the general administrative side of the Ministry of Education. Interest in physical education as a therapeutic device, including the medical value of physical exercises, declined, to be replaced by a view of the subject as an integral part of the education system.

The movement approach

Changes in content and method appeared after the war. Various forms of climbing apparatus were installed for younger children, with an emphasis on individual discovery of solutions to physical problems. Personal interpretation began to replace formal and uniform work. Another factor which influenced the development of the subject considerably was the introduction of the concept of 'movement'. It replaced 'posture' as the keyword in the post war years. Freedom, self-discovery and self-expression were encouraged in the 'movement' lesson. The movement approach proposed that activities could be educationally valid because of the intrinsic value of movement for its own sake, involving inner meanings and expressive qualities. This was in addition to the educational value of the functional skills performed and the extrinsic value of the physical, social and moral development gained through the subject. The development of these ideas was only possible because of the freedom of choice given to the teachers in the post-war period.

Many of the ideas originated in the work of Rudolf Laban in the late 1930s. The concept of movement was not an idea accepted readily by all teachers. The ideas became a focus for discussion and indeed controversy. Many remained sceptical of the new ideas, particularly male physical educationists. They were concerned about the threat to traditional activities and skills, especially major games. During the fifties and later, these difficulties were clarified to some extent, leaving the position not completely resolved, but more settled. In the infants school, movement training came to be used to describe all the work undertaken. In the junior schools, the majority of the work also came under the heading of movement, although swimming and the major games appeared separately for older children. In secondary schools, modern educational gymnastics and dance were distinguished from each other and from the formal, traditional work of 'Olympic' gymnastics. Movement education often co-existed with the therapeutic tradition of fitness and games skills.

The early fifties saw the arrival of a number of guides to the work in junior schools. In particular, the Ministry of Education set the scene with two important publications for primary schools called *Moving and Growing* and *Planning the Programme*. They were to replace the 1933 syllabus, and movement training was the underlying theme of both books. An interesting departure was that actual lesson plans were not presented. An open framework was offered, allowing teachers to interpret the work in their own way and to draw up schemes to meet the needs of the particular class they were teaching. In the sixties the movement approach dominated, although there was still resistance from those who considered the acquisition of skill the main aim of the subject. At this time the introduction of weight training and circuit training re-emphasised the therapeutic value of physical education.

In 1972, the Department of Education and Science issued a publication entitled *Movement*, designed to cover physical education in the primary schools. It focused on a consideration of the individual child and the provision of opportunities for direct experience and personal discovery. It gave no detailed schemes, but discussed a number of movement approaches to gymnastics, dance, games, swimming, athletics and outdoor activities. There were no parallel publications to cover physical education in the secondary schools. The assumption was that trained specialist teachers of physical education were equipped to teach and plan their subject competently. In fact, this lack of central guidance ensured a wide diversity of approaches in state schools. In the public schools, major games continued to dominate, although more modern approaches to gymnastics were investigated,

Figure 8.26 A lesson involving the movement approach, 1955

A reassessment of physical education

The latter part of the fifties had seen a great expansion in outdoor activities such as camping, walking, sailing and canoeing, which emphasised the recreational aspect of the subject. *Outward Bound* and similar courses were introduced, largely for character training, in a very similar way to the games of the public schools. In the sixties there was considerable development in the different types of activities accepted within the scope of physical education At a time of increasing affluence, local educational authorities, voluntary bodies and the private sector were able to provide facilities and equipment to allow people to take part in activities which would not have been possible in pre-war days. These included golf, squash, fencing, riding, water sports and many others largely unavailable to ordinary people in earlier times. Thus the increasing range of activities available out of school influenced to some extent the provision within schools. This resulted in a change of emphasis in some secondary schools from physical education towards physical recreation. It also meant a move from the development of high-level skills in a limited number of sports towards mass participation in many sports at a lower level of skill. Physical educationists had fought for parity of esteem for the subject in the curriculum over a long time. The 'recreation revolution' did much to damage this progress. It emphasised preparation for future physical recreation, rather than the educational value of the physical education programme offered in school.

The freedom enjoyed by the physical education teacher in the sixties allowed the subject to advance in only piecemeal fashion. There were few attempts to make a serious review of the development of the subject as a whole. However, the coming of the Bachelor of Education degrees in the seventies, which included physical education and movement studies, resulted in a complete reappraisal of the relationship between education, movement and physical education. This was caused mainly by the need to justify the subject in academic terms. At this time examinations at CSE level began to appear in a variety of areas including physical education, movement studies, sports studies, outdoor activities and related areas. These subjects usually included an examination of practical performance, written examinations involving anatomy and physiology, with some aspects of sport in society.

The arrival of the GCSE examination scheme reduced the variety of examinations offered because of the stringent requirements applied to the examination criteria. There has been a steady growth in the number of candidates taking physical education at GCSE level since its introduction. This indicates a growing recognition of the value of the examination amongst both physical educationists and schools in general. In 1986, the status of the subject was further enhanced by the introduction of examinations at GCE Advanced Level in two subjects – Physical Education and Sports Studies. Both these subjects have proved popular and the numbers taking the examination have continued to rise to nearly 8000 in 1995. Today there are also a number of vocational qualifications involving sport and leisure studies, for example, the GNVQ course in leisure and tourism. The development of these courses has been due to the employment opportunities offered by the growth in the fitness, health and leisure markets.

Figure 8.27 Outdoor activities are an important part of the school Physical Education curriculum

Recent changes in education

During the 1980s, there were a number of factors which influenced physical education. Many local authorities found that because of falling rolls, it was necessary to close some schools. In 1981 the government approved legislation which encouraged local authorities to sell off surplus playing fields. While there were obviously financial advantages for this action, the loss to the communities of much needed playing fields was a severe blow. Many sporting bodies protested at this policy, claiming it to be short-sighted and not in the public interest.

In some schools, particularly in the primary sector, there were strong moves against competitive sport. These actions were motivated by a particular view of education which saw competition, as opposed to co-operation, between pupils as ultimately harmful. It resulted, in some areas, in the abandoning of long-standing sporting fixtures between primary schools, the teaching of alternatives to games and sports, and the cancellation of sports days. In more recent years there has been a gradual reversal of this trend, with sports competition being seen as an important educational tool and the development of sporting excellence as valuable for the individual. Today team games are a central part of the national curriculum.

In 1985, the long-running teachers' pay dispute resulted in the curtailment of many of the regular extra-curricular activities for some period of time. This action affected sporting fixtures very badly. After the dispute was settled, and teachers' hours fixed, many staff chose not to resume their previous out-of-school sporting commitments. This resulted in a nation-wide decline in extra-curricular sporting activities which to date shows little sign of improving.

The concern in society in general for the health and fitness of the population was increased by a number of reports which suggested that fitness levels were low and declining. This affected the physical education in schools, through the introduction of heath-related fitness programmes, a return to the use of physical education for its therapeutic value in improving health.

The Education Acts of 1986 and 1988 have affected physical education in a number of ways. Most importantly, the freedom enjoyed by physical educationists in the post war period has been severely curtailed. The new national curriculum specified in broad terms the content of the subject for the future; however, it has left the method of delivery still in the hands of teachers.

Physical education was included in the national curriculum as a foundation subject, confirming its status as a major component of the curriculum. This means that attainment targets were set for the various age groups, together with programmes of study. For the years five to 16, there are four key stages. Details are given in chapter 10. As physical education was one of the last foundation subjects to be implemented, it has faced strong competition for curriculum time. In

Figure 8.28 Competitive sport in schools

some schools, timetabled physical education has been reduced, especially in key stage four, in order to accommodate all the other statutory subjects. There was a review of the national curriculum in 1994 by Sir Ron Dearing which proposed a number of changes largely relating to the areas of activity offered at the different key stages. The report also proposed a greater emphasis on games and increased opportunities for swimming as a separate subject. In addition, the review offers schools greater flexibility at key stage four, and if accepted, there may be opportunities to improve the amount of time given to physical education.

Another major change to the management of schools has been the transfer of control from the local authorities to school governors and the head teacher. Schools now have responsibility for their own budget which is based on the number of pupils in attendance. Local authorities in the past have always financed the use of off-site facilities such as swimming pools, sports centres, recreation grounds and outdoor activity centres. Today the extent to which these are available at any particular school will depend on the value placed on them by the school. Although the local authority still controls the use of schools for adult education and the youth service, it is the governors who manage community use of the school premises. The availability of facilities for local sports clubs and the charges to be made are decided by the governors. They have to balance the need to raise income against the ability of the local sporting community to pay. It might be that in this way more facilities will become available, although it is also possible that high charges will put them beyond the resources of local clubs.

Schools today are in fierce competition with one another for pupils, since budgets are now controlled by the numbers on their rolls. The school's popularity with parents in the community will depend on a wide variety of factors. One of these is likely to be the quality of the physical education programme, as well as the range and variety of sporting activities offered out of school. The need to market the school successfully may encourage schools to increase the resources available to physical education and also to develop the opportunities available for community involvement with the school.

SUMMARY

- Central government involvement in sport has always been fragmentary.
- There has been a long standing underfunding of sport by central government.
- An advisory Sports Council was established in 1965 and the independent executive Sports Council in 1972.
- Physical education was established in the 1944 Act for its educational value. The movement approach conflicted with traditional games teaching.
- Physical education moved away from educational values towards physical recreation and more recently towards health-related fitness.
- Various academic qualifications in physical education stimulated scrutiny of the subject (for example, B Ed, CSE, GCSE, A-Level).
- Physical education is now established in the national curriculum as a foundation subject.
- There has been an increasing influence of market forces on schools, physical education, sports facilities and sport.

Questions

1   Describe the various ways in which the government today is involved, both directly and indirectly, in sport and physical recreation.

2   Explain what is meant by the 'movement approach' to physical education and explain the influence it has had on the development of the subject since 1945.

3   The establishment of new examinations in physical education and related areas of study, both for prospective teachers and pupils, stimulated a detailed on-going analysis of the subject. Discuss the impact of the developments.

4   There have been many major developments in the education system in the last ten years, for example, the introduction of the national curriculum. Discuss these changes and the way they have affected physical education in schools.

5   The importance attached to physical education has changed greatly since the Education Act of 1870. Discuss the major trends and influences.

References

Birkley, Derek *Sport and the making of Britain* Manchester University Press (1993)

Brailsford, Dennis *British sport* Lutterworth Press (1992)

Coghlan, John *Sport and British Politics* Falmer Press (1990)

Hargreaves, John *Sport, power and culture* Polity Press (1986)

Holt, Richard *Sport and the British* Clarendon Press (1989)

Jones, Stephen *Sport, politics and the working class* Manchester University Press (1988)

Mason, Tony (ed) *Sport in Britain* Cambridge University Press (1989)

9 ORGANISATION OF SPORT

Objectives

To understand

- the origins of contemporary sport, and to see how they have shaped the structure and organisation of sport in England and Wales today
- the responsibility of governing bodies of sport; how they function and how they develop their elite teams and performers
- the way the British government came into sport and the role it plays
- the role of each of the many agencies established to assist the promotion and development of sport at elite and community levels
- the way opportunity for participation in sport has developed and how it continues to expand
- the factors that work against the involvement of certain groups in the community in the broad mass participation movement
- the ways in which facilities for sport and physical recreation are provided

The structure and organisation of sport in Britain is basically very simple. We have sports clubs and each sport has an 'umbrella' organisation, that is, a governing body. The governing body will administer the sport, organise competitions, promote development, maintain standards, ethics and discipline, and generally work to promote the best interests of that sport. It is responsible for seeing that the sport it governs plays according to the rules or laws of the game, which are in turn set by the international federation for the sport to which all national governing bodies are affiliated. Sometimes with some sports the national structure is broken down to regional or county governing bodies, which in turn are affiliated to the national body. For example, all football clubs belong to a County Football Association. County Football Associations are affiliated to the Football Association, so therefore every club has a voice in the democratic conduct of the sport. The FA is affiliated to the international body, the Fédération Internationale de Football Association (FIFA).

There are many people who participate in sport who do not belong to a club, such as canoeists or casual squash players. In this case such participants use publicly- or commercially-provided facilities on a pay-as-you-use basis. These participants are known as 'casual users'.

Public, commercial and private facilities

Public facilities in the main are provided by local authorities. For example, a local authority pays for the building and staffing of the local swimming pool and the users pay a fee to use it. In the same way a commercial company provides a facility, such as an ice-rink, and the users pay at the door.

Clubs are private and members pay a subscription to join and enjoy the facilities. These facilities have been provided by membership subscriptions and quite often by grants from the Sports Council, as long as clubs own the land or have a sufficiently long lease to warrant expenditure with money from the tax-payer.

The governing bodies of sport

Structure

The governing bodies of sport are voluntary organisations. They are elected by each sport to run that sport at national level. While many will have a professional salaried staff to manage affairs on a day-to-day basis, and some of the major sports have large staffs, those who decide policy are unpaid volunteers elected by members.

The methods of election may differ from sport to sport, but in all instances they are democratic elections. The elections are based on a democratic constitution which may only be changed by the members of the sport itself.

Neither the government, nor any other body, has a role in the running and conduct of a national governing body. However, from time to time outside organisations will try to influence affairs because sport has such a high profile in the international field. For example, the British government did try to prevent the British Olympic team from competing in Moscow in 1980 because the Soviet Union had invaded Afghanistan in late 1979. Likewise, successive governments in Britain did everything they legally could to prevent sporting contacts with South Africa before apartheid was abolished. In the first instance the government was largely unsuccessful, but in the latter case it was increasingly successful as the years went by. However, in these high profile situations, and in others that have arisen, the governing bodies have made the decision.

Finance

Governing bodies receive their income from four principal sources today. These are subscriptions from their members, sponsorship, television fees, and grants from the Sports Council. Some of the major governing bodies get income from gate-money from spectator events, and therefore, not having a great need for financial help, do not qualify for grants from the Sports Council. Some cannot attract television, and some have difficulty in obtaining sponsorship to any meaningful extent, so it is fair to say that no two governing bodies raise income in exactly the same way.

Remember that sport is not something separate from society; it is a part of our culture. Sport reflects the society in which it is practised and, therefore, as we briefly trace the development of sport from early in the nineteenth century to the present time, its development has to be seen against the social and economic background of the day.

The organisation of sport

The origins and nature of sport in England and Wales today are directly linked to the nineteenth century and, in particular, the latter half of the century. The industrial revolution saw a massive shift of population from the countryside to the towns, as work was sought in the factories, mills and mines. Against this working-class background the principal influence on the development of sport was the public schools, which grew rapidly in number to meet the needs and aspirations of an emerging middle class.

Early in the century headmasters of the then few public schools positively discouraged sport as this was seen to encourage hooliganism and bad behaviour. As the century wore on, attitudes changed to such an extent that the 'games cult' was seen increasingly as a force for good, and a force that instilled courage, leadership and character-forming qualities. The Universities of Oxford and Cambridge followed the pattern of team sport development of the public schools, as it was to these two institutions that the public schoolboys went for their higher education.

By mid-century sport had extended beyond the public schools and universities, and teams were springing up in the towns in increasing numbers, with soccer the main focus of attention. The developing industrial cities and soccer identified closely with each other as they do today. By the latter part of the century it was clear that some central organisation and control was needed in the developing sports to formalise rules, laws and competitions. This led to the formation, for example, of:

- The Football Association (FA) in 1863
- The Amateur Swimming Association (ASA) in 1869
- The Rugby Football Union (RFU) in 1871
- The Badminton Association of England (BA of E)
- The Hockey Association (HA) and the All England Women's Hockey Association (AEWHA) in 1895.

In some cases prestigious events led to the formation of a governing body. For example, the Henley Royal Regatta, started in 1839, eventually brought about the formation of the Amateur Rowing Association (ARA) in 1882. Likewise the first 'Wimbledon' Championship took place in 1877 leading to the establishment of the Lawn Tennis Association (LTA) in 1888. Oxford and Cambridge were competing in athletics since 1864, sixteen years before the Amateur Athletics Association was formed in 1880. So it was that well before the turn of the century, clubs from both ends of the social spectrum were in

Figure 9.1 The Henley Regatta

being; some sports such as soccer, often based on church or working men's clubs. Some of the most famous professional clubs, for example Aston Villa FC, sprang from such roots.

As the twentieth century dawned, the pattern of British sport was set with the development of voluntary sports organisations, the clubs, banded together for a common purpose of playing a particular sport. Matters continued in this way well into the second half of the century, as new sports took hold, with sports clubs and national governing bodies to administer and run each sport. As we approach the millennium the pattern of club and governing body structure continues and is the envy of the world.

Many clubs provided their own pitches and courts on land they owned, or which they leased, as they do today. At the same time municipal authorities, that is, local councils, have provided pitches, swimming pools, tennis courts and bowling greens. This has been to an increasing extent to cater for the swelling number of participants from an increasingly diverse social base for well over a hundred years. Factories, offices and churches, particularly between the two world wars of 1914 – 18 and 1939 – 45, frequently included sports sections in their social activities and often provided playing pitches of a high standard. An excellent example of this sort of provision was Cadburys, at Bournville in Birmingham, but there were, and are, many other such examples.

With the ending of the Second World War in 1945, sport in England and Wales re-started at the same point where it had largely finished in 1939, although it had continued as best it could during the war. The first post-war Olympic Games of 1948 took place in London on a make-do basis, a far cry from the extravaganzas of today, but very importantly, this event signalled an international return to some degree of normality.

The priorities in Britain were re-construction, jobs for the demobilised servicemen and women, and a drive to get back to normal. Any new deal for sport did not feature on the agenda. However, there were those who talked about the future for sport as Britain struggled to recover. In 1956 the Physical Education Department of the University of Birmingham published *Britain in the World of Sport* which signalled a new way forward and quickened the debate. Spurred on by this publication, the Central Council of Physical Recreation (CCPR) in 1957 appointed a small, but very influential committee under the chairmanship of Sir John Wolfenden with the following terms of reference.

'To examine the factors affecting the development of games, sports and outdoor activities in the United Kingdom and to make recommendations to the Central Council of Physical Recreation as to any practical measures which should be taken by statutory or voluntary bodies in order that these activities may play their full part in promoting the general welfare of the community.'

The Wolfenden Committee reported in 1960 with their publication *Sport and the Community,* which was to change the face of sport in Britain dramatically. Fifty-seven recommendations were made from which three fundamental issues arose. These issues may be summarised as follows:

- There should be a National Sport Development Council with public finance, to assist the development of the governing bodies of sport and to provide facilities.

- There should be statutory, that is, governmental, involvement in the financing of sport.

- A massive programme for more abundant facilities should be undertaken.

Figure 9.2 Structure of sport in England

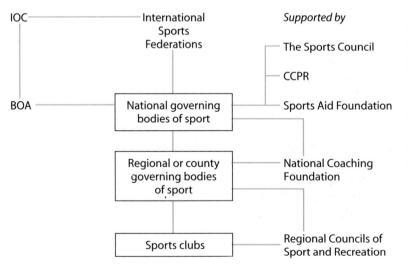

British sport was now at the crossroads. Should sport continue to develop as it had done since the nineteenth century, or should the government become involved with public finance to assist the way ahead and create a new climate in which British sport could flourish? In other words, should politics enter sport, because if the British government were to play a role, and in particular a financial role, would the voluntary nature of sport alter and therefore would sports bodies continue to be in control of their own sports?

The Sports Council

Although the Wolfenden Report was published in 1960, it took five years of discussion in and out of Parliament, and in the media, before positive action was taken to establish a National Sport Development Council. In the run-up to the October 1964 general election, the Labour Party declared in their election manifesto that, if elected, they would appoint a minister with responsibility for sport and would establish a 'Sports Council'. A Labour government was returned and Denis Howell was appointed as minister responsible for Sport. In February 1965 the government announced the setting up of the Sports Council as an advisory body to government, with the Minister in the chair supported by sixteen members appointed by the government. The terms of reference for this advisory Sports Council were simple, clear and all-embracing; the Council would be responsible for advising the government on all matters relating to the development of amateur sport and recreation.

Today the work of the Sports Council is still covered by these guidelines which were established in 1965, although great changes have been made over all.

In February 1972 the Conservative government, elected in June 1970, changed the constitutional status of the Sports Council when the Council was granted a Royal Charter by HM The Queen. This established it as an independent body with executive powers, as opposed to the advisory role. Sport now had the best of both worlds; it remained theoretically free of state control. However, it had increased state financial involvement through being voted grant-in-aid annually by Parliament to carry out its functions. This situation still exists, where the grant is now in excess of £50 million each year. The first chairman of this executive Sports Council was Roger Bannister, an eminent consultant neurologist and the first man to run the mile in under four minutes in 1954. He was supported by twenty-four members.

The terms of reference given to the advisory Sports Council in 1965 were largley those in the Royal Charter, and in particular, in the chapter dealing with 'furtherance of objects'. The first three, there are eight in all, summarise the task of the Council then and now:

(a) *to develop and improve the knowledge and practice of sport and physical recreation in the interests of social welfare and the enjoyment of leisure among the public at large in Great Britain, and to encourage the attainment of high standards in conjunction with the governing bodies of sport and physical recreation;*

(b) *to foster, support or undertake provision of facilities for sport and physical recreation;*

(c) *to carry out itself, or to encourage and support other persons or bodies in carrying out research and studies into matters concerning sport and physical recreation; and to disseminate knowledge and advice on these matters.*

The remaining five objectives deal with the powers to make grants and loans to further the work and define the role of the Council in relation to the government.

The Sports Council was asked to advise on matters concerning:

- the development of training and coaching
- priorities in sport development, that is, participation
- standards of provision for sports facilities, that is, how many swimming pools, sports halls, running tracks, golf courses, and so on, were needed and where
- co-ordination of the use of existing and new community resources, for example, greater use of school sports facilities and those of the armed services
- capital expenditure required to develop an expanding programme of facility provision
- research, both social and medical
- surveys of resources, that is, what did we have and what did we need?
- regional planning
- international competition involving British teams
- sport in foreign countries.

Since 1972, under the Royal Charter, the Sports Council has worked to encourage participation in sport at all levels by encouraging and stimulating the growth of facilities. It has also supported the governing bodies of sport to raise standards to compete more successfully at international level.

Because the structure of the UK is complex there are separate Sports Councils for Wales, Scotland and Northern Ireland. They deal with purely national matters. The Sports Council not only dealt with English affairs but also took on a Great Britain or United Kingdom role when required as, for example, when dealing with international affairs, or when foreign governments were involved, and this country needed to present itself as one unit and not four. This structure changed in 1996.

Facilities

The crucial step taken in developing a massive programme for more facilities was the setting up of the nine (later ten) Regional Sports Councils in England in the autumn of 1965 (they later became Regional Councils for Sport and Recreation) serviced by the Sports Council staff of the regional offices. The Sports Council for Wales acts as both a national body for Wales and in the role of a regional council for sport and recreation. The same arrangement exists in Scotland and Northern Ireland.

The Regional Councils for Sport and Recreation were consortia of local authority representatives, in the main the providers locally, and the regional or county governing bodies of sport, the users. In the beginning these Regional Councils were concerned only with facilities but, as the years went by they became involved with participation programmes. In 1996 the Regional Councils for Sport and Recreation were abolished as part of the government's restructuring arrangements.

Facilities are needed at three levels – national, regional and local.

National

National facilities are required for the staging of international events. Wembley, Twickenham, Lords and the National Stadium in Cardiff are all examples of national-scale facilities, but equally large indoor facilities are needed and these are in short supply.

In 1993 the Sports Council's strategy document *Sport in the Nineties – New Horizons* stated that, compared with other leading sporting nations, Britain still had a serious shortage of facilities capable of staging European and World Championship events. The National Indoor Arena in Birmingham and the facilities created in Sheffield for the 1991 World Student Games were welcome additions. Also the government grant of £73 millions to the City of Manchester for major facility provision to support the British bid for the Olympic Games in the year 2000, which sadly proved unsuccessful, further improved the position. Britain's first indoor cycling arena was opened in Manchester in 1994 at a cost of £9 million. These facilities will be used for the Commonwealth Games in 2002.

The National Sports Centres in England and Wales are under the control of the Sports Council and the Sports Council for Wales. They provide a wide range of specialist facilities for training and coaching to support the governing bodies. The centres found in England and Wales, together with their specialist activities are:

- Crystal Palace – Spectator events for swimming and athletics. Diving Institute
- Bisham Abbey – LTA Residential School for young players
- Lilleshall – FA Soccer School and high level gymnastics
- Holme Pierrepont – National Water Sports Centre
- Plas y Brenin – National Outdoor Activities Centre
- National Sports Centre for Wales, Cardiff – all purpose
- Plas Menai (North Wales) – National Outdoor Activities Centre for Wales.

Regional and local

Swimming pools

By early 1993 there were 1404 indoor pools in England and 114 in Wales, all owned by local authorities. A couple of years earlier the Department for Education had reported that 2496 primary schools and 855 secondary schools had pools. This meant that 13% of all primary schools and 23% of secondary schools had a pool.

Figure 9.3 Plas y Brenen National Outdoor Activities Centre

Public pools are a variety of different lengths and include training pools, learner pools, diving pools and leisure pools. It is estimated that a little more than 10% of all public pools are leisure pools, although nearer 40% of newly opened pools, or those under construction, are leisure pools.

Indoor sports halls and sports centres

Because the definition of a 'public sports hall' tends to differ, it is difficult to provide an exact figure for indoor sports halls and sports centres. However, in 1993 a regional breakdown showed that England had some 1510 indoor sports halls and Wales had 120, a far cry from thirty years ago when the whole of Great Britain had only two or three. It does not need great imagination to see how this growth of indoor facilities has benefited indoor sports such as basketball and volleyball.

Britain has long suffered in tennis for lack of indoor halls specifically dedicated to the game. The Indoor Tennis Initiative, a joint enterprise by the LTA, the All England Lawn Tennis Club, and the Sports Council which started in the mid-eighties, has today produced 470 indoor courts in England, with more in the pipeline.

Bowls has benefited and so has skating. We now have 315 indoor bowling rinks and 42 skating rinks in England and Wales. Many of the skating rinks were provided by local authorities, while most of the bowling rinks are provided and maintained by private companies.

Athletics tracks

There are 412 tracks in England and 24 in Wales, of which 40% have synthetic surfaces, a basic requirement for top-level domestic and international competition. The vast majority of tracks are in the ownership of local authorities.

Golf courses

The golf boom has continued strongly for many years and the recent cut-back in farming under European Union rules has resulted in more land becoming available for other uses. Golf has seized this opportunity. By 1991 England had the equivalent of 1270 18-hole golf courses and Wales had 121. Despite these impressive figures, the Sports Council estimates that a further 300 new courses are required to satisfy the existing demand.

Playing pitches

It has always proved difficult to count the number of playing pitches that exist, as some go out of use for other development while new ones appear. Playing fields are always under threat to building development, and with this in mind, the Sports Council has established a Register of Recreational Land in England.

Playing pitches are either owned privately by a club or a business

Figure 9.4 Regional capital grants to statutory, voluntary and commercial organisations 1992/93

Types of projects for which grants are awarded	Grants awarded (£)		
	Statutory (£)	Voluntary (£)	Commercial (£)
Sports hall	945 179	144 200	–
Swimming pool	71 300	15 000	–
Indoor specialist facility	196 800	772 500	221 500
Playing fields	86 000	110 497	–
Outdoor specialist facility	1 053 251	620 150	25 000
Changing rooms/pavilions	249 426	689 190	2 000
Floodlighting	94 000	72 211	–
Synthetic pitch	981 924	291 550	–
Multi-purpose games area	339 061	74 558	–
Equipment	26 000	117 347	20 000
Artificial wickets	–	4 700	–
Purchase land	–	7 675	–
Drainage	–	11 100	–
Country	–	–	14 000
Outdoor pitches	–	–	90 000
Totals	**£4 042 941**	**£2 930 678**	**£372 500**

[Source: Sports Council Report of Achievement 1992-93]

firm, or publicly by a local authority. If owned by a club, they are eligible for grants from the Sports Council to develop their facilities, under certain conditions.

By early 1993 there were 318 artificial grass pitches in England and 16 in Wales, with ten under construction. Remarkably, over 200 have been provided since 1988. This type of pitch is required for top club and international hockey, and they are also used for football to a considerable extent. They are the latest generation of all-weather pitches and, broadly speaking, live up to that name.

To illustrate how the Sports Council helps facility development financially, the table in figure 9.4 will help, but remember that not all facilities receive grants. The table shows that in the year 1992 – 93 more than £7 million was made available to support a very wide range of facilities.

Participation

The second major area of work for the Sports Council is participation. The Council was directed to work at two levels.

- the social welfare and enjoyment of the public at large, promoting 'Sport for All'.
- the encouragement of high standards in conjunction with the governing bodies of sport, that is, international competition.

While 'Sport for All' means exactly that, for the sake of simplicity we can describe separately the programmes that encourage a broader base of participation, and those which assist the raising of standards. They do link together as talented athletes rise through clubs and challenge for regional, national and international honours, and in so doing, move from one set of programmes to others.

Examine details of the Sports Council's Pyramid of sporting excellence in chapter 1 of this text.

'Sport for All'

The term 'Sport for All' owes its origin to the Committee for the Development of Sport of the Council of Europe. The Council of Europe, with its headquarters in Strasbourg, France, was set up in 1949 by the countries of Western Europe. It aims to develop greater unity and co-operation between people and nations by improving living conditions, developing human values and by upholding the principles of parliamentary democracy. This is a governmental organisation and the British government has been a member from the start.

'Sport for All' policies were first seen in Norway in 1966, and in 1972, under the executive Sports Council, the British 'Sport for All' campaign was launched. In 1976 the Council of Europe published the European 'Sport for All' charter to which the British Government was a signatory.

The launch of the British campaign was accompanied by the Sports Council's 'Sport for All' manifesto of which half a million copies were issued. This manifesto laid out a clear demand for a massive programme of new facilities to meet the increased participation that

The wide range and variety of activities covered by the word 'sport' in the 'Sport for All' slogan breaks down into four clear groups:

- Competitive games and sports, such as football, rugby, hockey, tennis and athletics.

- Outdoor activities such as climbing, walking, canoeing, sailing, pot-holing and camping.

- Movement and dance, which includes ballroom dancing, country dancing, aerobics, skating, keep-fit, Medau, League of Health and Beauty.

- Conditioning activities such as jogging, cycling to work, daily exercises and swimming.

the campaign would create. The campaign, since the beginning, and through until the present day, is concerned with the role of sport in British society. The emphasis is on attempting to provide the best possible opportunities for the greatest number of people. More recently it has attempted to be more selective with specific target groups such as school leavers, ethnic minorities, young mothers, the disabled, older and retired people.

The 'Sport for All' campaign

The Sports Council was, and remains, the catalyst and throughout, the on-going campaign has encouraged partners and organisations to join the campaign. In this way governing bodies of sport, local authorities through their leisure and amenity committees, local sports councils, sports centres and clubs have joined in to promote what they have to offer.

Since the beginning of the 'Sport for All' campaign the Sports Council has refined, sharpened and added to the aims of the campaign. Today these are:

- to increase the rate of participation overall
- to help improve performance at all levels
- to establish and reinforce the principle that the provision of opportunity to participate in sport and physical recreation is a social service
- to promote the concept that regular physical activity is beneficial to health
- to improve the quality of life

The objectives of the campaign are many and various and may be defined as:

- the promotion of sport within target groups of non-participants, for example, school leavers, the disabled, the family, mothers with young children
- the promotion of excellence in support of the governing bodies of sport
- targeting inner cities and areas of social deprivation
- attracting sponsorship and financial investment into sport
- the reduction of coronary heart disease
- the development of facilities for sport and physical recreation.
- the opening up of natural resources, such as rivers, lakes, reservoirs, the countryside, coastal areas, hills and mountains for recreational use

Over the years the Sports Council has launched a series of special targeted campaigns within the overall campaign such as:

- Sport for all the family (1975)
- Sport for all - come alive (1978)
- Sport for all disabled people (1981)
- Fifty+ – All to play for (1983)

- Ever thought of sport? (1985)
- What's your sport? (1987)
- Women in sport (1990)
- Year of sport (1991)

Since the mid-seventies the Sports Council has pursued a policy of attempting to bring sport and physical recreational opportunities to those areas in England which suffer social and economic disadvantages. A range of new initiatives were begun which aimed to demonstrate what could be achieved with a little money and enthusiastic people. As always, the purpose was to point the way so that other organisations, and in particular local authorities, would follow suit. The following are some of these initiatives which continue today:

- Football and the Community – the linking of professional football clubs with facilities open to the local community.

- Sport and the Unemployed – a range of pilot schemes to show how unemployed people could be offered participation opportunities suited to their needs and means.

- Outdoor activities for young people living in inner cities and urban areas.

- Action Sport – with the emphasis on people, this scheme set out to demonstrate the role sport could play in deprived urban areas. Concentration in depth on selected inner city areas was the plan, and the appointed leaders worked in whatever facilities were available – playgrounds, bomb sites, 'kick-about' areas, sports centres, and so on. Many local authorities picked up this type of scheme.

Evaluation

In 1985 an important report was produced for the Sports Council entitled *The Impact of 'Sport for All' policy 1966 – 1984*. This showed that, despite a general increase in participation, the pattern of non-participation remained very much as in 1972. In other words the groups that were largely non-participants in 1972 remained so in 1984. However, groups that were participants in 1972 had enlarged their numbers and had increased their rate of participation. The largely non-participant groups were identified as:

- low-paid and unskilled workers
- ethnic minorities
- school leavers
- parents of young children
- women generally
- unemployed youth.

As a result of these findings the Sports Council switched its policy to target these groups.

The General Household Survey (GHS), undertaken annually by the Office of Population Censuses and Surveys (OPCS), has included questions about participation in sport since 1973. This survey focuses only on those aged over 16 years and, therefore, could actually under-represent the true figures for participation. We now know that some

29 million adults took part in sport and recreation at least once at month in 1990 in Great Britain, which was an increase of two million since 1987.

The gap between men's and women's participation has narrowed and is continuing to do so. In England in 1987, 10.46 million women participated; three years later this had increased to 11.46 million. With men, 12.81 million took part in 1987; in 1990 this had moved up to 13.40 million. In percentage terms the increase in women's participation was 1% and men's was 0.75%.

It would be misleading to think that all was well, since a 1991 – 92 survey in Wales reported a drop in the rate of participation. This may have been caused by the recession but may equally have been a case of a small decline in the popularity of sport and physical recreation.

Participation in sport is highest among young people, but by the early 1990s participation was increasing at a faster rate among the middle-aged and elderly people. This proved that the targeting policy of the Sports Council was succeeding. Walking, snooker and swimming were the three most popular physical activities with men and with women, except that Keep Fit and aerobics replaced snooker.

Figure 9.5 Ten most popular sports in Great Britain 1990

Men		National participation(%)	Women		National participation (%)
1	Walking	44	**1**	Walking	38
2	Snooker	24	**2**	Keep fit/Aerobics	16
3	Swimming	14	**3**	Swimming	15
4	Cycling	12	**4**	Cycling	7
5	Darts	11	**5**	Snooker	5
6	Soccer	10	**6**	Darts	4
7	Golf	9	**7**	Badminton	3
8	Jog/cross country	8	**8**	Tenpin bowling	3
9	Weight training	8	**9**	Jog/cross country	2
10	Keep fit/Aerobics	6	**10**	Golf	2
				Tennis	2
				Weight training	2

[Source: OPCS 1992 General Houshold Survey 1990. Adults aged 16 or over participating the four weeks before interview.]

Figure 9.6 Participation rates in Great Britain 1987-1990

	Overall			**By socio-economic group**	
	1987 (%)	**1990 (%)**		**1987 (%)**	**1990 (%)**
Men	70	73	Professional	78	79
			Managerial	68	71
Women	52	57	Semi-skilled	51	55
			Unskilled	42	46
			Full-time students	89	90

[Source: Matheson J. 1991 Participation in Sport Series GHS no 17 (1991); OPCS 1992 GHS 1990.]

'Sport for All' has progressed since Sir Roger Bannister, the Chairman of the Sports Council launched the campaign shortly after the end of the Munich Olympic Games in 1972. Governing bodies of sport, local authority leisure and amenity committees, and many other organisations and agencies have supported and profited by their active support.

The development of excellence

Since 1965, the development of excellence in sport has been a prime objective. It was accepted that from this date onwards public finance would be directed towards the governing bodies of sport. This would help them promote their policies, to raise standards, and broaden the base from which selection for international teams could be made. The Sports Council, therefore, began immediately to advise the government on the level of current grants the governing bodies of sport needed to help improve their administration, coaching and development services. Money was also required to help pay for increased travel costs if governing bodies were to expand their international fixture lists. This was immediately agreed.

When the Sports Council became independent and executive these policies were continued. The principal difference was only that the Council now had their annual grant from Parliament and could, therefore, act without reference to the government. Today these 'assist' policies are still in force, refined and streamlined to fit the forward plans of the governing bodies. In the financial year 1992-93 the Sports Council provided more than £9 million to 81 national governing bodies of sport. This money helped pay for administration, international travel, preparation training of elite squads, national and regional development officers and coaches. The Sports Council offers and finances a range of support services for elite sport in the fields of sports science, sports medicine, coach education, and the all-important costly doping control.

The National Sport Centres

Governing bodies of sport have the priority use of the national centres which they use for the training and coaching of elite squads, and for the training of coaches. When these priorities have been met, the facilities are available to clubs and local users. Crystal Palace and Holme Pierrepont have national standard facilities for athletics, swimming and diving at the former, and rowing and canoeing at the latter. Bisham Abbey houses the Lawn Tennis Association's school of excellence, and Lilleshall hosts a similar institution for soccer. Traditionally the Sports Council subsidised the running expenses of the National Sports Centres; by 1992 this was running at £4.8 million. By 1993 the National Sports Centres have been run by private management companies. This means that the Sports Council sets the financial terms of reference for using the centres, gives grants to the governing bodies to use them, maintains and upgrades the facilities. However, it does not give annual subsidy to help with the running and operation.

The European Sport for All Charter, to which the British Government was a signatory in 1976, states in Article 1:

'Every individual shall have the right to participate in sport'.

The management company has the task of running the centres profitably. The Sports Council retains ownership of the centres. Facilities at the Centres are constantly being upgraded to meet governing body demands.

The future of the Sports Council

The final decision was made in 1995 and came into effect in 1996. There is now to be a UK Sports Council which will look after and promote UK interests nationally and internationally, and will be representative of the principal national organisations such as the BOA and the CCPR. At the same time a Sports Council for England is created, which will have complete responsibility for English affairs, and will stand alongside the existing Sports Councils for Scotland, Wales and Northern Ireland.

On 1 January 1996 the Regional Councils for Sport and recreation were abolished to be replaced by informal groups of regional - interests, which will no longer be serviced by the staff of the Sports Councils.

SUMMARY

- Since the Sports Council was established the growth of facilities at local and regional level has been considerable. However, the growth has not been the same at national level.
- The local authorities have been the main providers of facilities.
- The Sports Council has been the principal organisation in developing a strategy for facility provision. Together with local authorities, clubs and private enterprise it has seen much of its strategy fulfilled.
- The work of Regional Councils for Sport and Recreation has been critical from the start in driving forward the programme for facilities. They have also stimulated local authorities to spend on pools, sports centres, tracks, squash courts, golf courses, playing fields, and other facilities.
- 'Sport for All' continues to be a successful campaign to increase participation but some sections of the community have barely been touched by it.
- The Sports Council is concentrating on targeting groups that have not been previously involved to any great extent with 'Sport for All'.
- Participation in sport is increasingly regarded as a factor in the quality of life.
- A significantly large proportion of the Sports Council's annual grant from government is spent on helping the governing bodies of sport raise the standard of excellence.
- The National Sports Centres are widely used by governing bodies.

The Sports Aid Foundation (SAF)

In the seventies, countries of Western Europe were looking at ways to develop new policies if they were to continue to compete with any great chance of success against the communist countries and the USA. More financial assistance was required, it was argued, to assist high-level performers to compete with the heavily state subsidised full-time athletes of the communist countries and the sports scholarships schemes readily available in American universities and colleges.

In 1967 West Germany had started the *Sporthilfe* scheme to raise money from new and imaginative sources to fund part-time, and if necessary full-time, athletes preparing for international competition.

In 1975 the Sports Council, with the agreement of the British Olympic Association, picked up on this scheme. By early 1976 they had established the Sports Aid Foundation and were able to assist a few British competitors at the Montreal Olympic Games of that year. This was an acceptable method of injecting finance into elite performance. The money was used to help athletes with training and travel expenses, to pay the rent, to eat well, to buy equipment and generally manage themselves on little personal income. By passing such grants through the governing bodies, who in turn monitored needs and requirements, the athletes' amateur status was maintained, as defined by the International Olympic Committee and the International Sports Federations.

The structure of the SAF is very simple and is ruled by a board of governors, the majority of whom are wealthy men and women who enjoy sport. For example, the first chairman of the SAF was Paul Zetter of Zetters Pools Ltd. A committee of advisers is made up of distinguished 'wise men and women' of sport whose integrity and reputation is beyond reproach and who are in constant close touch with sport at the highest level. Their job is to receive applications from governing bodies on behalf of individual athletes, or sometimes teams, and then allocate grants. There is a professional staff which deals with the administration of the work and which services the board and the committee.

The SAF has raised millions of pounds through schemes, promotions and sponsorships backed by a wide range of major companies. In 1993 the newly-formed Foundation for Sports and the Arts donated £1.3 million to assist potential medallists at Olympic and world-level.

Technically and administratively the Sports Council could have given grants from their funds and not established the SAF. However, the Council decided not to do this as it might have been seen as politically insensitive when so many other social programmes were unfulfilled. In any case this was an opportunity to tap other voluntary sources of money imaginatively as elite level sport has a high sponsorship profile. The SAF has been, and continues to be, a great success story and contributes greatly to British successes at international level.

The National Coaching Foundation (NCF)

In 1976 efforts were made to establish some centralised coaching service to assist governing bodies in the training of sports coaches. This failed through lack of money and because those involved could not agree where the service should be located.

By 1983 the mood had changed and the regions of the Sports Council were responding to local needs for coach education with the co-operation of sports science departments at universities and colleges. It was decided, therefore, to attempt once again to set up a

The Royal Charter of 1972 stated that the Sports Council was to:

'…encourage the attainment of high standards in conjunction with the governing bodies of sport and physical recreation.'

national coach-education service with the co-operation of the British Association of National Coaches, but this time it was to be a network organisation. The National Coaching Foundation was established in Leeds, as guests of the then Leeds Polytechnic. It embraced the network universities, polytechnics and colleges involved in sports science, which in effect formed the coaching base. They had the knowledge, research and expertise that was required to develop a comprehensive coach-education programme.

A year later the NCF announced that, from thirty applicants, fourteen institutions of higher learning in England, Wales, Scotland, and Northern Ireland had been accepted as initial members of the network. The network institutions are responsible for running the courses in sports science for coaches at all levels. They do not teach the coaching of any particular sport. Instead they concentrate on such topics as physiology, biomechanics, nutrition and psychology, topics that apply to most if not all sports, in an effort to raise the standard of knowledge of coaches at whatever level they choose to work.

By 1992 a whole range of composite courses were well established. Advanced workshop programmes are currently offered. Courses are run at weekends and in the evening, and are very modestly priced. They are supported by publications, videos, information packs, fact sheets and databases.

In addition to the work with governing bodies and their coaches, by 1991 a little over 10 600 coaches had attended NCF courses organised either in conjunction with, or on behalf of, local authorities. This was a development not foreseen at the start but which shows the demand for good, informed coach-education. January 1991 saw the launch of the Diploma in Professional Studies (Sports Coaching) designed for experienced senior coaches with the status of a nationally recognised qualification.

In 1993 a review of the network of National Coaching Centres took place. It was decided that the existing structure and the development officers based at each of the institutions should be retained for a further three years. However, the institutions were to be grouped henceforth into four regional cell groups: the South; The Midlands; The North; and Scotland, Wales and Northern Ireland.

In each of these cell groups in England one officer specialises in work with local

> By 1986 the NCF was able to re-state its objectives, based on a few years of experience, as:
>
> '...The promotion of the education, instruction and training at national and local levels of honorary and professional coaches and other interested persons in performance-related knowledge applied to all kinds of sport and physical recreation.'

> The NCF is run by a Board of Directors composed of representatives of the following organisations:
>
> - National Association of Sports Coaches
> - British Association of Sports Science
> - The Sports Council and the Sports Councils for Wales, Scotland and Northern Ireland
> - British Association of Sport and Medicine
> - CCPR
> - British Olympic Association
> - National Coaching Centres (the Network)
>
> The professional staff is headed by a Chief Executive who is responsible for about fifty full- and part-time staff.

Figure 9.7 Coaching

authorities, one with governing bodies and one with institutions of further and higher learning, rather than each officer dealing with all three in his or her location.

In twelve years the whole coach-education system and structure had been developed greatly to give shape and cohesion. The harnessing of the academic research work to the practitioners in the field is now well established, and we are seeing the success of all of this in British performances at major international championships.

SUMMARY

- The Sports Aid Foundation has helped many hundreds of talented established and aspiring athletes to develop their potential free from financial worries.
- The National Coaching Foundation has raised the standard of coach-education considerably, has created a coaching hierarchy, and has brought many more people into the coaching structure.
- The two Foundations together have assisted elite sport greatly and have contributed to British sporting success in an ever-increasing competitive environment.

The British Olympic Association (BOA)

The British Olympic Association is the National Olympic Committee for Great Britain and Northern Ireland (NOC). Each governing body of each Olympic sport has a representative on the NOC which is serviced by a professional staff and headed by the General Secretary.

In the past, the main, often the only, task of the BOA was to organise the team, clothe it, transport it to the Olympic Games, look after it while at the Olympic venue and in due course return it home. Those days are long past, and although the Olympic Games, both summer and winter, take place every four years, the staff are kept busy with a whole range of initiatives in the intervening years.

Objectives of the BOA

- To encourage interest in the Olympic Games and to foster the aims and ideals of the Olympic movement throughout Great Britain in accordance with the principles and rules of the International Olympic Committee, and to focus public attention, with particular reference to the youth of the country, on the Olympic Games.
- To organise and co-ordinate British participation in the Olympic games and also to assist, when required, in the participation of Great Britain in any other games or festivals of sport held under the patronage of the IOC; to ensure that appropriate arrangements are made for the organisation of the Olympic games whenever they are awarded by the IOC to a host city in Great Britain.
- To assist governing bodies of Olympic sports in Great Britain in the preparation of competitors in their respective sports for the Olympic Games.

Figure 9.8 *The current structure of the BOA*

The Patron
(Her Majesty The Queen)
↓
The President
↓
BOA officers
(Chairman, Vice-Chairman, Honorary Treasurer)
↓
The National Olympic Committee
↓
The General Purposes Committee
↓
The Professional Staff:
(Headed by the General Secretary)
↓
Current Department Heads:
Technical Director (coaching, athlete preparation and support services)
Appeals Secretary (fund-raising)
Competitors' Employment Officer (careers work)
Public Affairs Director (PR, media, publications)
Medical Services Director (BOMC and other medical services)
Accountant (finances)
↓
The Committees:
Education Committee
Education Trustees
Medical Committee
BOMC Trustees
Physiotherapy Committee
Psychology Advisory Group
Coaches Advisory Group
Investment Committee
Note: BOMC - British Olympic Medical Centre

- To provide a forum for consultation among the governing bodies of Olympic sports and the sports associations as a means of representing their views to others.
- To subscribe, guarantee or lend money to any association or institution for any purpose calculated to further the objectives of the Association or to benefit amateur sport in Great Britain or for any charitable purposes.

The work of the BOA

The BOA was established as a voluntary organisation in 1905. British teams have competed in every summer Olympic Games since 1896 when the modern Olympic Games began, and traditionally Great Britain and Northern Ireland have two members on the International Olympic Committee (IOC). These two members are invited by the IOC to serve and are not elected by the BOA. They serve in an individual capacity and work to further the aims and objectives of the IOC. They are invited to attend meetings of the BOA. It is to the BOA that the IOC sends the formal invitation to take part in the Olympic Games. In turn the BOA asks its member governing bodies of sport to select teams and officials according to the arrangements laid down by the various international federations.

The major task of the BOA is fund-raising, as the British government does not give money to the Association which, in keeping with the broad Olympic policy, maintains a non-political stance. In the past, money had been accepted from the Sports Council, generally for administration, and the Council too has under-written the Olympic Appeal from time to time, in case it failed. Happily this contingency has never had to be called into action.

The Olympic Appeal

The Olympic Appeal runs for the best part of each four-yearly cycle. The appeal is directed at businesses and the average person. National and regional fund-raising events are held to bolster income. Sponsorship and merchandising contribute significantly. While the five-ring logo is the property of the IOC, in Britain the BOA has the legal right to use the logo when incorporated into the Association's own distinctive circular half Union flag. The Olympic sponsorship programme for the Seoul Olympics of 1988 netted the BOA some £3.7 million after tax. For the 1992 Olympic Games in Barcelona, the public appeal, merchandising and sponsorship raised an estimated £6 million tax paid.

It is unfortunate that, under existing legislation in Great Britain, money raised by the Olympic Appeal is subject to taxation like any other business. To many this seems a self-defeating operation where the Government gives money to sport on the one hand, for example, to the Sports Council, and then takes it away with the other, as with the BOA. This arrangement is virtually unique amongst the National Olympic Committees around the world.

In 1980 the government tried to prevent the BOA from taking the team to the Games in Moscow in support of President Carter of the USA. The USSR invasion of Afghanistan in late 1979 provoked many of the Western powers to threaten a boycott of the Games unless a withdrawal took place. There was no withdrawal forthcoming and the pressure was applied to the BOA. The appeal faltered as big business, not wishing to offend the government, withdrew financial support to a considerable extent. The BOA had to rely heavily on reserves which stretched their resources nearly to the limit. Since those days steps have been taken to ensure that, if ever any further political event endangered attendance, resources would be available.

Around 25 companies become official sponsors to the British Olympic team in exclusive product categories. For example, there is a radio and audio-visual category usually, and also a soft-drinks group. The companies officially accepted as sponsors may use the BOA marketing logo in their advertising, on their stationery, and of course on the packaging of their goods.

Merchandising is a relatively new field of interest for the BOA and they have taken their ideas from the major professional football clubs to some extent. In addition to general souvenir-type goods which carry the logo, replica team clothing for both the summer and winter Olympics is sold through high street retailers.

It could be that in the not too distant future the revenue raised from sponsorship and merchandising will outstrip that raised by the traditional appeal.

The Olympic Medical Centre

In 1987 the BOA opened its own medical centre for sports medicine and physiological testing of elite athletes from all Olympic disciplines, at Northwick Park in Harrow. This was a new departure from the traditional role of the BOA, and is in addition to current services offered by other organisations. There is a feeling in some quarters that this service is unnecessary today and is an example of empire-building by the BOA. What is certain is that it is a very expensive service to provide and there are debates over its future.

Technical services to governing bodies of sport

In an effort to take the best prepared team to the Olympic Games, a technical director was appointed in 1988 to provide new services to governing bodies in the fields of sports science, coaching and medicine. A 'consultant list' of professional experts now exists, involving doctors, physiologists, psychologists, physiotherapists, coaching advisers and biomechanics which governing bodies are able to call upon. These consultants and their services are available at the multi-sports 'camps' that the BOA organises at the National Sports Centres, and overseas if necessary. All of this develops group cohesion and is a clear signal to aspiring Olympic participants that they are being cared for, recognised and prepared.

Education

Today the spirit and ideal of 'Olympism' is being carried into schools and into universities and colleges. These programmes are concerned with the ethics of sport and the philosophical basis of the underlying concept of the meaning of the Olympic Games. Every year, just before Easter, the British Olympic Academy meets for a weekend where papers are read and discussions take place on a whole range of sporting topics. The majority of the participants are students who attend at a very modest fee subsidised by the BOA.

SUMMARY

The BOA:

- manages the British Olympic Team at the Olympic games.
- assists the governing bodies of Olympic sports to prepare for the Games.
- is the point of contact for the International Olympic Committee in all matters concerning the Olympic Games and events supported by the Olympic movement.
- is composed of representatives of all Olympic sports in Great Britain.
- runs a public appeal for funds to prepare, equip and transport teams to the Olympic Games.
- is totally independent of government, politics or any other organisation.
- promotes the concept and philosophy of the Olympic movement.

International Sports Organisation

The most prestigious body concerned with international sport is the International Olympic Committee (IOC), based in Lausanne, Switzerland. Established in June 1894 at the Congress of Paris the IOC is responsible for the control and development of the Olympic Games and the Olympic Movement in general. The IOC is a 'club' of non-elected people invited to serve, and as such, is often under criticism from developing countries which are represented in a very limited way with few members. Membership hovers around ninety and not every country therefore that has an Olympic committee is represented. Some countries, like Great Britain, have two members.

In 1967 the international federations of sport banded themselves together into the General Assembly of International Sports Federations (GAISF), in order to speak to the

Figure 9.9 International Sports Organisations

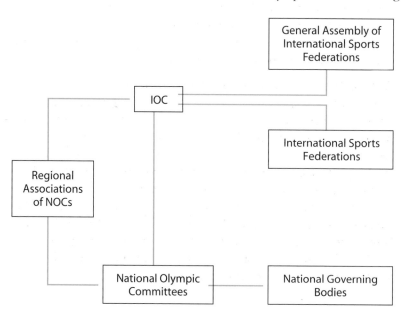

IOC, national governments, inter-national bodies and sponsors as a corporate organsation. The permanent secretariat of GAISF is in Monaco.

In a similar fashion, the National Olympic Committees, not only grouped themselves into regional bodies such as the European Confederation of NOCs or the Association of African NOCs but also establish-ed the Association of National Olympic Committees, a global body with a secretariat based in Paris.

Some see these structures as a threat to the IOC and there is no doubt that they represent powerful voices at the conference tables, but fundamentally they operate on a system of checks and balances.

On the governmental side, the Council of Europe was set up in 1949 to foster greater unity and co-operation between the nations of Europe by developing human values and principles of parliamentary democracy. It established a committee for the development of sport in 1975. Until then sport had been looked after by the Committee for Cultural Co-operation. The need for a free-standing committee for sport was acknowledged as early as 1968 but differing sports systems in member states presented problems. The 'Sport for All' European Charter was published in 1976. A series of initiatives have been taken by governments of Western Europe to embrace development policies, for example, sport and television, disabled sport, access to water, introduction to sport at schools, sports for immigrants, low cost facilities, drug abuse and violence in sport. Co-operation with international and national organisations is fundamental to the Council of Europe to promote harmonious and constructive relations.

SUMMARY

- The International Olympic Committee, set up in 1896, is responsible for the control and development of the Olympic Games and the Olympic movement in general.
- The General Assembly of International Sports Federations (GAISF) was set up in 1967.
- The National Olympic Committees have established a global body called the Association of National Olympic Committees in order to look after their interests.
- The Council of Europe (set up in 1949) established a Committee for the Development of Sport in 1975. It has been responsible for persuading many European countries to take on a large number of sporting initiatives.

The Central Council of Physical Recreation (CCPR)

Origins

In 1935 the Board of Education (today the Department for Education) announced the formation of the Central Council of Recreative Physical Training (CCRPT) under Royal patronage, backed by an impressive number of influential and powerful people in Great Britain. A combination of four factors created a favourable climate for this initiative at this time:

- concern about the health and morale of the nation, particularly among young people
- the problem of unemployment
- a recognition on the part of governing bodies of sport and physical recreation that greater strength could be gained by working together rather than in isolation
- developments in the justification for physical education.

The initiative attempted:

- to get the medical profession more closely linked with the physical educationalists
- to harness the technical knowledge of the physical education profession in the service of the voluntary youth movement
- to promote co-operation between the governing bodies of sport
- to recruit and train more voluntary leaders in sport and physical recreation
- to persuade local authorities to use their powers to provide more facilities
- to get the Board of Education more deeply involved with post-school activities
- to bring about some co-ordination and cohesion amongst those working in the wide field of post-school sport and physical recreation.

Six months after the announcement of the CCRPT, eighty-two national governing bodies were in membership, and the organisation was off to a flying start. National bodies fell into three categories:

- governing bodies of sport and physical recreation
- those which included physical recreation within their programmes, particularly the national voluntary youth organisations
- other interested national organisations, such as the British Medical Association and the National Union of Teachers.

In 1944 the Central Council of Recreative Physical Training became the Central Council of Physical Recreation (CCPR) and the work continued as before.

In 1957 the CCPR set up the Wolfenden Committee which reported in 1960 and, as explained in the section on the Sports Council, resulted in the establishment of the advisory Sports Council in early 1965. Between 1965 and 1972, when the Sports Council became an executive body by Royal Charter, the staff of the CCPR serviced the Regional Sports Councils and provided support to the Sports Council.

However, with the Sports Council becoming independent and executive, it was decided that the staff and assets of the CCPR, which included the National Sports Centres, should be formally transferred to the Sports Council, and the CCPR should go into voluntary liquidation. This latter step was not accepted, and in 1972 it was agreed that there should be a 'new' CCPR which is what we have today.

The objectives of the CCPR are:

- *'to constitute a standing forum where all national governing and representative bodies of sport and physical recreation may be represented and may collectively, or through special groups where appropriate, formulate and promote measures to improve and develop sport.'*

- *'to support the work of the specialist sports bodies, and to bring them together with other interested organisations.'*

The work of the CCPR

The CCPR has always had an uneasy relationship with the Sports Council because of two principal factors:

- the fact that the Sports Council, by an agreement in 1972, has to *'make such resources and facilities available to the CCPR . . . as may be reasonably required by the CCPR for the carrying out and implementation of the objects of the CCPR . . .'* The problem has always rested on what is defined as 'reasonably'

- the fact that the members of the Sports Council are appointed by the government, whereas the executive committee and the officers of the CCPR are democratically elected

Finance

The CCPR derives its funds from four main sources:

- donations from governing body members
- industry and commerce
- sales of publications and research material
- the Sports Council.

Organisation

The CCPR's membership hovers around 250, comprising both British and English national governing bodies which are grouped into six main divisions. These are:

- games and sports
- interested organisations
- major spectator sports
- movement and dance
- outdoor pursuits
- water recreation.

Each of these six divisions elects representatives to an executive committee, which in turn elects the chairman and deputy chairman to serve for a period of two years. At an annual general meeting the whole of the membership elects a President, who for many years has been HRH The Duke of Edinburgh.

Services

The primary responsibility of the CCPR is to represent the interests of its members, both singly and collectively. This responsibility is often exercised through:

- an annual conference where topical issues are discussed and publicised.
- liaison with the government, where concerns of the governing bodies are put directly to ministers, government departments and officials.
- liaison with local authorities. Since local authorities are the greatest providers of sports facilities, the CCPR ensures that they are continually updated on the needs of organised sport.

Likewise, sports bodies are kept informed on the effect of local authority policies on sport and recreation.

- assistance with financial management. Sport is now big business and has to be run like a business. The major sports can afford their own financial and legal advisers but many governing bodies cannot, and therefore welcome what the CCPR offers. Insurance is a growing issue for governing bodies, clubs and individuals. The CCPR has established contacts with insurers specialising in this field.

- international contacts where the CCPR has the opportunity to advance the cause of British sport overseas.

- an information service. The CCPR publishes a range of diverse reports, information booklets and leaflets which are made available to governing bodies, individual sportsmen and women, students, lecturers and teachers. A list of current publications is always available.

- development initiatives in the field of sponsorship, where the CCPR is very successful. The Council is uniquely equipped to assist its membership through the Sports Sponsorship Advisory Service, which establishes contacts between sports bodies and commercial partners, and sponsored awards, such as The Women in Sport Award, the Hanson Leadership Award, the National Pentathlete Award, and the Gatwick Airport Sports Achiever Award..

The image of the CCPR is linked to top-level sport, but one of its greatest on-going successes is the Community Sports Leaders Award (CSLA). This began in 1982 and aims to develop the existing voluntary effort in sport by recruiting from the community people who would like to become leaders and organisers in their chosen activity. The CSLA is awarded at three progressive levels: Preliminary, Basic Expedition Training, and Higher (Hanson Award). It is recognised as a qualification for the voluntary service element of The Duke of Edinburgh's Award. Schools, colleges and community organisations participate in this scheme.

By 1994, over 2500 courses had been organised which had resulted in some 35 000 qualified sports leaders, a considerable contribution to sport and physical recreation. To raise additional funds for leadership training the British Sports Trust has been set up under the Presidency of HRH The Duke of Edinburgh, and is supported by many 'captains' of industry and commerce.

There is a long-standing concern that the work of the Sports Council, the British Olympic Association and the Central Council of Physical Recreation does sometimes overlap. Efforts are constantly made to avoid such situations, as not only is it wasteful of resources but it also creates confusion. The media often draws attention to this and asks for the Minister for Sport to intervene in an effort to draw up precise demarcation lines. Such requests fail to take account of the fact that the BOA and the CCPR are voluntary organisations, while the

Sports Council, under its Royal Charter, has considerable independence of action. The Minister for Sport, therefore, has little legal power to assist, but he has influence and moral authority which he exercises from time to time. The sports organisations are aware of the overlapping problems and constantly work to eliminate these.

SUMMARY

The CCPR:

- is an effective forum for the governing bodies of sport and other national organisations that have sport within their responsibility.
- is a voluntary organisation that promotes measures to improve and develop sport and physical recreation.
- is funded by the Sports Council by a formal agreement.
- takes up contentious issues and lobbies Parliament and politicians on behalf of sport.
- liaises with statutory bodies on behalf of sport.
- provides a range of support services to its members.
- is very effective with sponsorship matters.
- runs an imaginative and successful Community Sports Leadership Award.

British Sports Association for the Disabled (BSAD)

The place sport plays in the lives of disabled people is due, particularly, to Sir Ludwig Guttman, a neurosurgeon who founded the BSAD in 1961. The work of Sir Ludwig in this field was the inspiration for others in many countries. A lasting testimony to him is the Ludwig Guttman Sports Centre at Stoke Mandeville, Aylesbury in Buckinghamshire.

Objectives of BSAD

- to provide, develop and co-ordinate opportunities in sport and recreation for people with disabilities.
- to work in partnership with other relevant agencies, including the British Paralympic Association, the UK Sports Association for People with Mental Handicap, the National Disability Sports Organisations, the governing bodies of sport, and the Sports Council.

The BSAD has charitable status which has advantageous associated tax arrangements.

Organisation

The BSAD has its headquarters in London and operates through ten regional offices in England. There are separate Sports Associations for the Disabled in Wales, Scotland and Northern Ireland. The BSAD has a membership of some 50 000 individual members and 550 clubs, schools and associations.

Finance

In the main, the funding of BSAD is from:

Figure 9.10 Wheelchair basketball

- the Sports Council's annual grant
- local authority grants
- donations and sponsorship
- charitable trusts
- funding in kind through use of facilities and assistance with the staging of events by local authorities.

Structure and management

BSAD has an executive committee, supported by a national advisory council, all of whom give their services in a voluntary capacity. To carry out policy, a small professional staff under a chief executive is responsible for development, the organisation of events, operations, and administration. Sponsorship often pays the salary of some staff. For example, the BBC Children In Need Appeal funds the post of National Development Officer – Young People, while British Telecom funds the Swimming Co-ordinator.

HRH The Princess of Wales is the patron of BSAD, and the British government offers full recognition to the role and functions of the Association.

The work

- In 1963 the first annual National Multi-Disabled Games was introduced.
- In association with the national governing bodies of sport the Association now organises around 15 national championships annually.
- In 1974 the first World Games for Disabled Youth was held
- In 1984 a Profile Classification System was introduced which defines degrees of disability covering a wide range of competitive and recreational sports.
- The Association works with special schools and residencies to introduce teachers to activities for people with severe or multiple disabilities.
- 'Activity Days' are organised with colleges and schools in liaison with coaches.
- Leaflets, booklets and guidelines are published, often in association with national governing bodies of sport, to explain the special requirements of disabled people who wish to participate in sport.
- Competition is provided for athletes with a disability from the grassroots to the highest levels of sporting excellence – 'Sport for All'.
- The Association continues to establish training opportunities for teachers to help them deliver the physical education curriculum to those with disabilities, as it does with youth leaders.
- BSAD plays a role in the setting of policies which control sports

Other organisations concerned with sport for the disabled

The following national organisations are members of the British Paralympic Association:

- British Blind Sports
- British Wheelchair Sports Foundation
- British Amputee Sports Association
- British Les Autres Sports Association
- Cerebral Palsy Sport
- British Deaf Sports Council
- UK Sports Association for People with Mental Handicap

The British Paralympic Association co-ordinates international competition and manages the British Team at the Paralympics.

provision. At national level this involves work with the government, the Sports Council and the governing bodies of sport. At regional level, an input is made to the strategies of the Regional Councils for Sport and Recreation, and local authority policy statements.

● Overall, through its many activities, the Association attempts, with considerable success, to raise the profile of sport for disabled people.

● The Association supplies a considerable number of British athletes to the Paralympics which takes place in association with the Olympic Games every four years. In parallel fashion to the national governing bodies of sport, and their affiliation to the BOA, the BSAD is a member of the British Paralympic Association (BPA). In turn, the BPA relates to the International Paralympic Committee which has the responsibility for staging the Paralympic Games.

SUMMARY

● BSAD is the largest of several organisations developing sport and physical recreation for people with disabilities.

● BSAD works with the governing bodies of sport and the Sports Council to promote their objectives.

● The government and local government look to the BSAD for advice on matters concerning sport for disabled people.

● BSAD is concerned with both grassroots sport and sport at élite level.

● BSAD is a voluntary, charitable organisation, funded by the Sports Council but reliant on sponsorship and donations to a considerable extent.

● BSAD co-ordinates and works with partners to achieve joint objectives.

The national governing bodies of sport

Organisations such as the Sports Council, SAF, NCF, BOA and CCPR have a role to play in supporting the governing bodies which form the core of organised sport in Great Britain. Often in Britain when any group of like-minded people get together to take part in any activity they form a club. They may then appoint a chairperson, secretary, treasurer and committee in a democractic fashion, to act in the best interests of the group. Sport being essentially a social activity also develops in this way. Relatively new sports, such as bicycle polo, triathlon, roller hockey, hang gliding and dragon boat racing have formed clubs and national governing bodies just as soccer, rugby and hockey did in the second half of the nineteenth century.

Facilities

Depending on the sport, clubs will seek the facilities they need in the private, commercial or public domain. Sports requiring playing fields may hire them from a local authority or provide them themselves on land they own, rent or lease. Those needing indoor facilities, such as basketball or volleyball, will need to hire these at an indoor sports centre, a school or perhaps a church-hall, using the existing administrative systems. Badminton, for example, is a sport which uses all of these venues, and any other hall that will accommodate a court. Squash players form themselves into private clubs, sometimes linked with tennis or golf clubs, at commercial squash facilities, and also at sports centres where squash is basically a pay-as-you-play activity. Rowing, water-skiing and sailing clubs will usually have a club house at the water they use, while sports that require hills, mountains, caves and open space will often base their clubs at a pub, a youth or community centre. They then plan their activities from that location using natural resources, either with permission, if privately owned, freely, or with a licence if open to the public.

Over the years the national governing bodies have become far more aware of, and knowledgeable about, the type of facilities they require. Often led by their international federations today they can readily define the type of surface they prefer to play on, the standard of lighting that is required, and the colour of the background against which to play in a sports hall. To lead, and assist, the Technical Unit for Sport at the Sports Council, staffed by architects, engineers and quantity surveyors, publishes technical reports and data sheets which are available to all potential providers so that the latest in design or materials technology is available.

At national level governing bodies have an on-going dialogue with the Sports Council. This has as a principal objective the provision of national-scale facilities for every sport. The Council's Indoor Arenas Strategy, established in 1991, demonstrates the need for more national-scale indoor provision. Additions, up-grading and refurbishment of facilities at the national sports centres are always carried out at the wishes of the governing bodies. An example of this was the provision of the national slalom centre for the British Canoe Union at the National Watersports Centre at Holme Pierrepont, and the wild-water canoe centre at Bala in North Wales.

Participation

While the 'Sport for All' campaign is concerned with increasing participation at club and grass-root levels in particular, it also includes élite sport. It is the task of the governing bodies to develop and encourage excellence assisted by the other support agencies. The development of squads at various age-levels and standards, and of top national competition, is solely the responsibility of governing bodies as they prepare for the challenge of international events.

Finance is mainly provided by members' subscriptions, the Sports Council and by sponsorship. Support services, such as the SAF and the NCF are in place to help raise standards, as is the facility provision programmes at national and regional levels. However, in the final analysis, it is the individual governing bodies which have the responsibility for achieving success. They have the power, the authority and control over their organisation and structure, and the Sports Council exists to help them achieve their objectives if money is a problem. In the 15-year period between 1978 and 1993 the Council's current grant-aid to governing bodies rose from £3.2 million to £9.3 million per annum. For example, as 1993 was drawing to a close the Sports Council agreed to make a further £190 000 available to governing bodies due to participate in the 1996 Summer Olympic Games in Atlanta.

Unlike many other European countries, governing bodies of sport are not exempt from tax. Despite the fact that they are voluntary, non-profit making organisations, have no shareholders, pay no dividends, they are treated no differently from any business or commercial enterprise. If the voluntary sport sector is to thrive in Great Britain, then a review of its tax burden is very long overdue.

Britain, as far as is known, is the only country in the world which taxes its Olympic competitors. In 1992 the Swedish government waived VAT on ticket sales for the European Football Championships to help develop football in that country and because it contributed to the national interest. No British government to date has ever favoured sport in this way.

- The BOA paid £750 000 in corporation tax on the Olympic Appeal of 1988; some 11% of the £7 million raised to participate in Barcelona.

- The Rugby Football Union pays around £1 million in taxes a year, half of which is corporation tax.

- The Lawn Tennis Association, like the RFU, pays over £1 million in Corporation Tax arising from the profits of the Wimbledon Championships.

- The then British Amateur Athletics Board in 1989 paid £450 000 in tax on its marketing enterprises.

SUMMARY

- Governing bodies control and manage their sport.
- Those with big earning capacity, such as football, rugby or cricket, provide their own national facilities; the remaining majority rely on the Sports Council or local authorities.
- There is a shortage of national-scale indoor facilities for governing bodies to use.
- The Sports Council grants aid to bodies which need assistance to achieve excellence.
- Taxation is a heavy burden on sports bodies.
- Governing bodies control their own organisation, programmes and destiny; they are voluntary bodies.

Figure 9.11   The South African team at the Barcelona Olympics

Local authorities

Local authorities are administrative areas of government that look after local affairs, such as education, social services, housing, public health and recreation. Councillors are elected to serve on local authorities and they represent wards which are very local areas. Throughout most of England and Wales we live under a two-tier system of local government with county councils and district councils between them providing a wide range of services.

In heavily populated areas such as London, Birmingham, Sheffield, or Manchester, the cities provide all the services and are known as metropolitan districts.

Earlier sections have shown that local authorities have a long and distinguished history of provision for sport and recreation dating back to the nineteenth century, with parks, swimming baths and recreation grounds. Education authorities, which are a fundamental part of county and metropolitan structures, offer further education, or, as it was known years ago, 'night-school.' A wide range of educational, leisure and physical recreation classes are on offer to the general public, often, in the past, at heavily subsidised fees.

Regional Councils for Sport and Recreation

The establishment of the nine (later ten) Regional Sports Councils in England, and the Sports Councils for Wales and Scotland in 1965, is considered to be the most significant action yet taken in the drive to create a new vision for sport in Britain. Northern Ireland followed suit a little later.

Today it is quite common to see in towns and cities, signs showing 'to the sports centre'; it was not so in 1970. In 1972 the Sports Council asked for 815 sports centres by the end of ten years. By 1981, 700 centres had been built in England alone, thanks to local authorities bringing to reality the early policies and plans of the Regional Sports Councils. Today there are over 1500 in England. The Regional Councils for Sport and Recreation were abolished by the government as at 1 January 1996.

Local government reorganisation

A major reorganisation of local government took place in 1974. This triggered off a proliferation of local authority committees for leisure, amenity, recreation and sport, which took over from the long-established separate committees for parks and swimming baths. These new committees have responsibility for most leisure activities, embracing everything from swimming pools, sports centres and playing fields to libraries, museums and pop concerts. They are serviced by recreation departments. There are few local authorities which do not have some type of structure along these lines. It was normal for the chairpersons and chief officers of the recreation committees to serve on the Regional Councils for Sport and

Recreation and contribute to policy and action. At this local level 'Sport for All' has become a reality for so many.

Recreation departments

Most recreation departments report to a specific recreation committee, but some are located within larger departments such as Education. In all cases, recreation and leisure departments are run by professional staff who act on the policy decided by their committees, within the budget made available by the county, metropolitan or district council. The recreation committee has the responsibility for the promotion of activities for the benefit of local people, and provides facilities such as swimming pools, sports centres, playing fields, artificial ski-slopes, squash courts and municipal golf courses. Development officers are appointed to promote and motivate participation, establish clubs, and create a climate that encourages all age groups and abilities to take part.

Today, as a direct result of government intervention, many of the services offered by local authorities are put out to compulsory competitive tendering (CCT), including recreation. The service required is described and private enterprise is invited to tender. Often the staff of the recreation department itself will bid. This is an effort to obtain best value for money. Since 1989 we have seen many local authority sports facilities being run by commercial operators, but under local authority control. Such an arrangement raises the question of whether traditional local services for recreation will continue to be available to the public at large, or whether 'market forces' will mean higher charges and therefore will prevent some from participating. If this turns out to be the case it will undermine the philosophy that has held force since 1973 when the House of Lords Select Committee on Sport and Leisure described provision for sport and physical recreation as 'a social service'. There is a growing concern that, under financial pressure from the government, local authorities are being forced to cut back on expenditure and this includes recreation.

Local education authorities

Education Authorities are committees within county councils and metropolitan district councils. They have a statutory duty laid upon them by Parliament to provide educational services under the law. Many famous education acts have shaped the style and structure of education in Great Britain. The Butler Education Act of 1944, although aimed at the way education was to be organised in the post-war years, indirectly contributed greatly to the development of sport. Section 53 of this Act placed a statutory responsibility upon education authorities to provide facilities for physical education and games where previously this had been optional. Thus the framework was established for post-war children to have a sound grounding in sport and physical recreation.

As the building of new schools has taken place, an increasing range of facilities has been available to every generation of school children, and with sound management, many of these facilities are made available to the public in the evenings and at weekends. This is the on-going policy of 'dual-use'. Many of the new schools built in the late sixties and seventies involved more money from local authorities for enhancing, enlarging and making additions to the facilities provided by the education authority. This arrangement is known as **'joint provision'.**

The **'dual-use policy'**, distinct from the 'joint provision' policy, has ranged from schools enthusiastic to offer this public service to those somewhat more reluctant to open up their facilities, and in some cases refusing to do so. Overall though, education authorities continue to offer both facilities and a continuing and imaginative range of programmes to learn a sport, improve performance, and develop clubs. The Sports Council has continued to press in these areas and in 1993 reported that they had financially supported 62 dual use/joint provision schemes that had a total value of £13 million in the previous year. Additionally the Sports Council funds posts at dual-use facilities in order to improve the management and marketing of these facilities.

SUMMARY

- Local authorities are a tier of government that looks after local interests, including recreation.
- Local authorities are the main providers of sports facilities in Great Britain.
- Regional Councils for Sport and Recreation were bodies composed of local authority councillors and officers, and representatives of regional and county governing bodies of sport. Together they developed policies.
- Regional Councils for Sport and Recreation were concerned with programmes for both facility and participation provision.
- Local education authorities have a wide range of facilities in schools. The policy of 'dual-use' endeavours to open these up to the public after school hours and at weekends. This policy is not universally accepted by all schools.
- The policy of 'joint-provision', whereby additional money is added to that being spent by the education authority to enhance the physical education and sports facilities in a school, continues to be successful.
- Education authorities are traditionally providers of a wide range of sport and physical recreation courses and opportunities in evening classes.
- Governmental pressure on local government in financial matters is raising concern that the amount of money being spent locally on sport and physical recreation is falling.

Current administration issues

Sport reflects the society in which it is practised. Sport will always be confronted by problems as it attempts to mould itself to the ever-changing environment. This is a world which is constantly changing demographically, economically, socially, politically and culturally.

> *'Any effective strategy for sport must be tailored to the shapes and tastes of the society for which it is designed.'*
>
> *Sport in the Nineties – New Horizons,*
> Sports Council, 1993

Some threats to sport today were not evident ten or twenty years ago, while others from that time have disappeared. Drug-abuse and rampant commercialism in sport did not trouble sport in the fifties or sixties, but unlike today, amateurism and professionalism was a burning issue.

Financial resources

Since 1965 the Sports Council has been grossly under-funded. This has inhibited developments on a number of fronts, notably in the provision of large-scale national facilities. Other countries have been quicker to recognise the economic and social values of success and its value to national prestige, and accordingly, have invested heavily in sport development. Conditions are improving however with the establishment of the Foundation for Sport and the Arts in 1991, which has at its disposal around £60 million per annum from the football pools industry, with £40 million of this earmarked for sport. Unfortunately this money is being spent without an overall strategy.

The National Lottery is a further source of money for sport. The National Lottery Bill (1992) stated that funds allotted to sport should be held and distributed by the Sports Council (83.3%), the Sports Council for Wales (5%), the Scottish Sports Council (8.9%) and the Sports Council for Northern Ireland (2.8%). This provides a welcome annual injection of resources and will help those major projects that the Sports Council is not able to fund from its annual grant-in-aid by the government.

By the end of February 1995 the Sports Council had at its disposal £36 million with more coming in weekly. A lottery awards panel was established and at their first meeting in March of that year, they had a little over five hundred applications for projects which together totalled £208 million. A first list of successful projects was announced in the early spring . By 6 December 1995 the Sports Council had given £122 million to 751 approved schems, the total cost of which was £248 million. By the same date 43,000 general enquiries had been made and 2,188 schems had been submitted.

This vast injection of money into facilities will change the face of Britain. For thirty years ths Sports Council had struggled to meet demands; now it can do so.

Local government

There are plans for local government to be reorganised, to create more unitary authorities where two-tier authorities exist at present. Such a reorganisation would mean that all services, including recreation, would be provided by one local authority rather than having both county and district councils each providing a range of services. The medium- and long-term effect on sport and physical recreation will only be seen in time, but what is certain is that there will always be a need for local authorities to ensure that leisure opportunities are available to their local communities. Experience has shown that in times of financial restrictions leisure services are vulnerable. This will continue to be so until a statutory requirement is placed on local authorities to provide opportunities for sport and recreation to a standard laid down by law, as it is for education.

Commercialism and sponsorship

Sport and leisure spending contributes greatly to the economy of Great Britain. It exceeds spending on gas and electricity. It was estimated by the Henley Centre for Forecasting in 1993 that consumers spend £2.06 billion on sports goods and equipment, £2.01 billion on clothing and footwear, and £1.61 billion on sports participation annually. Between 1986 and 1991 consumer spending on sport rose by 28% which, even allowing for inflation, is considerable.

It can, therefore, be seen that sport contributes greatly to the economy and that overall it is a big business in Great Britain. It can also be seen that the money made available to sport by the government, while obviously welcome, is a very small percentage of the money raised by sport from goods, services and taxes.

SUMMARY

- Sport has to move with the times.
- With vastly increased commercialism and sponsorship in sport, ethical values are at risk and need careful guarding.
- The Foundation for Sport and the Arts and the National Lottery are welcome and provide much needed resources for sport.
- There are concerns that yet another reorganisation of local government may affect sport adversely.
- Sport must continue to demand that provision for it and physical recreation becomes a statutory responsibility of local authorities as it is for education and social services, for example.
- Political action to support and encourage sport is welcome; intervention in the running of sport is not.
- Sport internationally is of political significance and, if used sensitively, can be of national value.
- The government's stated objectives for sport and physical education are welcome and are guidelines for sports administrators.
- Sport reflects the society in which it is practised; it is not something apart from human daily life.
- Drug-abuse in sport is a stain on the morality of sport. It is cheating and has no place in sport.
- Sport, morally and ethically, represents social values of society.

Questions

1 Describe the major organisational developments in sport in England and Wales since 1960.
2 Describe the way the 'Sport for All' campaign has been promoted and assess its successes and failures.
3 Analyse the role local authorities have played, and continue to play, in the promotion of sport and physical recreation.

4 Analyse the role and function of:
   a The Sports Aid Foundation.
   b The National Coaching Foundation.
   c The British Sports Association for the Disabled.

5 A Royal Charter established the Sports Council as an independent body in 1972. Describe the rôle the Council has played in furthering the aims and objectives laid down in the Charter, giving examples of policies pursued to achieve success.

6 Describe the way governing bodies of sport function with respect to:
   a Finance.
   b Development of excellence.
   c Rules of competition.
   d International competition.

7 What is the role and function of the British Olympic Association and the Central Council of Physical Recreation in the promotion of sport?

8 How is excellence in sport developed in Great Britain?

9 The growth in facility provision since 1965 has been considerable. Describe how this has come about.

10 *'The main concern of most people, however, is that access to sport should be readily available and affordable. This remains the primary aim of the (Sports) Council.'* [Sports Council Annual Report 1988].

   Describe the work of the organisations that strive to bring this situation about and point to any factors that obstruct this work.

11 Lately the Sports Council has attempted a greater degree of selectivity with specific target groups as it continues to promote 'Sport for All'.
   a Which are these target groups?
   b Why did the Council take this decision?
   c What is being done to increase participation within these groups?

12 Describe and analyse some of the major problems facing sport as we approach the millennium and hazard an opinion as to whether these will be resolved satisfactorily.

References

Coghlan J F *Sport and British Politics since 1960*, Falmer Press (1990)

McIntosh P *Sport in Society* (revised), West London Press (1987)

Holt R *Sport and the British*, Oxford University Press (1989)

Sports Council

1982: *Sport in the community — the next ten years*

1988: *Sport in the community — into the nineties*

1993: *Sport in the nineties — new horizons, Part two: the context*

10 CONTEMPORARY ISSUES

Objectives

To understand
- the nature of sport and physical education
- the significance of sport in society
- the way in which sporting activities relate to political issues and national identity
- the role which sport plays in economic affairs
- why different groups in society have unequal sporting opportunities
- the way in which sport is able to overcome social inequality
- why many forms of deviant behaviour are linked to sporting activities

This chapter will examine the relationship between sport, physical education and contemporary society, considering a number of issues that are relevant to this relationship. In doing this, the chapter will also study the science of sociology and the ways in which sociological information on sport may be collected. The first section will provide a theoretical framework to explain the sociological approach taken and the reasons why sport is a significant field of study.

We will consider the role sport plays in society and how events in society affect sport. It has been suggested that sport reflects the society in which it is practised and is not separate from our everyday life.

To investigate these contemporary issues, we will take a sociological approach. It is necessary, therefore, to understand what the sociology of sport is, and examine the value of the sociological approach. We will identify:
- various types of theories
- ways of collecting sociological information on sport
- definitions of the nature and current state of sport and physical education in contemporary society.

Towards a sociological understanding of sport
Sport studies and physical education courses often have not been regarded as serious or intellectual because sport itself is seen as fun rather than serious. It is either seen as associated with the body rather than the mind, and, therefore, is non-intellectual, or as part of leisure rather than work, making it less important.

Within these courses, more emphasis has been placed upon a study of the physical attributes of the performer: physiology and biomechanics to improve, for example, fitness and technique, with a more recent application of psychological techniques to mentally prepare the performer. However, studies that enable someone to perform better in their sport, still do not explain why sport is a significant aspect of society to study, and more than 'just a game'.

Studying sport

As sport became more organised and structured in post-industrial society, so academics began to take an interest in it. The original studies were dominated by the physical sciences because research developed through sciences such as biology and physics, making them the only sciences available for researchers to apply to understanding human behaviour. Sport is a physical activity and it makes sense, therefore, to study its physical elements.

The initial studies focused on such aspects of sport as the acquisition of skill and the study of movement. However, these studies do not explain the phenomenon of sport, and this is where the sociological study of sport is applicable.

Sociology

Sociology has two main concerns:

- examining interactions and inter-dependence.
- examining how human behaviour becomes regulated.

The sociology of sport is a sub-discipline of the science of sociology. Within sociological research in its wider sense, the main considerations are with the way in which people live in groups within society, and therefore interact with other people throughout their everyday life. While we all are different and individual, we have to interact with others both socially with friends and professionally with work colleagues. Also, as a result of interdependence, we rely on other people to provide the services that we, ourselves, are not equipped to provide, such as medicine, education, food and housing. We provide our own service in turn, whether it be as teachers, shop workers, or some other task. This interaction also has some regularity to it, since we have to live according to certain standards of behaviour, otherwise society would break down. For example, we have to follow regulations about not injuring other people or stealing their possessions, in order for us to be able to live together in groups. In this way, human behaviour also has some sort of regularity to it, since we act in accordance with certain rules.

These considerations may be applied to sport, in order to look at the interactions of sportspersons, and the patterns of behaviour that emerge in sporting settings.

The sociology of sport

The sociology of sport has only really developed since 1970, when the media made sport more visible to the wider society. Before this time, sport was seen as being trivial because it was associated with the unimportant factors of being playful and physical, rather than serious and intellectual. However, it is now recognised that sport plays a large

Figure 10.1 Human behaviour at a sports event ,

part in everyday life, through its relationship to the economy, politics, the media, leisure and education, as will be discussed in later sections.

The sociology of sport considers the relationship between sport and society. It also considers social processes within sport. For example, it can analyse such social processes in sport as socialisation, social stratification and conflict between different groups in society. It also looks at the interactions between people in sport, since sport occurs in a social setting.

The sociology of sport is often controversial because it raises questions about the people in power who have control over society and specifically sport in society. It asks for changes to the system in order to give money, facilities and equality of opportunity to groups such as women, people with disabilities and ethnic minorities. It therefore threatens the people who benefit under the current situation.

Theories in the sociology of sport

Functionalism

Functionalism sees society as made up of various institutions, the family being the most basic unit. These institutions work together for the benefit of the society as a whole. Individuals are socialised into the society through the influence of the institutions. It is not possible for individuals to change society as they have little control over their own lives. Change occurs when institutions readjust to meet new needs.

Sport is seen as having a functional position in society as a whole. It reinforces the dominant values and ways of behaving. It enables people to adapt to new economic and social pressures, such as the requirements of work and coping with urban living. As such, sport is seen as one way in which groups alter to meet changes in social order. Thus sport socialises and integrates. It is sometimes seen as allowing people some choice and self determination in the increasingly controlled world of modern living.

It uses a scientific approach to research into sport by collecting hard data through objective measurement. Survey type methods are often used and scientific definitions are essential. Sport may be classified in terms of rules and regulations, by the degree of organisation and the element of competition. Once it has been defined in these terms it is possible to work out the amount of sport available to such groups as women, people with disabilities, and the unskilled working class. These 'hard' facts lead to policy formation and then action.

Sport is viewed in all its different forms as a unique social activity providing particular opportunities for physical self-expression. The approach may be criticised for separating sport from the wider pressures of society and not considering the link between sport and such variables as power and conflict. In a capitalist society with wide social divisions, it is not clear for whom sport is functional – society as a whole, the state, workers, black people or others? Functionalism therefore does not take sufficient account of the historical circumstances which affect sport in society, in particular, class, power and economic inequalities.

Social action theory

The relationship of the individual to society is of central importance in social action theory. This theory considers that society is created by social interaction. In the process of interacting with each other, people form institutions such as schools and factories. These institutions in turn influence people partly because of the pressure to observe the rules of the institution. Although it is necessary to have people in power for society to function efficiently, those groups which gain power tend to use it first of all in their own interest. It is accepted that individuals are affected by social institutions; nevertheless it is more important to understand the meanings that individuals experience in their own social lives

This approach accepts that sport is produced and developed at a particular time through the relationships and social networks of people who share similar views. The links between these people and their social interdependence is a key idea. Sports development is not, therefore, controlled by the overall social, economic or political situation. It is determined by the relationships between people based on the relative amounts of power they have in society. The way these relationships are built up and the way they lead to change is an open-ended process. It is essential to study these fluid patterns through practical, not theoretical research. Thus sport has developed in a complex way alongside those aspects of society such as class structure, education, bureaucracy, and the family.

Social action emphasises not only the historical situation but also the way people can intervene in social processes and change them. Power struggles between like-minded individuals are seen as more important than the inequalities of capitalist society. Thus the split of football into soccer and rugby should be studied by considering the structure and dynamics of the overall social context within which the game was being played at the time.

However, the influence of functionalism can be seen in the focus on the particular roles or functions of sport for people. It can also be seen in the view of sport as a counterbalance to the pressure and constraints of modern industrial and urban life.

Marxism

For Marx, society functioned through conflict generated by different classes pursuing their own interests. He argued that in capitalist societies power is in the hands of those who own the means of production, while those with least power are those who have to sell their labour in order to earn a living.

This approach suggests that sport is conditioned by the economic structures of capitalism. Thus modern sport came about with the birth of the capitalist methods of production. It is yet another means by which capitalist owners extract surplus value from the working class in order to produce profit. Sport produces a healthy, efficient and disciplined work force ideal for developing capitalist values such as competitiveness. The dominant class which controls sport then co-operates with the state to further nationalistic ambitions. Sport is, therefore, a mere by-product of the materialistic forces of society.

There are contrasting views of sport within the Marxist tradition. Some suggest that due to the alienation of work, leisure and sport are an opportunity for freedom and enjoyment. Others see sport as part of the 'culture industry' where those in power create leisure to deceive the working class. In this classic 'bread and circuses' version, there is no place for sport as a creative activity. Even when seen as distinct from production, sport is merely a part of class domination and exploitation.

Another Marxist approach rejects the crude idea of social control, while maintaining the importance of capitalist production methods. Sport is thought of as neither a form of human freedom nor structural slavery. Rather it is a historical process of conflict between social classes with dominant groups having continuously to win over subordinate groups.

Although the Marxist approach is very sensitive to the complex nature of sport in modern society, it does show sport as continuing the domination of the ruling class, in spite of its possibility for producing opposition, change and freedom.

Interactionism

This is one of a number of relatively new approaches to sociology based on attempts to include individual meaning and intention in sociological theory. In contrast to structuralist views, this approach works from the individual towards society. It stresses the fact that it is people who actually create society. The symbolic means of communication, including language, dress and gesture, are emphasised. Although it is accepted that society does constrain and form individuals, there is always the opportunity for some creative action. Through the use of language, people negotiate the various social roles they are expected to play.

For interactionists, social institutions such as the family, club or peer group are seen not as separate from people, but as the product of the interaction of the various people involved. Thus a football club should be considered as more than a group of administrators and players. It is important to consider the way they all interact and negotiate their various roles within the club. Their resulting role

'Sporting activity, we contend, can never be adequately explained purely as an instrument of social harmony, or as a means of self-expression, or as a vehicle for satisfying individual needs; for this ignores the divisions and conflicts, and the inequalities of power in societies, which if we care to look more closely, register themselves in sports. Nor can their social role be explained simply as a means whereby the masses are manipulated into conformity with the social order, capitalist or otherwise, for to do so is to regard people as passive dupes, and it ignores their capacity to resist control and to stamp sports with their own culture.'

John Hargreaves

performance will decide the nature of the club and how it might change in the future.

The strength of the theory is the insight it provides into the micro-level of society, when it deals with clubs, groups and small organisations. Its weakness has been its failure to deal with large-scale issues, such as power and structure. Thus in explaining sport, it is mainly concerned with the experiences of sportspeople. It looks at how they interact with each other in social groups and in turn how they affect external social factors.

In order to undertake sports research, participant observation has often been used. In this method, the researcher is actually involved in the social action which is to be described and understood. As such it is highly qualitative, but the data produced can be tabulated and categorised.

Collecting data on the sociology of sport

There are two main ways of collecting data on sport: quantitative and qualitative.

Quantitative methods

Quantitative research tries to uncover the causes of events, prove the cause by statistical significance, and so be able to generalise these findings to a wider population. For example, a researcher could hypothesise that a television advertising campaign will improve attendance at a sport centre's aerobics classes. They would compare the attendance records at aerobics classes in two similar sport centres, with one centre being advertised and the other not receiving any advertising. They would then statistically analyse the findings. Finally they would make recommendations to all sport centres about their advertising requirements based on the statistics of this research. Quantitative research, therefore, will use methods such as surveys and laboratory-based work, isolating the participants from interferences, to make sure that nothing influences their highly controlled experiments. Quantitative methods are fully described in chapter 11.

Qualitative research

Qualitative research tries to understand the phenomenon of sport, before attempting to quantify the process. As stated before, learning how to improve sport performance does not explain why sport is significant as a form of activity. Qualitative researchers believe that sport can only be understood if looked at from the viewpoint of the participants, and examined in its natural setting. Therefore, while quantitative research looks for universal laws that govern all partici-pants' behaviour and can be used to assist in general training programmes for all sportspersons, qualitative research asks questions such as why people get involved in sport. In order to answer these questions, qualitative researchers use methods such as interviewing and observing sports participants to understand their perceptions of the meanings associated with sports events.

Sport and physical education in the UK

Before analysing the issues that have been identified as important in contemporary sport, it is necessary to define what we mean by this concept of 'sport'. The term 'sport' is readily used in social conversation, in the media and in more formal analyses of certain types of activity, and yet it is a difficult concept to define.

Sport is a subculture in its own right. When talking about a culture or subculture, we assume these consist of a group of people who adhere to certain beliefs, values and norms of behaviour. Cultures can be made up of the whole society who have laws imposed upon them to determine the accepted values and behaviour patterns, for example, what the government says is legal and illegal, such as murder and theft. Within these cultures, there are subcultures, which share some, but not all of the larger culture. People who have been imprisoned are therefore believed to have rejected the wider culture and to have broken some of the normal behaviour patterns, and so are isolated from the culture and form a criminal or delinquent subculture. Sport is a subculture, since many of the rules (for example, off-side in football, LBW in cricket) are meaningless outside the activity, and are accepted only for the duration of the activity. People have to learn the norms, values and beliefs of the sporting subculture in order for it to function. Any deviation from these norms will involve a penalty, rather like the penalty of imprisonment given to the convict.

Characteristics of the sporting subculture

What makes most people accept without question that professional football is a sport, whereas professional snooker is not? It is necesary to define the term 'sport' before discussing issues within the activity.

- Sport is physical activity, demanding complex physical skills and physical exertion. Therefore, snooker is not a sport.
- Sport is usually competitive and determined by formal and organised conditions, with rules being enforced by umpires or referees. Therefore, professional football is a sport, whereas children kicking a ball around in a park is not a sport.

When physical activity is free of formal rules and spontaneous, it is considered to be play. Similarly, with adults enjoying a game of tennis or a round of golf, these activities are often more play-like since, although rules will apply, they often are not enforced by an outside official and may be manipulated to make the game more even and enjoyable, for example, giving somebody a few free points. This is called recreation, literally meaning to re-create, to relax, enjoy oneself, to unwind after a hard day at work, often with health benefits. Snooker, on the other hand, has the institutionalised regulations, but lacks the physical exertion, and is, therefore, also a game, rather than a sport.

People can be involved in sporting activities in a variety of ways and with varying degrees of commitment.

According to the European Sports Charter, 'sport means all forms of physical activity which, through casual or organised participation, aim at expressing or improving physical fitness and mental well-being, forming social relationships or obtaining results in competition at all levels'.

For details of Sports Council policy, see Chapter 9. This section deals with the actual involvement of people in sport. At the foundation level, school physical education is largely responsible for teaching basic skills, and this will be discussed in the next section.

Levels of involvement in sport

Primary involvement

In primary involvement, people are involved in sport directly, as sportspersons. The Sports Council adopted a sports development continuum of involvement in sport from:

- foundation (basic skills)
- to participation (sport as leisure)
- to performance (improving standards)
- to excellence (national standards).

Participation in sport as a leisure pursuit is the most popular form of sporting involvement. Leisure may be defined as those activities that people do in their free time. This is time that is free from work, domestic responsibilities and physical necessities such as eating and sleeping for their own sake. Leisure also includes forms of activity that are satisfying rather than being undertaken out of necessity or duty.

Secondary involvement

People can be involved in sport, without actually playing, in two main ways: as a producer, for example, the managers, coaches and umpires; and as a consumer or spectator.

Figure 10.2 A lesson in physical education

The nature of physical education in the UK

The place of physical education in the school curriculum was debated at length in the 1980s and 1990s, by government ministers in the UK. The main curriculum changes resulting from these debates have involved such things as:

- pupil-centred learning, with students learning 'how to learn'
- health-focused physical education
- linking physical education with other subject areas
- development of assessment procedures
- improved partnerships with the local community.

One of the most significant developments in school physical education has been in offering it as an examinable subject at both GCSE and A-level standard in England, Wales and Northern Ireland, and at Standard Grade and Higher Grade in Scotland. However, by far the greatest development during the late 1980s and early 1990s has been the National Curriculum for Physical Education.

The national curriculum for physical education

The curriculum has been developed to provide equal opportunities for all pupils irrespective of age, ability, sex, race or religion within school physical education. At the time of going to press, the national curriculum makes physical education compulsory for all pupils aged between five and 16, and focuses upon developing the following skills:

- physical activity and healthy lifestyles
- positive attitudes to others and to the environment
- learning safe practice
- using information technology capabilities within physical education. Pupils should be taught in ways appropriate to their abilities and appropriate provision should be made for pupils with special needs.

The programmes of study are organised within key stages for different age groups.

Key stage 1 is for pupils aged five to seven, and pupils are expected to follow three areas of activity: games, gymnastic activities and dance. Pupils learn to develop simple skills and eventually sequences of movement, independently at first and then with a partner.

Key stage 2 is for pupils aged seven to 11 years, following six areas of activity: games, gymnastic activities, dance, athletic activities, outdoor and adventurous activities and swimming. Pupils improve motor skills and co-ordination, develop more complex patterns of movement, sustain energetic activity, gain an understanding of the effects of exercise upon their bodies, and plan and evaluate performance in more detail.

Key stage 3 is for pupils aged 11 to 14 years, following games and one other of the six areas in key stage 2 each year, and two half-units of the six areas to include either gymnastic activities or dance. Pupils refine their motor skills, undertake more complex movements, learn rules, tactics, and how to prepare for, and recover from, activities.

Key stage 4 is for pupils aged 14 to 16, following games and one other area of activity. Pupils undertake different roles, as performer, coach and official, and begin to work out preparation programmes.

The inclusion of physical education as a compulsory subject within the National Curriculum shows very clearly that sport and physical activity are considered to be more than 'just games'. They are now valued by the government as appropriate and valuable pursuits for the nation at large, although the Dearing Report of 1994 still promoted games as the most important activity.

The value of sport in society

Sport is valued by society for a number of reasons. The health benefits are well documented and considered elsewhere in this book. Similarly, the psychological advantages such as stress-relief and improved self-concept are studied in chapters 6 and 7. However, the significance of sport extends beyond this. It has become one of the key institutions within society. Sport permeates through all levels of society from the family through to the government.

'Sport makes a positive contribution to national morale, health and the economy. There is no doubt that regular physical activity reduces the risk of coronary heart disease, helps prevent brittle bone disease, reduces stress and enhances self-esteem. To have an increasingly active nation is to reduce the incidence of ill-health and increase the quality of life for millions. We also know that sport creates wealth. It now accounts for nearly £10bn of consumer expenditure and just under half a million jobs. Approximately 1.7% of GDP is contributed by sport and related industries.'

Sports Council, 1993, *Sport in the Nineties — New Horizons*

Sport and the family

For many families, sport has provided a collective focus. Many of the most popular sports are now those which may be undertaken as a group, from sailing, through mountain-bike riding, to swimming and jogging. Sport can also dominate family life when one or more members of the family have committed themselves to competition. Family schedules (meal-times and domestic chores) have to be altered to accommodate family members who attend training sessions and matches.

Sport and education

Sport is an integral part of school physical education, with competitive team games being emphasised throughout all key stages as a requirement. Sport is also important in the extended school curriculum, through inter-school matches, and with increasing partnerships to involve the local community in the school and use of its facilities.

Sport and the economy

The Sports Council has indicated that sport is now a huge part of the economy, both in terms of the revenue generated through media coverage of events and ticket sales, and also through the number of people employed in the leisure industry. The extent and nature of this relationship will be explored in more depth in the next section.

Sport and politics

It is a popular notion that sport should be free of politics, and yet the government determines, to a large extent, the very nature of sport through its policies. It is important to recognise that this demonstrates the significance of sport in society. Governments have often used sport as a political weapon, to make a statement about activities in another country, for example, the sporting boycotts against South Africa during their years of operating a system of apartheid. There is also a relationship between sport and national identity. The success of sports teams in international events becomes the success of the country.

Figure 10.3 Family sport

SUMMARY

- The sociology of sport investigates the relationship between sport and society.
- The four over-arching theories used in the sociology of sport are Functionalism, Social Action, Marxism and Interactionism.
- Studies of sport may include both quantitative and qualitative data.
- Sport, physical education, leisure and play are defined differently but all are significant in society.

Questions

1 Explain what is meant by 'the sociology of sport' and outline one sociological theory which may be used in a study of sport.
2 What is the difference between quantitative research and qualitative research?
3 Devise a physical education lesson for one of the key stages specified in the national curriculum, which takes into account the factors stated as central to good teaching.

A macro-sociological understanding of sport

It was suggested at the beginning of the chapter that sport is often seen as lacking reality and that for many people, sport is an escape from the real world. This section will consider the ways in which sport is, in fact, very real. It is very much a part of everyday life, firstly in its relationship to political issues focusing on national identity, and then, in the economic significance of sport and associated activities. This examination of how sport reflects society and integrates with social institutions is termed 'macro sociology'.

Sport and national identity

Freedom in Sport arose from a concern with the way that governments were imposing sporting boycotts on South Africa as a statement against the system of apartheid. This is just one example of the way that politics has infiltrated the arena of sport, preventing sportspersons from participating in international sporting contests against particular nations on the basis of the political policies of governments.

Governments have long been involved in sport, both at national and at international levels. Nationally, governments are involved in the organisation of sport and the provision of facilities as described in chapters 8 and 9. For example, the Sports Council, a government-funded body, has had a number of strategies to promote involvement of the population in sport. Also, the police are involved in controlling large events to make them safe for the players and spectators and to control, for example, football hooliganism.

Internationally, sport has been used in international politics in three main ways:

- as propaganda – to promote a nation through sporting success
- for sanctions – to make a statement about the national policies of other countries

It is a popular argument that sport should be free of politics and any political involvement. An example of such a belief is the *Freedom in Sport* organisation which was set up in London, with the stated objective *'to uphold the right of the individual to have freedom of choice to participate where, and against whom, he or she should wish in pursuing his or her sporting interests'*, and aiming *'to assist participation in sport free from interference or influence by government or any other organisation or individual'*.

● in diplomatic relations between nations.

This section is concerned mainly with the ways in which governments have used sport to improve national identity, promoting one nation's interests at the expense of other nations. Governments often promote national teams in Olympic sports and World Cup sports more than teams in other sports because their success will be witnessed on the world stage, therefore promoting the image of the nation around the world. Such international success can also be used to promote political ideology. For example, in the 1936 Olympic Games that were hosted by Germany in Berlin at the time of Hitler's rule, the Nazi's used the Olympics to 'prove' the superiority of the Aryan people through their athletic successes.

It is possible to argue that sport can promote positive international relations because sport promotes contact between nations, friendly competition and an understanding of other nation's values and cultures. However, sport can have the opposite effect of reinforcing an 'us versus them' mentality and increased international conflict. This was clearly shown in America's boycott of the 1980 Olympic Games in Moscow and the Soviet Union's decision not to send a team to the 1984 Olympic Games in Los Angeles.

National identity and the Olympic Games

When the French Baron, Pierre de Coubertin revived the Olympic Games in 1896, he proposed that the Olympics could ultimately promote world peace, by serving as a meeting place for the upper classes in a co-operative environment. He also stated that the Games were to be free of governmental interference and that politics was not to be a factor in the Olympic Movement. However, de Coubertin also stated that *'anyone who participates in the Games exalts his country and his race by so doing'*. Thus the founder of the modern Olympic movement laid the foundations for political and nationalistic abuse of the Olympic Games.

Symbols of nationalism in the Olympic Games

The structure of the Olympic Games reinforces nationalism. Sportspersons may only enter the Olympics as representatives of a nation; they may not participate as individuals.

When sportspersons enter the opening ceremony, they wear national kit and, as representatives of their nations, they parade behind their respective national flags.

When athletes are awarded medals, the flags of the first three placed sportspersons are flown, and the national anthem of the winning sportsperson is played.

There have also been unofficial medal tables, promoted by the media, to demonstrate which country 'won' the Olympics.

There are many instances of political and nationalistic intervention in the modern Olympic Games. Olympic sportspersons have been described by Edwards (1981) as *'little more that foot soldiers engaged in a global ideological and political warfare camouflaged under the pageantry of international sport competition'*. For example, in the 1936 'Nazi' Olympics, Hitler walked out of the Olympic arena whenever a black sportsperson was successful, in order to demonstrate his beliefs in Aryan superiority. In 1948, Germany and Japan were excluded from the London Olympics as a result of their role (and defeat) in the Second World War. There have been many national boycotts of the Olympic Games as statements about the national policies of the host nation .

Suggestions to reform the Olympic Games to remove or reduce nationalistic tendencies have included:

- removing the national symbols of sportsperson's uniforms, national anthems and flags
- removing team games whereby sportspersons have to represent their country and leave these for World Cup competitions
- having multiple sites for the Games instead of one host nation
  This would undermine the opportunities for host nations to use the Games to promote national policies. It would also give poorer nations the opportunity to bring the Olympics to their countries, since multiple sites will reduce the cost for each of the host cities.

Globalisation

This is the process whereby nations are increasingly being linked together and people are becoming more interdependent through improvements in communication and travel. It may be argued that national identity becomes blurred as, for example, McDonald's restaurants and advertisements may be seen throughout the world, transcending cultural or political barriers. Within sport, the process of globalisation may be seen in the sponsorship of events, with Coca Cola being the most obvious example of a universal sponsor. It can also be seen in the way players are recruited to play for teams in countries other than their own. Globalisation also allows sports to spread into new nations. For example, the Superbowl (the final of the American Football Championship) is now popular in the United Kingdom, whilst the 1994 soccer World Cup (the British national sport) was hosted very successfully by the United States of America. Is this process of globalisation an indication of the breaking down of nationalism and chauvinism, and a recognition of cultural diversity? Or is globalisation a sign of expanding capitalism as corporations such as Coca Cola spread their influence around the world and sport becomes controlled less by national governments and more by corporate boards ?

Sport and the economy

The considerable annual spending of the British population on sports consumables is discussed at length in chapter 9. This indicates the role of sport and leisure in the national economy. This section considers aspects of this relationship in more depth.

Commercialism and sponsorship

The relationship between sport and commercialism has benefited sport through generating an income for the players and clubs. It has also enabled companies to exercise control over sport through the power that money brings.

Definitions

'Commercialism' is the process of attempting to gain money from an activity (for example, sport) rather than being interested in the activity purely for its own sake.

'Sponsorship' is when a company will pay for their products to be publicly displayed, or advertised, usually in an attempt to increase the sales of their goods. The practices of commercialism and sponsorship are, therefore, inextricably linked within sport.

Why are commercial companies interested in sport?

There is a considerable amount of money to be made in sporting activities, in the sale of tickets, in the fees for media rights to cover events, and in activities, such as food sales. When sports are televised, they are seen by a large proportion of the population. Companies research into who watches sports events and they then advertise their products to these groups via billboards around the stadia, logos on players' shirts, and so on. The larger the audience, the better it is for the advertiser. International events allow for the 'globalisation' of products to sell them around the world. This is often helped by world famous players endorsing certain products.

How has commercialism affected sport?

Coakley (1994) suggests that commercialism has created three main changes in sport:

The format

Sports have been changed to speed up events to prevent boredom. For example, by introducing sudden death penalty shoot outs to ensure a final result in soccer, rather than by playing more extra time.

Points awarded for scoring have been increased to add excitement. For example, in rugby union, a try is now worth five points, to encourage teams to run with the ball rather than kick for penalties. It makes a more exciting scoreline.

In America, many sports are organised to provide commercial breaks when they are being televised, to enable sponsors to advertise their products.

The players

Commercialisation has meant that players are now more than just sportspersons. They are also entertainers,

Figure 10.4 Commercialism in sport

to please the spectators who may have limited knowledge of the technical aspects of the sport.

Therefore, in tennis, players such as Andre Agassi have become known as the 'crowd's favourite' as a result of such things as wearing T-shirts that reveal his torso, and his interaction with the crowd. Agassi himself said that 'image is everything'. Other players have been criticised for spoiling the game for the spectator through their consistent serving of aces.

Players are also encouraged to take greater risks to entertain the spectators. This improves the spectacle for the commercial companies sponsoring the events who need increased viewers. Consequently, ice-skaters may well undertake more complex jumps, and contact sport players will risk injury and endure pain to play a more entertaining game.

Some sports have even been invented as entertainment, such as the Gladiators and professional wrestling.

The organisation

As sports become more commercialised, so the control of the sport moves away from the performer and into the hands of the managers, owners and the sponsoring companies and the media. Thus, performers may well have a decreasing say in the organisation of their own sport as a direct result of its commercialisation.

The commercial success of sport has much to do with the involvement of the media in raising the profile of sports events and bringing them to the public's attention. Without this high visibility of sport, commercial companies would not have an audience for the goods they wish to promote. It is necessary, therefore, to consider the inter-relationship of commercialism, the media and sport.

Sport and the media

The relationship between sport and the media is important since most people experience sport through the media, rather than through active participation or watching events live.

Definitions

The mass media is usually defined as the organised means of communication by which large numbers of different people can be reached quickly. The media includes the printed media (newspapers, magazines, books) and broadcast media (radio, television, movies).

Contemporary media coverage of sport

Newspapers

There are two main types of newspaper: the tabloid papers such as *The Sun;* and the broadsheet or quality papers such as *The Times*. The tabloid papers usually attract a more working class readership and up to a quarter of the paper may be devoted to sport. The greater coverage of sports tends to be in papers with the highest working class readership, such as *The Sun*. The coverage in the tabloids also focuses

---

Historical development

The development of the modern mass media dates from as far back as the fifteenth century, with the key developments being as follows:

1440 Johann Gutenberg invented the movable type printing press

1889 Thomas Edison invented the kinematoscope – the forerunner of motion pictures

1916 First radio broadcast

1923 First television broadcast

1935 Technicolour

1963 First instant replay on television

more on the popular sports of football and horse racing with minority sports receiving little, if any, coverage. The broadsheets have a more middle class readership. Although proportionately less of the paper is usually devoted to sport, the coverage is more varied, covering a wider range of sports and often involving critical analysis of the events and issues surrounding sport.

Television

Coverage of sport on the television developed since the 1950s and became very popular because events could be seen as they happened rather than waiting until the newspaper report the next day. The most popular programmes are Grandstand, Wimbledon, the Grand National and the World Cups in Football and Rugby Union, and, of course, the Olympic Games every four years. The soccer World Cup is said to attract around 30 million viewers in the UK (half of the British population), while the Rugby Union Cup Final held in the UK in 1992 attracted 150 million viewers around the globe. There are also many sport-related programmes and quiz shows such as the long-running BBC 1's *A Question of Sport.*

The cost of the television rights for the Olympic Games has also risen dramatically in recent years, and in 1992 the rights to the Barcelona Olympics cost $401 million.

Value of spectator sport

It is easy to justify the values of participating in sport. However, the media can provide information and knowledge about the sports event and about the players. This 'secondary' involvement in sport can be enjoyable, providing a release from everyday tensions and a focus for socialising with friends. Spectators are able to associate with a team or player and experience the excitement of the event and feel a part of the end result. Camera angles also enable viewers to feel as if they are actually involved in the event, with cameras actually positioned on, for example, Formula One racing cars. However, there should be some concern that time spent watching sport is time that is not being spent actively involved in sport. There is some evidence that in populations with high levels of television viewing, fitness levels decline.

Style of media coverage of sport

When the media covers sports events, it does not provide merely a factual account of the events. It presents the sport according to the interpretations of the journalists and reporters, who often dramatise events to make them more entertaining. Newspaper journalists can do this through the style of writing, use of dramatic headlines, and photographs of particular incidents. They can present an image of the game of being particularly violent or one-sided through one photograph. This was exemplified through the coverage of football hooliganism, with headlines such as 'Savage! Animals!' and photographs of people being crushed to death during the Hillsborough tragedy. On the television, there is usually a limited

To be certain of high viewing figures the television companies are prepared to pay large sums of money for the broadcasting rights to events:

1989 BBC paid £11 million for a six-year contract to cover the World Snooker Championships

1990 BBC paid more than £12 million for a four-year contract to cover Wimbledon

1992 BSkyB paid £2 million to cover the Cricket World Cup

1992 ITV paid £10 million to cover the 1995 Rugby World Cup

1992 BSkyB paid £304 million for a five-year contract to cover the Premier Football League.

camera angle range, and so anything that is not seen is described by the commentator. The commentator can also exaggerate the action to make it seem more dramatic than it may be without the commentary.

Effects of media coverage on the player

The media often focuses on sports personalities rather than the event itself, discussing their personal lives in preference to an analysis of their sporting ability. This is more often the case for female sportspersons, who may well have their status as a wife and mother referred to, suggesting that their sporting performance is secondary to their career and perceived place in society. This type of comment is inherently sexist. There are also claims of racism in media coverage. It is suggested that the emphasis is often placed on the poor performance of black sportspersons while white sportspersons receive more positive comments.

Effects of television coverage on sport

Making sports

Many sports have been altered in quite fundamental ways through their involvement with the media. Events that are exciting to watch, such as sprints and downhill skiing, are maximised. In skiing the giant slalom and mogul events have been created to provide more downhill ski events. Also, sport-type activities such as snooker have been 'made' by television. Snooker is less dramatic but is easy to televise, requiring limited camera angles to cover the table. It also fills large amounts of television time quite cheaply. Subsequently, from 1972 when Alex Higgins won £480 for the World Championship, the prize money rose to £20 000 when Steve Davis won in 1981. This was due to the television coverage and the resultant interest of Embassy Cigarettes as sponsors. By 1983 Steve Davis had become a millionaire and the highest paid sports personality in Britain.

Figure 10.5 Steve Davis

Breaking sports

In contrast to this, some sports have lost popularity because of a lack of media interest. When table tennis lost its television coverage in 1978, there was a drop in membership of table tennis clubs by over one third in the next ten years. In ice skating, the compulsory figures have been marginalised because they are not so interesting for spectators.

Manipulating sports

There have been changes to the appearance of sports to make them more attractive for television. For example, the white football was used in soccer because the brown leather ball could not be picked out from the grass by television. The Australian World Series Cricket had players wearing yellow shirts and blue pads, instead of the traditional white kit. Many sports events have also been timetabled to take place at prime television time. The Los Angeles Olympics in 1984 held the marathon event in the heat of the day because it was good for television. American Football has compulsory time-outs for commercial breaks. There have also been cases of boxing matches being held late at night in the UK to be at prime time for American television. The late night boxing also means that they are held too late for newspapers to get a report into the papers the next day, and so the only way for people to find out the result of the fight is through the broadcast media. Many of the 1994 Soccer World Cup matches were also held in the midday heat in the USA in order to be seen live in the evening in Europe.

The future of the sport-media relationship

In the latter part of the twentieth century, the relationship between sport and the media moved to a new era. This was because technological advances produced such developments as the satellite. This enabled the spectator to watch sports events live from anywhere in the world. Also the sports organisers demanded rights for media coverage, and refused the media automatic access to information. Many sportspersons now attend courses to learn how to handle the media. They have had to become much more professional in dealing with the media as they achieve a higher profile.

Many problems have been identified in this relationship. The increased money involved in the media rights to events has meant that the media may well be able to exercise control over the events that they have effectively 'bought'. Thus the media has almost taken control of the sport out of the hands of the governing body. As sportspersons become media figures, so they too have additional pressures placed upon them. These include pressures to perform too often as they are in the public eye, which may lead to fatigue and sometimes to drug abuse. The sportspersons have to maintain the standards of performance expected of them.

SUMMARY

- Sport can be used by government for political purposes.
- Sport and leisure have a significant impact on the economy today.
- Sponsorship and the commercialisation of sport has changed the nature of sport.
- This presents sports with both advantages and disadvantages.

Questions

1 Choose one sports event that has been televised, and note as many examples of commercialism as you can find, during the course of the event.

2 Write a factual report of a sports event and compare the style of your report with the reports in both a tabloid and broadsheet newspaper the following day.

A micro-sociological understanding of sport

This section will consider the social structure of society, looking at the different groups of people that exist within a society and their relative involvement in sport. This analysis will consider how sport may reinforce social inequalities between these different groups in society. It will also show how sport may be used as an arena for the disadvantaged groups to resist, using a 'micro-sociological' approach.

People's involvement in sport may be affected by their status in society, in other words, the amount of power and money they have in relation to other people. Each person in society has a number of ascribed attributes (those determined at birth), such as our gender, race and age. We also have some achieved attributes (those which are earned), such as social class. The first part of this section will consider how these attributes affect a person's involvement in sport. The second part of this section will then investigate the ways in which different social groups may come into conflict, leading to deviant behaviour which is sometimes witnessed in sporting contexts.

Sport and social structure

The quotation from the Sports Council seems to suggest that sport has the capacity to provide equality of opportunity for all participants, regardless of their position within society. The reasoning behind this opinion is that sport, in many ways, replaces the conventions of everyday life by providing the alternative set of rules and regulations of the sport itself by being a 'subculture'. Therefore, in boxing, for example, government laws about assault on another person are 'suspended' to enable physical assault to take place legally in the sport. In many sports new laws are imposed to enforce rules such as 'offside' which are meaningless outside the sports event. In the same way, the participants are able to leave behind the conventions of their lives, and adopt a new athletic identity in the sports context. Thus, the inequalities of everyday life are replaced by a situation where we are all equal, and our status in the real world is suspended. Thus in sport a director would take part on an equal footing with one of his or her employees.

The problem with the idea that sport provides equality of opportunity is that the very nature of sport emphasises competition and dominance. Therefore, within individual sports, for example, the participants are not usually trying to co-operate or be equal with each other, but instead they are attempting to defeat the opponent. In addition to this, the realities of the 'real' world do affect people's involvement in sport. How much money a person has available will influence the equipment used and the type of club joined. The stereotypes of some groups in society concerning, for example, women's abilities, influence the sporting opportunities available to these groups. Therefore, to a certain extent, sport mirrors society and many of the inequalities found in society go through into sport. By studying

'Sport enhances community spirit, equality of opportunity, personal development and social integration ... Sport can and should provide a context within which everyone can come together on equal terms to participate and reach their full potential regardless of race, social class, gender, age, ability or religious belief.'

Sports Council, 1993, *Sport in the Nineties – New Horizons*

Figure 10.6 In boxing, laws about assault are suspended

sport we are able to learn much about the wider society.

When we consider the way in which society is organised and structured, it is evident that there are some individuals and groups in society who have traditionally held the 'power' positions (for example, the Prime Minister and school head teachers). There are other groups who have been denied access to these positions. The people who have usually held the positions of power have tended to be white, male and middle class (in contrast to the exclusion of almost all other groups). This leads to social stratification of society, whereby there is a hierarchy, or a social ladder, with the people in power at the top and those who do not have power at the bottom.

This system of social stratification has also been visible in sport as identified by the Sports Council in the 1980s and 1990s. In 1982, the Sports Council published a document entitled *Sport in the Community – The Next Ten Years*. It recommended a strategy to provide social equality in sporting opportunities. In setting a number of participation targets, this policy identified a number of target groups who were under-represented in terms of sports involvement, namely, women, middle and older age people, older teenagers, the unemployed, ethnic minorities and people with disabilities. The review of this policy, published in the document *Sport in the Nineties – New Horizons* (Sports Council, 1993) demonstrated that, while some of these groups had become more active, on the whole they remained relatively underrepresented in sport.

Age

The Sports Council's policies for sport in the late 1980s and the early 1990s were particularly concerned with promoting sport within three broad age groups. It was felt that these were critical periods in the life cycle for shaping sporting participation :

- 13 – 24 years is usually a time when individuals define their own identity and interests which may stay with them for life.
- 45 – 59 years is usually the age when many people experience freedom from family responsibilities and employment and therefore take on new activities into retirement.
- the elderly (60+) as a group which is under-represented in terms of sporting involvement. Within these groups, it must be noted that people have different experiences according to their gender, race and social class, amongst other variables.

General trends in sports participation across the age groups may be

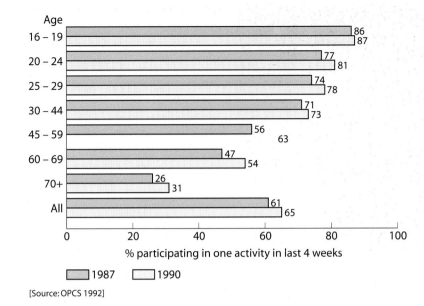

% participating in one activity in last 4 weeks

[Source: OPCS 1992]

Figure 10.7 Age and participation in sport, 1987 and 1990

seen in figure 10.7. From this figure, it may be seen that there is a general trend toward decreased involvement in sport and physical activity with age.

In considering age structures, it is important to be aware of chronological age, and also the social meaning attached to these stages in the life cycle. These stages may be described as: infancy, childhood, adolescence, adulthood, middle age, and old age, and will affect social behaviour in a number of ways. They may determine the social roles people are expected to play at each stage as they move from childhood to legally being an adult, and adopt the roles of, for example, parent and worker.

To illustrate the significance of age upon our opportunities, we know that our age determines, for example, our voting rights, when we can drive a car, consume alcohol, and also when we can join certain sports teams or enter specific events. There have also existed a number of social stereotypes. These define age-appropriate behaviour, including the importance of 'play' activities for children and sports for adolescents, and a widely held belief in the past that sport was not appropriate as an adult activity. The Protestant Work Ethic, that time should be spent in productive rather than frivolous activities, greatly influenced adult society in the past. As such, adult leisure activities were considered inappropriate and a waste of time. The Sports Council figures, however, do demonstrate that in recent decades in the UK, adults have become more active in sporting activities.

Infancy and childhood

Young people on the whole tend to enjoy sport and to be interested in a wide range of physical activities. Physical education is a foundation subject in the National Curriculum, which means it is required for all pupils aged between five and 16. This is intended to provide all young people with the opportunity to be involved in sport and physical activity, in order to encourage commitment to sport into adulthood.

Sport has been identified as having a crucial role to play in the socialisation of individuals. The nature of living in a society is such that people are constantly interacting within a social group, whether the group is the family, work colleagues, or friends. Different social groups have different subcultures (beliefs, expected standards of behaviour,

Figure 10.8 The social stages

attitudes). Each time we join a new subculture we have to learn how to act within it and this is the process of socialisation. For example, people often behave differently depending on whether they are with their family, their work colleagues or their friends because the cultures are different.

Although socialisation is an on-going process, since people join new cultures throughout their lives, much of the fundamental socialisation takes place as a young child. At this time families and early friends teach basic values and accepted behaviour patterns. Often through play activities, children learn how to share and interact, and may practise adult activities, such as pretending to be a parent or at work.

From this informal play, children progress to more formal sports activities. Sport is one arena where people can learn how to interact with others in a different environment. On the one hand, participants have to be socialised in to the culture of sport, that is, how to behave in this new situation, learning the rules of the game. On the other hand, sport can help to socialise the participants into society, by teaching them to work with others, learning to take responsibility for the consequences of their actions. For example, a poor tackle in hockey can lead to a penalty against the team, in the same way as inappropriate behaviour in society can lead to a 'penalty' which can be anything from friends being annoyed through to a police arrest.

Children are taught acceptable forms of behaviour when they are very young, so that they may be socialised into society. Sport and play can assist in this process. As children grow up, they start to make their own decisions about how to behave, within acceptable frameworks.

Adolescence

This may be defined as the period when children become adults. There are two main emphases in this stage of a person's life. Firstly, children learn to be adults and therefore adopt the norms of the adult culture, such as dressing in adult clothes, drinking, smoking, and also engagement in sports rather than play activities. Secondly, adolescence is a period when children are often at variance with the adult culture. They may rebel against the imposed culture because it is perceived as inappropriate and irrelevant. They subsequently form their own adult identity.

Within adolescence, there are a number of physiological changes as the child goes through puberty. These include developing reproductive capacities with subsequent hormonal changes, and also gaining height and weight. As a result of these physical changes, the adolescent has to learn to cope with a 'new' body and emotions and therefore redefine their concept of themselves. Sport is one arena in which the adolescent can learn how this adult body works, and also learn to control and direct the emotions which often accompany the hormonal changes.

There are also a number of psychological adaptations at adolescence, as the person adopts adult relationships with peers of both sexes, prepares for employment, and acquires independence from his or her parents. Sport again may enable the adolescent to practise adult roles by playing roles in sport of, for example, a key player within a team, or a team captain. Sport also provides the opportunity for adolescents to socialise with their peers to strengthen youth cultures and form their own adult identity.

Once again, it is important to be aware of the gender, race and social class differences in people's experiences of the adolescent phase.

Adulthood and middle age

The adult population has become increasingly active in sport participation in recent decades. People in their 30s and early 40s tend to become involved in 'fitness' sports such as swimming, jogging and keep fit, with increased awareness of the relationship between exercise and health. This age group also tends to be most actively involved in sports such as ten pin bowling and cycling which are often family activities.

The most popular sports amongst people in their late 40s and 50s are walking, swimming, golf and bowling. It is this age band who showed the most dramatic increases in sports involvement in the Sports Council survey between 1987 and 1990.

The elderly

The 60+ age group also became increasingly involved in sport in the 1980s, most notably in walking, and also in sports such as bowls. The reason for the lower levels of sports participation in this age group, compared to younger age groups, is often attributed to a decline in physical ability and mobility. However, there are also a number of social factors which should be considered, for example:

- that people in the 60+ age group lacked sufficient sporting experiences in their youth to acquire interest
- the effects of 'ageism'; that there has traditionally been a lack of opportunity and encouragement for older people
- the lack of role models in some sports to demonstrate the possibility of involvement in sport in later years.

Despite this, it is important to realise that there has been an increase in participation in sport and physical activity. This is probably due to changes in society's attitudes, approving sporting involvement for ageing adults. Some sports have role models and more opportunities to take part. For example, Masters competitions in swimming and athletics, and veteran levels in rowing. It is likely that this trend will continue as the more active younger generations bring their positive attitudes toward sport into their own old age.

Social class

One of the most significant factors determining the opportunities people have to participate in sport is their social class background.

In figure 10.9, it is evident that, aside from students who have uniquely available sporting opportunities and facilities, professional workers are the most actively involved group in the population. This table identifies socio-economic group by employment. It is important therefore to consider the case of the unemployed who tend to be under-represented in sports involvement. This is in spite of government initiatives such as to offer concessions to get the unemployed involved in sporting activities.

Figure 10.9 Participation and socio-economic group, 1987 and 1990

% participating in one activity in last 4 weeks

1987   1990

[Source: OPCS 1992]

What is social class?

Social class is the term used to define social inequalities, that is, that certain groups have greater access to wealth, income and power than others. While social class is often defined as a person's employment, it should not be seen as a one-dimensional concept. Factors such as a person's family background, education and income also contribute to social class.

Oppressive or functional

While it is commonly believed that social class means social inequality, sociologists differ in their opinions on the basis of this inequality.

Social class and sporting involvement in a historical context

By the late nineteenth century, as a long-term result of the industrial revolution, the working classes had more time and money to pursue leisure activities. The working week decreased initially to 54 hours, and by 1920 to 48 hours, with the gradual introduction of weekends free from work. Between 1875 and 1900 real wages also increased by one third.

From the 1870s onwards, sport became commercialised as the attendance of the working classes at football and horse racing events increased. Certain sports remained essentially middle class, in particular badminton, hockey and tennis, with money being a crucial determining factor. Additionally, sport was very much a male domain, allowing working class males the opportunity to find a collective self consciousness and become heroes in their local communities.

Despite the increased involvement of the working class, sport was still controlled by the middle class in terms of ownership and management. While those in public schools were being prepared for leadership roles through team games, the working classes were given drill and therapeutic gymnastics to provide discipline and improve health.

Social class and school sports

It appears that children from low-income families have poorer health than other children, which may undermine their physical abilities. Also, children of these families will have less money to spend on sports equipment, and often less space at home to practise sport. The schools themselves may magnify social class differences, since schools situated in more affluent areas often have better sports facilities at the school than those in working class areas.

Many children from working class families are expected to carry out domestic responsibilities. These may include looking after younger children in the family, having a part-time job and doing housework, and helping out parents who may work long hours to earn more money. These children therefore may be limited in any involvement in extra-curricular sport, especially if it takes place after school.

While the National Curriculum aims to offer all young people a broad and balanced programme of physical education, it is evident that some young people may be disadvantaged as a result of social inequality.

Social mobility

Society may be considered to be stratified, that is, as a ladder with people on different rungs according to their status, in terms of wealth and power. It is important to realise that people are able to climb or descend this ladder, thus creating the process of social mobility. Different societies have different social structures:

- **Closed societies**, such as the Indian caste system, are those where the positions of members are fixed for life
- **Open societies**, such as in America and Europe, are those where theoretically all positions in society are available to be filled by the people best qualified. Thus positions people hold in society may be changed as a result of achievement or failure.

Social mobility and sport

The nature of sport itself offers participants the opportunity to develop a number of skills useful for success in life:

- physical abilities in sport to become a skilled performer and possibly pursue a career in sport
- attitudes and behaviour patterns, for example, leadership, which can be used in career development
- motivation to achieve, learning the desire to be successful in sport, which carries over into life in general
- since sport developed from middle class activities, it can be said to socialise participants into middle class norms, values and behaviour patterns.

Sport also provides social mobility opportunities:

- educational achievement, for example, in the USA, where students can gain sports scholarships to get a university education
- sponsorship – some companies will sponsor sportspersons and offer them employment when they retire from full-time competition
- career as a Physical Education teacher or sports coach.

Race and ethnicity

In the second half of the twentieth century, many countries including the United Kingdom, moved from being predominantly white to being multi-racial. This was because many people, largely from Africa, Asia and the Caribbean, arrived to fill vacant positions in the work force. Much of the work carried out by the immigrants was originally in relatively unskilled and low paid jobs which did not attract sufficient white workers, particularly in public transport. Despite high achievement by many black people, the association of black people with low-status work has persisted until today. It has resulted in black people being regarded as second class citizens by some people in society. As in many other areas of society, the experiences of the black citizen is mirrored in processes in sport. By tracing the progress of the black sportsperson it can aid understanding of the experiences of black people in the wider society in general.

Definitions

When discussing a person's race and ethnicity, it is important to be aware of what is meant by these terms:

- Race is the physical characteristics of an individual (for example, skin colour).
- Ethnicity is the cultural adherence of a person or group (for example, religious beliefs, lifestyle).

The term 'racism', which is a description of the practice of oppression of one person or group by another, is by definition based upon a person being physically different. It is important to consider also the notion of ethnocentrism which is the assumption that any culture (religion, lifestyle) that is different is also inferior.

It is the acceptance that 'different' means 'inferior' that creates the problems often seen in a multi-racial, multi-cultural society. It is necessary to distinguish between different races in order to recognise that racism exists, and to discuss the mechanisms of racism. However, this needs to be done in a socially acceptable way. Black people are often referred to as 'West Indian' or 'Asian' because of their ancestry. These terms are no longer universally appropriate, since young black people in the United Kingdom who were born in Britain, hold British passports and are British educated, are therefore of British nationality and not West Indian or Asian other than in ancestry. Such terminology is unacceptable since many white people may have, for example, Italian or German ancestors, but are still considered to be British citizens. The terms 'black' and 'white' recognise that in some societies, being black is significant, because the society has historically been dominated by whites and being black is different (and therefore inferior).

'I know that I am a black man in a white world'.

Jackie Robinson

Figure 10.10 Jackie Robinson, on the right, was the first black baseball player to play in a white American team

Racism and sport

The focus of this section is to consider the ways in which racism manifests itself. There are four main issues to consider, the four Ss.

Sports Council findings

Ethnic minorities are one of the target groups identified by the Sports Council as under-represented in sports involvement, as demonstrated in the figure 10.11.

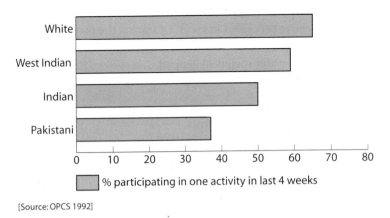

% participating in one activity in last 4 weeks

[Source: OPCS 1992]

Figure 10.11   Participation in sport and origin

Stereotyping

Racial discrimination has excluded black people from achieving in the workplace, and so many black people have entered sport as an arena where they can be successful. Many young blacks have therefore spent more time improving their sporting abilities than their academic abilities. This has produced two stereotypes or beliefs: black people are naturally good at sport, and black people are not intelligent.

Stacking

Having entered sport, black people become guided into certain sports, and certain positions within teams, and are excluded from others. Black sportspersons tend to predominate in sports such as track and field, basketball and boxing. These sports tend to be cheap to play, require little equipment and can be practised without needing to attend special clubs or centres. This is relevant since the census indicates that there is a relationship between race and social class, with black people being predominantly in lower working class categories.

Within these sports, black players tend to dominate certain positions, usually those requiring physical rather than intellectual or decision-making abilities, and also on the periphery of the team, such as wingers in football and rugby, hitters rather than setters in volleyball. This seems to result from a stereotype that black people somehow have a natural, genetic capacity to be quick and powerful, but lack high intellectual abilities.

Social immobility

Black people very rarely progress from the position of sportsperson to the position of coach, manager or sports administrator, which offer longer-term career prospects and greater power in the control of sports organisations. Social mobility for the black sportsperson therefore appears to be limited.

Physiological explanations

The performance differentials of black and white sportspersons has sometimes been explained by physiological factors with some evidence suggesting that there are physical differences between races which account for the predominance of black sportspersons in sports demanding speed and power (for example, sprint events in track and field). The suggestion is that black people have longer legs, narrower hips, wider calf bones, greater arm circumference, denser bones and an elongated body structure which causes more efficient heat dissipation. In addition there are theories that American slavery weeded out the weak, as only the strongest survived the cramped conditions on the boats taking black slaves to the United States of America, and their descendants are therefore a 'super race' of today.

The limitations of these theories are that most of the research has been carried out on highly trained black sportspersons, and therefore the results may be due to a training effect rather than indicative of genetic endowment. The theories also generalise, ignoring the differences between black sportspersons, and similarities of black and white sportspersons in similar sports.

Furthermore, these theories fail to explain a number of factors.

- that few black sportspersons are seen in sports that they would be physiologically suited to according to these theories, for example, canoeing and rowing

- that black sportspersons have been successful in sports they are not suited to (for example, swimming because of bone density, although Antony Nesty of Surinam won the 100 metre butterfly gold medal in the 1984 Olympic Games)

- that there are differentials in performance between young black and white children at such an early stage in their physical development that physiological differences would seem to be as a result of social learning rather than any genetic differences.

Mechanisms of racism in sport

There are three main types of racism (the three Is).

- **Individual racism** is overt or blatant racism, involving individual acts of oppression on the grounds of someone's race. This can include racist activities or comments. For example, a senior member of a first class cricket club when asked about the absence of black players, was quoted as follows: 'When these immigrants come to our country, they don't know the first thing about cricket . . . I don't see why we should bend over backwards to go looking for these . . . Bloody Pakistanis'

- **Ideological racism** is created by people stating ideas so strongly that they become believed as fact. The South African apartheid structure was a particular ideological system that excluded black sportspersons from certain areas of society. For example, black swimmers were excluded from the national swimming team on the basis that 'some sports the African is not suited for: in swimming the water closes their pores and they cannot get rid of carbon dioxide, so they tire quickly.' These ideas are not based on fact, but can be believed and so create discrimination.

- In **institutional racism** within society, the power positions tend to be held by white, middle class males, for example, sports coaches and managers. If these people maintain ideological stereotypes about black people, they are unlikely to appoint black people to positions of power, therefore the oppressed populations do not achieve the power that is necessary to change the

Figure 10.12   John Barnes

system. For example in the late 1980s and early 1990s in the UK, fifty per cent of the national Track and Field team were black but there were no national black coaches, despite there being suitabley qualified candidates available. Consequently, there was no black voice at a high level to speak out against the very racism that was present, and so the system perpetuated itself.

This process is likely to be repeated since young black children tend to have black role models. They will be likely to want to be like their role model which will again reproduce rather than challenge the current situation.

An example of how institutional racism operates may be seen in a study by Carrington (1982) examining the over-representation of 'West Indian' pupils in school sports in London. It was found that the physical education teachers held stereotypes that the black pupils had natural physical prowess and they channelled pupils into sport. This often helped the pupils give up academic studies in order to practise sport, thus reproducing the stereotype. The pupils themselves were attracted to sport as they had internalised the idea that they were non-academic and saw sport as a means of achieving success in life.

Gender

The quotations in the margin are examples of a historical attitude toward women. They illustrate the accepted assumption that women have inferior abilities and physical weakness. This has limited women's opportunities in all spheres in society, including employment, education and sport.

With regard to sport, women are becoming more active in certain sports, but are not as involved as men.

This is apparent at all levels of sport, from sport as a leisure activity through to international players, from children learning skills to coaches, managers and journalists. For example, in the Olympic Games, women constitute only one third of the competitors and approximately 10% of the coaches. In leisure management, although more women than men enter leisure as a career, more men progress to managerial positions. These trends reflect an historical tradition that is proving slow to change.

Definitions

'Sex' is defined as the biological aspects of a person, distinguishing whether they are male or female. These are characteristics we are born with and they are permanent.

'Gender' refers to the social, cultural and psychological aspects of expected sex-role behaviour, known as masculinity and femininity.

'Female, by virtue of a certain incapacity, they are weaker and cooler by nature than males and we must regard the female character as a kind of natural defectiveness.'

Aristotle

'There is a good principle which created light and men and a bad principle which created chaos, darkness and women'.

Pythagoras

[Cited in Lucas, 1990]

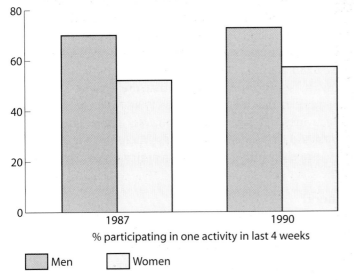

% participating in one activity in last 4 weeks

☐ Men ☐ Women

[Source: Matheson, J 1991]

Figure 10.13 Participation rates by sex, 1987 and 1990

These expectations vary between societies and throughout history.

'Stereotyping' is conventional unquestioned beliefs about behaviour patterns of individuals or groups.

Gender stereotypes and sport

The society we live in expects certain standards of behaviour of its members. Some of these standards are enforced by law and breach of the law can lead to penalties, including imprisonment, for example, for theft, or injuring another person. There are also other subtle ways of regulating people's behaviour. As we grow, we learn appropriate behaviour by being taught 'acceptable' and 'unacceptable' ways of doing things, for example, eating with our mouths closed, being respectful of our elders. Similarly, we learn how to behave in accordance with our gender. Men are expected to be physically big, competitive and assertive, whereas women are expected to be slim, passive and non-competitive.

These stereotypes are relevant since the development of muscle and assertiveness are usually integral to sports involvement. Yet these are characteristics that are perceived to be non-feminine. Sports have developed from competitive and violent activities, such as sprinting and throwing events from hunting days, team sports from medieval games. These were considered masculine activities and not appropriate for females.

For the majority of people, 'norms' of behaviour are learned firstly through parents, and later through peers, particularly in school.

Historical perspectives

Physical education for girls started in the public schools of the mid to late nineteenth century, and was based upon deportment (posture), social dance and callisthenics (gymnastics for elegance and grace). In other words, it was developed very much within the socially defined concept of femininity.

An extensive study by Scraton (1986) identified three key constraints on physical education for girls:

Physical ability

When physical education was first developed for girls, it was on the understanding that it was to be separate and different from boys, since girls were weaker and more fragile than boys. Even early feminists such as Dorothea Beale (1868) believed that while boys played cricket, girls could walk and do some callisthenic exercises. As a result of the belief in this innate physical difference between boys and girls, it was felt that women's sports should not involve endurance, strength or physical contact. Subsequently, men's sports were adapted to be appropriate for women. For example, netball was an adaptation of basketball, limiting space, speed and contact in the rules of the game, and hockey and lacrosse prevent contact with the ball by using an implement. It is interesting to note that the biggest increases in women's sport in the 1980s and early 1990s were in keep fit and aerobic activities. These both emphasise grace and aesthetic movements, and also slimness. These are therefore compatible with femininity, especially with the style of dress that accompanies involvement in these activities.

Motherhood

In the twentieth century, there developed a belief that physical education could make women physically fit to prepare them for motherhood. However, emphasis was placed on the care that had to be taken not to over-stress women, as this could sap their energies and undermine their ability to reproduce. While modern society has largely progressed from this opinion, women's sporting opportunities are still hampered by domestic responsibilities, particularly working class females. Working class girls are often expected to carry out domestic chores after school such as housework or looking after younger brothers and sisters.

Sexuality

In the Victorian and Edwardian eras, women were seen to be responsible for morality through their behaviour and style of dress. Any moral lapses on behalf of men were attributed to the misleading influence of an immoral woman! Women's dress had to completely cover their bodies: high necks, sleeves to the wrist, and skirts to the ground, with tight corsets underneath, limiting the ability of a female to move freely in a sporting situation. This remained the case until the World War of 1914 to 1918 when middle class women joined the working class females who already made up much of the workforce, to replace the men who had gone away to fight. Women's clothing, of necessity, became more practical and less restrictive to enable them to work more easily. A similar advance in women's clothing was made after the Second World War.

Sport as a male preserve

Physiological myths have been used to argue the case against women's involvement in sport, for example, that women will have child bearing problems, will suffer damage to their reproductive organs, and will develop unattractive muscles. In fact, female sportspersons often have easier deliveries because they have more developed pelvic muscles, female reproductive organs are actually more protected than males', and it is only possible to develop muscle bulk in the presence of the hormone, testosterone. Muscle tone and conditioning are more likely as a result of training than muscle bulk. Even the evidence that women

Figure 10.14 Women's rugby

may suffer amenorrhoea (stopping of menstrual cycle) is not a reason for stating that women should not do sport. Iron supplements are available to counteract the possibility of anaemia, and a normal menstrual cycle usually resumes on finishing heavy training. The differences that we observe in men's and women's involvement in sprot must be due to factors other than physiology.

Restricted opportunities

Even today, there are less sporting opportunities available to women. In the Olympic Games, there are no bobsled, boxing, ice hockey, soccer, weight-lifting or wrestling events for women. In track and field athletics, the pole vault, triple jump and hammer were not recognised for women until some limited competitions in the early 1990s, and the 5 000 metres and steeplechase were still excluded. In clubs where there are both male and female competitors, it can be the case that women suffer from inferior equipment and facilities. Women's sports also receive less sponsorship, which is related to the inequality of media coverage of men's and women's sport.

Media coverage

It is possible to see from even the most casual observations of the media that female sportspersons are comparatively under-represented in sports coverage in newspapers, magazines and on the television. When women do receive coverage, it tends to trivialise women's sport, with attention being paid to their physical appearance and marital status. Photographs often show female sportspersons in passive rather than active poses, trends which are not seen in the coverage of men's sport. In addition, in coverage of women's sport, there is often comparison to the male equivalent, which does not happen in reverse in men's sport. This indicates that the men's game is the 'norm' and the women's game merely a hybrid, for example, there are usually two categories of sport such as 'soccer' and 'women's soccer', 'basketball' and 'women's basketball', showing that there is no need to qualify the male version since it is the norm. There are also considerably fewer female sports journalists, commentators and photographers. To some extent this is to be expected since there are fewer women than men involved in sport, and therefore the media personnel and media coverage will reflect this.

Gender stereotyping, sport and men

It is relatively easy to understand how male dominance in society (patriarchy) and in sport, can affect women's involvement and progress, but it is important to recognise that patriarchy can also oppress men:

- Men are expected to be competitive and to achieve, since these are required traits of people (usually men) working in a capitalist society. Yet only one person can win, which means everyone else has to cope with effectively being a loser

- Men learn through sport that they are superior to women, and therefore should avoid any feminine characteristics, such as involvement in aesthetic sports such as dance. This limits their own sporting opportunities
- Boys are often taught the principle of 'no pain, no gain' and learn to treat their bodies as a machine to do a job in sport. They also learn to suppress emotions, thus losing awareness of their bodies and emotional responses.

Sport and deviance

This section will consider sport's role in socialising people into deviant behaviour, that is, behaviour which involves cheating, violence, and other acts which are considered to be socially unacceptable. In particular, attention will be paid to deviance amongst sportspersons, in the form of violence and drug abuse. Also deviance amongst spectators, in the form of crowd violence or 'hooligan' activities will be considered.

Deviance amongst sportspersons

Deviance in sport involves breaking the rules of the game. Some infringements of the rules have become so common that they are considered to be minor offences, as people become so used to witnessing them that they are no longer shocked by the offence. This is most evident in the use of the term 'professional foul' to describe tackles in soccer which are carried out as a means to an end. The foul is in some way understandable and therefore almost acceptable.

Minor offences in sport include faking injuries to provoke a yellow card, intentionally falling in a tackle to give the impression of having been fouled, and holding an opponent back.

Major offences include intentionally causing an injury, and the use of drugs to improve performance. This would give an unnatural advantage in strength, endurance, speed or tolerance of pain.

Defining deviance amongst sportspersons is difficult since much of the behaviour that is acceptable in sport would be considered deviant in everyday life. For example, Formula One racing drivers regularly speed, and participants in boxing and other contact sports are 'guilty' of assault. Deviance occurs when participants step outside the rules of the sport, just as deviance in society is defined as illegal or unlawful behaviour. It is possible to identify two types of deviance.

Positive deviance

This involves an overcommitment to sport, whereby the participant will do almost anything to achieve the end result. Types of positive deviance include enduring personal injury in order to keep training and playing. It was noted in an earlier section that many men adhere to the 'no pain, no gain' principle. However, many female sportspersons have also adopted this attitude as they become socialised into the athletic culture. This identity becomes more important than any socialisation to a feminine identity. This may be taken a step further when injury is accepted within sport to the extent that inflicting pain upon others is seen as just being a part of the game by both the injurer and the injured.

Negative deviance

Negative deviance involves violation of the rules. It is often connected to positive deviance, since people may violate the rules in a desperate attempt to win the event. The most obvious example of this type of deviance is in the use of performance-enhancing drugs. Some drugs may be taken to mask pain. An extreme version of positive deviance, was seen in the case of Birgit Dressel, who died in 1987 as a result of severe drug abuse, including over four hundred injections of a large variety of substances, which had been used to help her continue training while suffering from extreme pain in the lower spinal region. Other drugs used are stimulants such as caffeine and amphetamines to increase endurance and alertness, sedatives to improve accuracy, and hormones such as anabolic steroids to help improve power and also to develop aggression. In one famous case Ben Johnson was tested positive for the use of anabolic steroids after winning the 100 metres men's sprint in a world record time in the 1988 Olympic Games. In 1994 in the soccer World Cup finals, Diego Maradonna was found to have taken a cocktail of drugs in order to improve his physical performance. Regular drug testing has now been imposed as a deterrent to sportspersons considering taking drugs. The publicity surrounding these international affairs has demonstrated the consequences of testing positive. Sportspersons desperate to use drugs are now experimenting in the use of masking drugs to prevent detection.

Deviance amongst sportspersons has become as technical as the training itself, for those who wish to pursue these methods of improving performance. With sportspersons, the motivation to cheat may be attributed to a desire to succeed.

Deviance among spectators

Football hooliganism

Football hooliganism is a contemporary example of the type of deviant behaviour that may be seen amongst sport spectators. Football hooliganism has been defined as *'those people who were dealt with by the police for offences occuring in connection with attendance at football matches'* (Sports Council and Sport Science Research Council, 1978).

The most common types of offences are physical assaults, missile throwing, verbal abuse, vandalism, theft and possession of weapons.

Who are the hooligans?

Often described in newspapers as 'mindless morons', football hooliganism seems to have meaning for the participants. The hooligans themselves are people who have been socialised into this culture and stick to these meanings. The majority of football hooligans are male, in their late teens, and working class, although some gang leaders have been found to be middle class. Hooligans also tend to be very loyal supporters and are very knowledgeable about their club. Hooliganism has sometimes been linked to adolescents (see earlier section) who were using football as a focus for developing their own adult identity whilst rebelling against the imposed adult culture.

Historical trends

Football hooliganism is not a modern phenomenon. In ancient societies, violence amongst spectators similar to contemporary football hooliganism was witnessed during chariot races. Between 1895 and 1914, there were 254 incidences of football hooliganism recorded in the Football Association minutes. Levels of football hooliganism dropped in the 1930s, but picked up after the Second World War and accelerated during the 1960s. This was sensationalised by the media who saw these events as newsworthy, and captured them in headlines such as 'Soccer Marches to War' (The Sun, 1965), and more recently in headlines such as 'Savages! Animals!'. Besides Great Britain, many other countries have been identified as having similar problems, including Germany, Holland and Italy.

Recent trends in football hooliganism have included the involvement of skinheads who symbolised an exaggerated working class style, with cropped hair, industrial boots, braces and an emphasis on hardness and masculinity. Football hooliganism has also become increasingly organised, with groups such as the InterCity Firm (West Ham supporters). They use normal as opposed to official train services and ask younger members to look for the opposition. They also operate a no-alcohol policy to maintain a clear head for fighting.

From the late 1970s onwards, football hooliganism became more violent. Petrol bombs, stabbings and ultimately hooligan activities contributed to the Heysel Stadium disaster in Brussels in 1985 with 39 deaths. There is also some evidence of National Front involvement in many hooligan activities. This is a politically right wing group who believe in racial purity, and may in part explain the racist nature of much football hooliganism.

A number of theorists have presented opinions of the nature and causes of football hooliganism.

Genetic theories

Based on the work of Peter Marsh, these theories distinguish between real violence and ritual violence or 'aggro'. Football hooliganism is argued

Figure 10.15 Football hooliganism at the England vs Ireland match, 1995

to be an example of the latter whereby weapons are displayed but not used, and potentially lethal action is aborted early. 'Aggro' is thus based on a set of rules, to get submission without causing injury. Problems with this theory arise when ritual escalates into real violence, especially if people do not know, or choose to ignore, the rules.

Marxist theories

Largely originating from the work of Ian Taylor and John Clarke, who believe that as football has become more professional and the players more affluent, so the game has moved away from its working class roots. Football hooliganism is seen as a resistance movement by the working class fans to this 'bourgeoisification' of their game.

Figurational sociology

This was initially applied to an understanding of football hooliganism by Norbert Elias, and subsequently by Eric Dunning and others. The idea of a figuration is used to explain the interdependence of people with each other within society. It is shown that these relationships are dynamic, changing through history and in different societies. Within football hooliganism, there are the relationships of the law maker, the law breaker and the law enforcer to be considered. There are two principles of the figurational approach.

The ordered segmentation theory states that within working class communities, people are protective of their territory and will combine to fight against a common enemy who is seen to threaten it. Therefore, one housing estate will fight against another, but they will combine to fight a 'foreigner' from another area. In football, the foreigner is the fan of another team, which may be a Derby fan in a game against Leicester, a southern team against the north of England, or an international team against England. The explanation of this is the 'violent masculine style' that is prevalent in working class communities, where aggression and fighting are positively valued for males.

The second theory is that of a civilising process, suggesting that governments have increasingly made laws to regulate people's behaviour and, in particular, to stop violence. Society, as a whole, may be seen to have become less tolerant of violence and high levels of emotion. Thus there are fewer opportunities available for people to express strong feelings. Hence, football hooliganism may be seen as a quest for excitement. This is an area where the strong emotions and physical violence repressed by civilised societies may be expressed.

Despite a number of reports and measures to deal with the problem of football hooliganism, the phenomenon still continues. This is possibly because the solutions offered look to eliminate the activities without a complete understanding of the causes.

- The Justice Taylor report after the Hillsborough tragedy indicated that part of the problem of football hooliganism was complacency. A main recommendation concerned the squalid conditions at football grounds, which may encourage equally squalid behaviour. The report recommended that improved conditions would improve behaviour. These specifically included all-seater stadia and new facilities for spectators.

- Police solutions have included removing firearms, segregation, and closed circuit television. The cost of policing football is approximately ten million pounds per season, involving one thousand officers each week to police both the ground and the local area. Violent and threatening behaviour away from the ground can be dealt with under the Public Order Act of 1986. There is also a National Football Intelligence Unit at New Scotland Yard, attempting to identify the causes and extent of the problem. Critics of the police solutions suggest that if people are treated like caged animals in pens, they will act like animals. Also the repression of the problem at the ground merely means that the problem will occur elsewhere (train stations and public houses being prime targets) since the cause of the problem has not been dealt with. This is also evident in the weaponry used. When firearms are removed, hooligans have found ways to use stanley knife blades in a rolled up newspaper and penny coins sharpened to a point to be used as missiles. Removing the weapons does not remove the problem.

- Figurationalists argue that if football hooliganism is a product of a violent masculine style, then this can be undermined by introducing a female presence at football which will have a civilising effect on the hooligans.

Hooliganism has been used as a 'case study' as a form of deviant behaviour in the sports context. It is by no means the only, or even the most severe, form of deviancy. However, it is useful to use it to illustrate the possible roots of deviancy, also to show how difficult it is to identify the causes, and subsequently the problems, involved in eliminating harmful deviant behaviour.

SUMMARY

This section has considered the ways in which our personal qualities may affect our involvement in sport and the mechanisms by which this may happen. It has been suggested that:

- People are treated differently because of their age, social class, gender, race, and disability. This means that people do not have equal access to sporting activities and that people are expected to behave differently because of their perceived qualities.
- Some people do not conform to expected forms of behaviour, and act outside the 'rules', whether these are laws of the land, rules of the sports event or behaviour that is socially acceptable. This is called 'deviant' behaviour.

Questions

1 Write a report on yourself, or a friend, documenting the ways in which you think that your age, social class, race and gender affects your involvement in sporting activities. Give examples of situations in sport where you feel you have been treated differently or unfairly because of your age, social class, race, gender or disability.

2 Watch a sports event, either on television or live, and list the number of ways in which sportspersons may be deviant. Do they fake injury? Do they unnecessarily foul? What is the result of their action? Do they gain advantage from it?

3 Go to a sports event, and instead of watching the match, watch the crowd and make notes on how they behave. What do they do if the contest gets boring? What happens when a goal is scored or a race is won? Are there particular players who are cheered or jeered? How does the crowd treat the referee or umpire?

References

Cashmore E *Making Sense of Sport*, Routledge (1990)

Coakley, J. *Sport in Society*, Times Mirror Publishing (1994)

Elias N, Dunning E *Quest for Excitement: Sport and Leisure in the Civilising Process*, Blackwell (1986)

McPherson B D, Curtis J E, Loy J W *The Social Significance of Sport*, Human Kinetics Books (1989)

SCAA *Physical Education in the National Curriculum: Draft Proposals,* London (1994)

Sports Council *Sport in the Nineties — New Horizons* London, The Sports Council (1993)

11 DEALING WITH DATA

Objective

- To give students the theoretical background and practical skills necessary to carry out meaningful investigations and research in the field of physical education and sport

Many different methods are used to investigate problems relevant to human activity. However, they all follow a set of principles which govern the process of problem solving in general. The 'scientific' method of problem solving uses logical methods to answer these four basic questions:

- What is the precise, nature and scope of the problem under investigation? What exactly are we looking for?
- How is the problem to be investigated? What methods are we going to use?
- What can be found out from this investigation? What results will we find?
- What do the results of the investigation mean? How can we link our results with what we already know about the subject?

Characteristics of investigation methods

Worthwhile investigation using structured problem solving needs a careful and controlled approach. The following six principles should be followed:

- **Systematic**: Be clear about what you are studying and the methods to be used. This will enable you to collect relevant data to investigate your problem.
- **Logical**: Present your research in such a way that other researchers can easily follow your methods and understand your conclusions.
- **Empirical**: Only draw objective conclusions after analysis of relevant data.
- **Reductive**: Any general conclusions you draw are formed from a number of individual pieces of data.
- **Replicable**: Other researchers may repeat your investigation in the same way and get the same results.

- **Refutable**: New evidence may lead to your results being questioned at a later date.

The scientific method of investigation

Most approaches to scientific methods of investigation use 'structured' problem-solving to extend present understanding or create new knowledge. In general, there are four key steps in the problem-solving method of investigation:

1 **Problem identification** – The precise nature of the problem is clearly defined and the area of research agreed.

2 **Hypothesis formulation** – The anticipated results are stated based on either theory or previous research.

3 **Data collection** – Appropriate methods are used to collect relevant information which can be analysed to test the specified hypothesis.

4 **Analysis and interpretation of the results** – The collected data is analysed to accept or reject the specified hypothesis. The resultant findings are incorporated into the general body of knowledge in the subject area.

Classification of methods of investigation

There are different kinds of problems in the areas of physical education and sports studies. Therefore there are different methods of investigation used to find solutions to these problems depending upon the nature of the phenomena under investigation. There are four basic types of approaches used depending upon the nature of the problem being investigation and these are:

1 **Analytical methods** – These methods use the study of existing information in an attempt to provide an overview of complex issues. Such approaches might involve in-depth studies of philosophical and historical issues or reviews of literature in the field of study.

2 **Descriptive methods** – These methods attempt to determine the current state of such things as knowledge, attitudes and behaviours related to specific issues. Such approaches often use survey techniques which rely on questionnaire and interview techniques.

3 **Experimental methods –** Traditionally regarded as the most 'scientific' of all the approaches used, the researcher attempts to manipulate the influence of variables in order to arrive at cause-effect relationships, rather than rely upon existing data. Examples of such approaches include the use of both controlled 'laboratory' and 'field' investigations.

4 **Creative methods** – These methods tend to concentrate upon the qualitative aspects of form and composition in the performing arts such as dance.

Example of method of investigation:

Philosophy - mind, body and sport

History - sport developments in modern society

Review - physical activity and health

Questionaire - survey of health and activity

Interview - survey of sports injuries

Laboratory - cardiovascular responses to exercise

Field - effects of warm-up on performance

Choreography - artistic merits of an original dance

417

In the rest of this chapter we will concentrate on the experimental and descriptive approaches used as methods of investigation associated with human activities.

Experimental ways of gathering data

An experiment involves applying a set of procedures to a subject of interest in order to answer a specific question about the subject using the scientific rules of evidence. Normally the question to be answered is posed as a research hypothesis which states some anticipated result. The hypothesis is often stated as a null hypothesis, of 'no-difference', which can then be tested by experimentation. The experimental study needs to be designed in such a way that the null hypothesis is either accepted or rejected. To do this we would apply a statistical procedure to the results obtained from the experimental data collected.

The researcher usually manipulates some sort of treatment variable to cause things to occur as a result. This is carried out in order to identify a possible 'cause and effect' relationship. The researcher also attempts to control all other known influential factors, except the treatment variable itself. If these other variables are controlled, then it may be presumed that any effects noted from the experimental procedure may be a result of the treatment being applied.

Example 1: A laboratory experiment

Suppose a researcher wishes to determine the possible influence of nutritional intake on the performance of high-intensity exercise in young healthy subjects.

Research hypothesis: it is proposed that the nutritional composition of diet may have influence on the ability to sustain short-term, high-intensity exercise.

Null hypothesis: it is stated that there is no difference in the time to exhaustion following three different diets which are (a) mixed, (b) high carbohydrate and (c) high protein/low carbohydrate.

Treatment variable: the nutritional composition of food intake in terms of the predominant nutrient supplied by each of the three diets.

Other influential variables: a variety of factors known to affect performance of short-term, high-intensity exercise such as:

a prior warm-up

b level of fitness

c fatigue

d familiarity with the task

e motivation

f environmental conditions

Experimental design

● **Subjects** – a group of 30 healthy, trained volunteers who have consented in writing to take part in the experiment.

● **Treatments** – three groups of ten subjects randomly assigned to three separate diets each of one week nutritional intake on either

CAUTIONARY NOTE: Before embarking on any experimental research investigation, written approval should be obtained from the appropriate ethical organisation concerned. You must also obtain written 'subject informed consent' from volunteers invited to take part in the experimental procedures.

a mixed diet, a high protein/low carbohydrate diet, and a high carbohydrate diet.

Treatment variable – the amount of carbohydrate in daily diet.

● **Experimental protocol** – warm-up exercise on a bicycle ergometer. This is followed by exercise at a load equivalent to the individual's previously determined maximal aerobic power at a fixed pedal rate (90 rev. min^{-1}) until the ability to maintain the required rate declines.

Experimental variable – total time to termination of the exercise in seconds.

● **Controls applied:**

a a standard 10-minute warm-up exercise at low 'steady state' level.

b subjects with similar levels of fitness assigned to three groups.

c subjects free from residual fatigue effects of previous exercise or training.

d subjects habituated thoroughly to the experimental exercise task involved.

e no externally applied motivational or other stimuli applied to the subjects.

f laboratory environmental conditions controlled for temperature and humidity.

Figure 11.1 Mean (SD) exercise performance times (seconds) of subjects following mixed (M), high protein (P) and high carbohydrate (C) dietary treatments

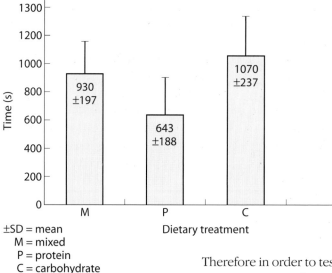

±SD = mean
M = mixed
P = protein
C = carbohydrate

Experimental results

The graph of the data obtained from the experiment in Figure 11.1 illustrates the way in which the treatment variable of carbohydrate intake level (known as the independent variable) exerted its effect upon the experimental variable of exercise duration in seconds (known as the dependent variable). This assumes that all of the other known influencing variables have been suitably controlled.

From the results obtained it can be observed that the level of carbohydrate intake appears to influence the duration of performance of short-term, high-intensity exercise under the conditions specified.

Therefore in order to test the original null hypothesis or no-diffence it is necessary to apply a suitable statistical test to the data obtained.

Using the t statistic for uncorrelated data to test the difference between the means obtained:

$$t = \frac{\overline{X1} - \overline{X2}}{\sqrt{\dfrac{(SD_1)^2}{N_1} - \dfrac{(SD_2)^2}{N_2}}}$$

where 1, 2 = means of first and second treatments

and SD_1, SD_2 = standard deviations of first and second treatments with N_1, N_2 = number of subjects.

$$t = \frac{1070 - 643}{\sqrt{\frac{(237)^2}{10} - \frac{(188)^2}{10}}} = \frac{427}{45.6} = 9.36$$

Since the t value calculated (9.36) is greater than the t value tabled in the t-statistic distribution, (3.56 with 8 degrees of freedom at the $p < 0.01$ level), the null hypothesis is rejected. It is concluded that there is a significant difference in the exercise performance time associated with the high carbohydrate compared with the high protein/low carbohydrate diet.

However, in the case of the high carbohydrate versus the mixed diet, since the t value calculated (3.35) is not greater than the t value tabled (3.36), the null hypothesis is accepted. Therefore it is concluded that there is no significant difference in exercise performance associated with these two diets.

Example 2: A field experiment

Suppose a researcher wishes to determine the possible influence of fluid hydration level on the performance of endurance-running capacity in young healthy subjects.

Research hypothesis: it is proposed that the level of fluid hydration in the body may have an influence on the running capacity over a sustained period of time.

Null-hypothesis: it is stated that there is no difference in the total distance achieved in a one-hour endurance run following three levels of hydration. These include 'normal' fluid intake, hyperhydration (high fluid intake) and hypohydration (low fluid intake).

Treatment variable: the degree of hydration associated with the three levels of fluid intake.

Other influential variables: a variety of factors known to affect performance at long-term endurance exercise such as:

a environmental conditions

b level of fitness

c nutritional status

d fatigue

e motivation

f clothing

Experimental design

- **Subject**s – a group of 10 healthy, trained volunteers who have consented in writing to take part in the experiment.
- **Treatment** – Each subject randomly assigned to three separate fluid intake treatments of one week duration. These involve 'normal' fluid intake (control), high fluid intake (hyperhydration) and low fluid intake (hypohydration).

CAUTIONARY NOTE: Before embarking on any experimental research investigation, written approval should be obtained from the appropriate ethical organisation concerned. You must also obtain written 'subject informed consent' from volunteers invited to take part in the experimental procedures.

Treatment variable – the level of fluid intake associated with hydration state.

● **Experimental protocol** – warm-up exercise followed by a one-hour endurance run for optimal distance over a flat measured course. This is repeated with one week between each treatment.

Experimental variable – total distance achieved in one hour of running.

● **Controls applied:**

a standard environmental conditions with respect to temperature and humidity.

b standard clothing used by each individual in each run.

c subjects with similar levels of endurance fitness performing each run.

d subjects free from residual fatigue effects of previous exercise/training, with one week between each run.

e subjects' diets standardised to ensure energy intake maintained at constant level over the period of the study.

f no externally applied motivational stimuli to the subjects.

Experimental results

The graph of the data obtained from the experiment in Figure 11.2 illustrates the way in which the treatment variable of hydration level (the independent variable) exerted its effect upon the experimental variable of distance covered in one hour of endurance running (the dependent variable). This assumes of course that all of the other known influencing variables have been suitably controlled.

From the results obtained it can be seen that the level of hydration associated with different fluid intakes over the seven days prior to each run, influenced the distance achieved in the performance of a one-hour endurance run under the conditions specified. Therefore, in order to test the original hypothesis of no-difference it is necessary to apply a suitable statistical test to the data obtained.

Using the t statistic for correlated data to test the difference between the means obtained:

$$t = \frac{D}{\sqrt{\dfrac{N\Sigma D^2 - (\Sigma D)^2}{N-1}}}$$

Where D = the difference between each subject's distance on two separate runs

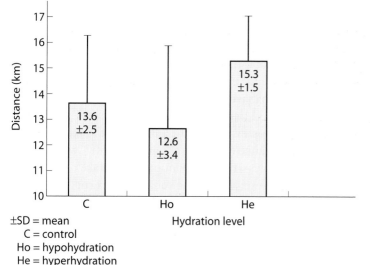

Figure11.2 Mean (SD) running distances (kilometres) of subjects following control (C), hypohydration (Ho) and Hyperhydration (He) treatments

±SD = mean
  C = control
Ho = hypohydration
He = hyperhydration

and N = the number of subjects.

$$t = \frac{28}{\sqrt{\dfrac{10(184) - (28)^2}{9}}} = \frac{28}{10.8} = 2.59$$

Since the t value computed (2.59) is greater than the t-statistic distribution (2.26 with 9 degrees of freedom at the $p<0.05$ level), the null hypothesis is rejected. Therefore it is concluded that there is a significant difference in distance achieved during endurance running associated with the hyperhydrated compared with the hypohydrated treatment.

However, in the case of the control versus the hypohydrated regimen = t, since the t value computed (0.95) is not greater than the tabled t value (2.26),, the null hypothesis is accepted. Therefore, it is concluded that there is no significant difference in exercise distance achieved with these two hydration treatments.

Interpretation of experimental results

Experimental investigations attempt to establish a cause and effect relationship by manipulating of an independent variable so as to determine the influence upon a dependent variable. However, it is important to note that cause and effect are not always easily established. While two separate variables may be related, this does not necessarily imply that one causes the other to occur. In the examples above, enhanced exercise performance duration or distance may have been due to some other variables not accounted for in the experimental design. For example, the time of day in which the experiments were conducted could have an impact.

Therefore, the establishment of a cause and effect relationship requires the use of logical approaches to properly designed experiments. The only reasonable explanation for the outcome observed by the experimental procedures is the use of the treatment variable. In the case of the previous examples, the effects on the experimental variables – time or distance (the dependent variables) – were caused by the treatment variables – the type of nutrient or intake or hydration level (the independent variables) in the subjects concerned.

To ensure that logical approaches are used to arrive at reasonable explanations for the outcomes observed from experimental investigations, it is necessary to:

1 Establish a sound theoretical framework for the experiment on the basis of literature in the field of study.

2 Apply an appropriate design for the experimental procedures to allow for the effects of the independent variable used.

3 Select and control the appropriate independent variable in the experimental design.

4 Select and accurately measure the most appropriate dependent variable in the experiment protocol.

5 Use the correct statistical model and analytical procedures for the processing of the results obtained.

6 Ensure the correct interpretation of the results in the light of other existing evidence related to the field of investigation.

Survey, interview and questionnaire approaches to gathering data

A survey is concerned with the process of taking a broad, general or comprehensive view of a situation, and is not limited to any particular method of collecting information. However, in practice, the survey approach often uses specific techniques for gathering data, such as questionnaires, interviews, or observational methods to provide information. What distinguishes the survey approach is the form of data collection and the methods used for the analysis of such information.

Surveys take the form of a structured or systematic set of data. This involves a set of variables collected over a specified number of cases which is called a 'variable by case matrix'. The same set of information is collected from a given number of individuals to provide a data matrix such as the one in figure 11.3.

Figure 11.3 Data matrix

Cases (number of people) Variables	Person 1	Person 2	Person 100
Age (yrs)	15	16	14
Height (cm)	165	160	156
Body mass (Kg)	61	58	55
Activity Level	High	Moderate	Low

For each case in the matrix, information is obtained on each variable so that a structured set of data is assembled. Techniques for generating the data itself may not be as structured and often the most convenient method used for survey investigation is by use of a questionnaire. Survey analysis which uses the 'variable by case matrix' often allows comparison of cases on the variables or sets of variables concerned.

One of the main uses of surveys is to describe the specific characteristics of a sub-set of cases being investigated. If it is required to know how activity level varies with age (in figure 11.3), a 'variable by case matrix' will allow the information to be processed. However, survey investigators often attempt to provide information on the likely causes of the phenomena being studied. The researcher may note variations in the physical characteristics of height and body mass for example, which may influence participation in physical activity. In other words, survey research can provide an understanding of what influences such things as activity level. This is done by observing the differences in this variable across cases, and by identifying other characteristics which are linked systematically, such as physique. In this way, the survey attempts to establish why things happen, by a detailed comparison of the specific characteristics of a group or sub-set of cases. It would also be possible to speculate on why physique might influence physical activity levels in young people. However, care should be taken when assuming cause and effect relationships since the observed relationship may not indicate a causal link.

Surveys often use a range of methods in order to produce the data required to investigate a particular topic. The techniques by which data are collected may vary considerably. These may include the direct observation of each subject or case involved in the study, an interview conducted with each subject, a self-completed questionnaire by each subject, or a combination of these techniques.

Essentially the survey approach represents a method of collecting, organising and analysing data to provide meaningful information on measures relevant to the topic of interest to the researcher.

Example 3: A lifestyle survey in young people

Suppose a researcher wishes to assess those health-related behaviours and other factors which contribute towards the health of young people in school, using a lifestyle survey by means of a self-completed questionnaire. A sample of six schools selected with a local education authority is chosen to represent the types of schools provided within that district. Within each school, whole tutor groups of boys and girls in each age group from 11 to 16 years old are chosen to make up the sample of the young school-age population for investigation.

The necessary approval by the various authorities, such as LEA, local ethical committee, headteachers, teachers, parents and governors of the schools concerned, must be obtained. A lifestyle questionnaire is then designed to find out what young people think and do about their own health, by identifying the known health-related behaviours and other factors which influence young people's health.

Suitable questions are drawn up from reliable sources, relating to those lifestyle factors which are acknowledged to influence health including age, sex, physique, ethnic background, dietary patterns, physical activity, leisure time pursuits, smoking and alcohol habits, drug and sexual health awareness or knowledge, and health beliefs. A simple, attractive, structured questionnaire which asks questions related to each topic area is designed with additional space provided for respondents to identify any other health concerns they may have.

A small pilot scheme should first be trialled among representatives of a similar sample of young people in a similar population and the appropriate amendments made. The full survey is then delivered to the selected schools for distribution by the teachers involved. Each pupil in the tutor group completes the questionnaire in approximately 20 to 30 minutes of lesson time. Completed questionnaires are collected directly from the schools, with over a 90% response rate.

The following results (figures 11.4 to 11.7) were obtained from those sections of a questionnaire dealing with body mass, physical activity, smoking and alcohol consumption respectively. This provided a framework for the interpretation of the findings.

Figure11.4 A personal view of body mass by 15/16 year olds

1 What do the findings suggest about the personal views of young males and females regarding their own body mass?
2 What differences in perception of body mass sexist between young males and females?
3 Suggest some factors which might influence the perception of body mass in young males and females.

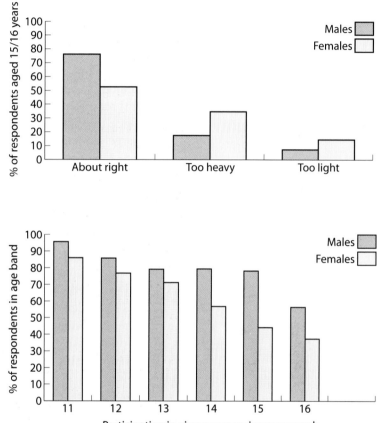

Figure11.5 Exercise habits by age

1 Overall, what trend can be detected in participation in vigorous physical activity in young people 11 to 16 years of age?
2 What differences can be detected in participation in vigorous physical activity between males and females 11 to 16 years of age?
3 Suggest some factors which are likely to influence participation in vigorous physical activity over the age range investigated.

Figure11.6 Smoking habits by age

1 How does the trend in smoking habits compare with the trend in alcohol intake over the age range investigated?
2 Suggest some factors which may influence the uptake of use of tobacco and alcohol among young people in this age range.

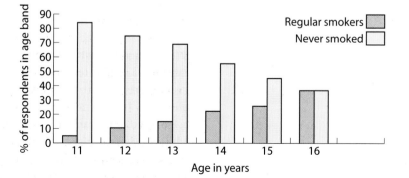

Figure11.7 Alcohol use by age

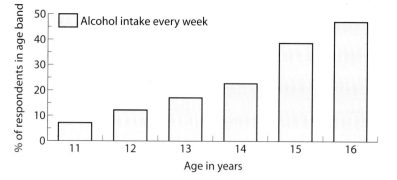

Survey approaches

Survey methods vary according to the nature of the investigation but there are three main approaches used: observation, interview and questionnaire techniques. The decision to use a particular technique depends largely upon the nature of the investigation (see figure 11.8).

Observation

This approach can be used for generating data by observing subjects directly or by making video tape recordings of subjects or events. It is necessary to define precisely the specific items to be observed, to have a method of recording these items noting the type of occurrence, its frequency or timing. It is also necessary for the observer to be trained in making observations to ensure correct and reliable recordings and to keep to the criteria which specifies the event.

Suppose for example a survey was being conducted to determine the characteristic patterns of play which lead up to the scoring of goals by teams during the World Cup soccer tournament. It would be necessary to define the territorial location of initial possession of the ball by the attacking side, the number of passes leading up to the goal, and the contribution of individual team members toward the movement. It would then be possible to compare the styles of play among the teams taking part, provided the same observers, using the same techniques, are following carefully specified criteria for observational recording of the specific events concerned.

Interviews

This approach can be used for generating data similar to that required using a questionnaire. However, the interview is conducted either face-to-face or by telephone, since it is considered important to interact directly with subjects concerned, especially where sensitive issues are being investigated, for example, in a study of ethnic background. It is often vital to develop a rapport with the interviewee, with reassurance given and encouragement provided in order to generate candid information. It may also overcome any confusion or lack of understanding, as well as detect subtle differences between verbal and non-verbal responses.

Figure 11.8 Choosing a suitable non-experimental approach to gathering data

First consider the following
1 The topic being investigated
2 The time available
3 The resources needed

Questionnaires	Advantages	Disadvantages
If questions to be answered are relatively simple and many responses are needed for the analysis then this technique is preferable.	1 Cheaper than other methods 2 Quicker to obtain a greater number of responses 3 Standardised better in order to reduce bias 4 Analysis of data obtained more straight forward	1 In-depth information not possible 2 Complex or personal questions cannot be used effectively 3 Low response rates likely (e.g. postal questionnaire $N \sim 50\%$) 4 Respondents need adequate literary skills

Interviews	Advantages	Disadvantages
If detailed or in-depth information is required, or if personal or sensitive topics are to be studied, then this technique is preferable.	1 Schedule allows flexibility for the interviewee's situation 2 Detailed information can be obtained directly 3 Sensitive questions can be used effectively 4 Information can be obtained from people with literacy problems	1 Interviewing skills need to be developed 2 Costs increase in terms of training, time, travel 3 Bias more likely since difficulty in treating each interviewee the same 4 Time, cost and resources limit numbers to be included

The disadvantages of face-to-face interviews are the time and effort needed to arrange them and the levels of skill required by the interviewer to ensure good quality information. Telephone interviews may overcome some of these problems.

The interview format may also vary according to whether it is structured or unstructured. Structured interviews use the same questions, in a constant order for each subject, so that responses are easier to compare in the subsequent analysis. Unstructured interviews require highly-trained interviewers and may yield a large amount of detailed information making comparisons between subjects difficult. In either case, such interviews may also be used with small samples to verify information gained from larger numbers of people using questionnaire approaches.

Structured interview forms should be devised in the same way as questionnaires but with a flexible layout in order to record additional information. Unstructured interview forms may only be a list of subject headings with space left available to write down the information provided. Recording the interview on tape may make analysis easier. Whichever technique is used, the interviewer should only ask the questions on the forms in the order set down, and should be prepared to explain any unfamiliar terms. The interviewer needs to listen carefully, to try not to interrupt and to provide standardised prompts where necessary. The information provided should be recorded as accurately as possible without modification to ensure that the data is collected in a standardised way. Finally, any interviewee's question should be answered and recorded at the end of the interview, along with gratitude expressed for the co-operation provided.

Questionnaires

This approach can be used to determine knowledge, attitudes, beliefs or behaviours of individuals, and is the most popular data-gathering tool in survey research. However, it does have two major problems: the design of a reliable, valid questionnaire instrument, and the need to convince the intended recipients, who may have little interest in the study, to respond willingly, honestly and promptly to the request for information. To provide reliable information, the questionnaire must give consistent measures over time and from person to person. It should have 'content validity' in that the questions proposed are the best ones to obtain the information which is required. This can usually be ensured by referral to expertise in the subject of study, or by conducting a pilot study to check that the information meets with intended aims and objectives of the investigation.

Procedures for data-gathering using a questionnaire

It is important to plan and thoroughly prepare the questionnaire instrument used in survey investigation, in order to generate the most valid and reliable results. The following stages should be included in the process of construction, dissemination and analysis of the questionnaire:

Determine the exact objective(s) of the questionnaire

1 Identify the precise information required.
2 Consider how each piece of information is to be analysed.
3 Identify variable(s) to be included for study so that appropriate questions can be generated.
4 Define the specific purpose(s) for which the information gathered will be used, such as:

- a simple description of the responder's replies as a percentage
- a comparative analysis of the response of the respective groups studied
- the identification of relationships between or among variables investigated.

Identify the sample of respondents needed

1 Identify the specific population group at which the study is aimed.
2 Draw a sample (or sub-set) from the population and ensure that it is representative by using stratification (for example, age bands).

Take a random sample from each strata.

3 Ensure that the sample drawn is based upon the variables to be included in the study so that the results can be applied generally to other similar samples.

4 Set the appropriate sample size in order to ensure a proper representation of the population from which the sample is drawn. Make the time and resources available.

Formulate the questions

1 In question formulation, consider the specific objective of each question and how the information obtained is to be analysed.

2 Devise a table to identify categories of responses to be obtained, the comparisons which will be required and how the individual data gathered contributes to the aims and objectives of the study.

3 Choose an appropriate format for the questions. Use either:

- **open-ended questions**, such as, 'what type of leisure activity do you participate in each week?' This type of format has certain limitations since it is open to interpretations, difficult to categorise the result, and is not easily analysed.

- **closed questions**, which can be used in a variety of forms including:

    a **rankings**, in which respondents list their activities in order of preference. For example: 1 — Television, 2 — Sport, 3 — Reading, 4 — Music, 5 — Cinema.

    b **scalings,** which can be used to indicate respondent's relative commitment to certain types of activity. For example: sport participation — never, rarely, sometimes, often, frequently.

    c a **Likert 5-Point Scale** with assumed equal intervals. For example, physical education should be required at least once per week as part of the curriculum:

Strongly agree	Agree	Undecided	Disagree	Strongly disagree

d **categories** in which respondents are permitted only two choices. For example: yes/no, true/false.

4 Consider the following principles in the questionnaire design:

- use only one single idea per question
- use words with only one meaning
- keep questions as short as possible
- ensure grammatical accuracy of questions
- avoid value-laden words or implications
- use a balance of open/closed questions.

Design the questionnaire

Since the appearance and layout of a questionnaire can influence the willingness of respondents to complete it and return it, it is important that care should be given to the format by noting the following points:

- include the name and address of the researcher.
- give clear, concise instructions for answering the questions, with examples where difficulties may arise.
- begin with easier questions leading to others which require more time and thought.
- keep the length of the questionnaire to a minimum.
- indicate the approximate time required to complete the questionnaire.
- include a covering letter.
- express thanks to the respondent for completion and return of the questionnaire.

Conduct a pilot study

This involves one or more preliminary exercises in order to overcome any problems which may arise subsequently:

- use a 'trial run' among friends and acquaintances in order to obtain constructive critical comments.
- use a 'trial run' among a small sample of respondents from the population you intend to use.
- use these 'trial run' results to analyse whether or not the questions measure what they are supposed to measure.
- change the format and or structure of the questionnaire and revise questions in the light of the 'trial runs'.

Write a covering letter

The success of a questionnaire often depends on a well-constructed covering letter, which though brief and to the point, explains the purposes and importance of the investigation. It should also be tactful and provide assurance of confidentiality on the part of the respondent by specifying how the privacy and anonymity will be maintained. It is necessary to address the respondent by coded reference, not by name directly. The covering letter should be constructed with the following points in mind:

- the letter should appeal to the respondent's co-operation.
- the letter should be endorsed by a recognised authority.
- the investigators should be named with their status and address identified.
- acknowledgement should be given to the supervisor of the study.
- to increase the response rate, prior contact should be made with the respondents by letter or phone call requesting participation in the study.
- summary of the results should be offered to the respondent.

- a return date should be stated, repeating it on the questionnaire itself.
- the letter should be carefully checked for overall layout, grammar and spelling before signing it.

Distribute the questionnaire

Consider the timing and method of distribution, avoiding holidays or other busy times of the year. If the questionaire is to be mailed, a self-addressed stamped envelope should be included for the returned questionnaire. Alternatively, direct drop-off and pick-up can be arranged if it is possible, to make contact with the sample group directly through focal points.

Follow-up

Since response rates may vary enormously, it is usual to arrange follow-up. After about two weeks after receipt of the questionnaire, it will be necessary to send another copy, plus covering letter and stamped self-addressed envelope to non-responders, with a further postcard reminder if necessary. Such follow-up procedures increase the return rate from 30% and 60% of initial returns by an additional 10% to 25% after follow-up. The aim should be to obtain a total response rate of 75% to 90% if possible.

Analyse the results

Depending upon the type of analysis planned during the design of the study, it will often be necessary to code the information obtained from questionnaires into convenient types of data, such as nominal or ordinal. This should be done before the application of the appropriate numerical or statistical procedures. These procedures are used to summarise the results obtained in suitable tabular or graphical form with the appropriate interpretive written analysis of the results.

Preparing the report

The final production of the complete report should be carried out in accordance with the principles laid down by the appropriate authority.

Example 4: A questionnaire for use in a lifestyle survey

In a survey of young people the following sections of a questionnaire dealing with activity and fitness, tobacco and alcohol useage, have been used as part of the Trent Regional Health Authority's Lifestyle Survey among boys and girls aged 11–16 years of age. The authors wish to thank Trent Health for their kind permission to include extracts from the survey questionnaire.

We are asking many young people across the East Midlands and South Yorkshire to take part in this survey.

We are trying to find out what you think and do about health. Your answers will help us to plan health education and so help other young people.

Your school was randomly chosen to take part in the survey.

This is not a test, but please do not talk to anyone else about what answer you should give. The only right answers are the one that describe you best. Only you know what the right answers are for you.

Please answer honestly.

You don't need to put your name on your answers.

Please read each question in turn, and don't think too long before you answer. If you make a mistake, cross it out clearly and put in the right answer.

When your group has finished, put all your answers in an envelope before sealing it and giving it in. The envelope will not be opened in school.

No-one will know which is your questionnaire.

Your teachers will not see them.

Thank you for your help.

4. ACTIVITY AND FITNESS
This part is about your physical activity and fitness.

I feel that I have enough.

Tick one box for each item.	no	yes
overall stamina - I can keep going as long as I need to	1. ☐	2. ☐
joint suppleness - I can bend and stretch as much as I need to	1. ☐	2. ☐
strength - I am as strong as I need to be	1. ☐	2. ☐

Every week, I usually do at least 20 minutes continuous activity -

Write a number or 'none' for each item.

keep fit or exercises	..............days a week
any kind of dancing	..............days a week
swimming	..............days a week
sport	..............days a week
please say what	....
brisk, long walks (e.g. to school or a paper round)	..............days a week
jogging or running	..............days a week
hard work at home or in the garden	..............days a week
cycling (e.g. to school or the shops)	..............days a week
other activity	..............days a week

please say what ....

I think I do enough daily activity - 1. ☐ no   2. ☐ yes
If no, please say why not ....

To increase my activity and fitness I would need -
Tick one or more boxes.

☐ better health   ☐ facilities after school
☐ more time   ☐ more money
☐ more will power   ☐ facilities nearer home
☐ other, please say what   ....

5. TOBACCO

**Whether you are a smoker, an ex-smoker or have never
smoked, please answer these questions.
Tick one box for each item.**

	no	yes
I live in the same house as someone who smokes	1. ☐	2. ☐
I have friends who smoke	1. ☐	2. ☐
I use no-smoking areas when I can	1. ☐	2. ☐
I think there should be more	1. ☐	2. ☐

separate areas for smokers and non-smokers - if yes please say where

....

Please read the following statements carefully.
Tick the one box that describes you best.

1. ☐ I have never smoked.
2. ☐ I have only smoked once or twice.
3. ☐ I used to smoke sometimes, but I have given it up now.
4. ☐ I sometimes smoke, but I don't smoke every week.
5. ☐ I smoke between one and six cigarettes a week.
6. ☐ I smoke more than six cigarettes a week.

In a week I usually smoke -
Write a number of 'none' in the space.
..............cigarettes a week.

If you don't smoke, go on to Part 6: Alcohol.

I have been a smoker for .... **years and** ....**months.**

When I smoke I am usually -
Tick one or more boxes.
- [ ] with friends of my own age
- [ ] with friends of all ages
- [ ] with relatives.
- [ ] on my own

I usually smoke -
Tick one or more boxes.
- [ ] at home
- [ ] at parties
- [ ] in pubs
- [ ] other - please say where
- [ ] youth club
- [ ] night club or discos
- [ ] at sporting events

....

I would like to stop smoking -

1. [ ] no   2. [ ] yes   3. [ ] don't know

6. ALCOHOL

Please read the following statements carefully
Tick the one box that describes you best.

1. [ ] I have never had a taste of alcohol - go on to next section
2. [ ] I have only tried alcohol once or twice.
3. [ ] I have an alcoholic drink on special occasions, such as birthdays, Christmas or New Year.
4. [ ] I sometimes have an alcoholic drink now, but no more than once or twice month.
5. [ ] I have an alcoholic drink about once a week.
6. [ ] I have an alcoholic drink more often than once a week.

I drink -
Tick one or more boxes, even if you have only tried alcohol once or twice.
- [ ] at home
- [ ] at parties
- [ ] in pubs
- [ ] other - please say where
- [ ] youth club
- [ ] night club or discos
- [ ] at sporting events

....

When I drink I am -

Tick one or more boxes, even if you have only tried alcohol once or twice.

- ☐ with friends of my own age.
- ☐ with friends of all ages.
- ☐ with relatives.
- ☐ on my own.

Now think back over the last full week, Friday to the following Thursday.

Over the last week, Friday to the following Thursday, altogether drank -

Write a number or put a dash in each box like this. (–)
Include home-brewed alcohol.
Do not include fruit juices, fizzy or soft drinks as low alcohol drinks.

Marking	Fri	Sat	Sun	Mon	Tue	Wed	Thu
1/2 pints of ordinary beers, ordinary lagers or cider							
1/2 pints of strong beers, strong lagers or ciders							
1/2 pints of shandy							
Pub size glasses of ordinary wine							
Pub size measures of spirits or liqueurs (e.g. whisky, gin or vodka)							
Pub size measures of sherry, martini or port							
Other alcoholic drinks (e.g. cocktails)							
1/2 pints of low alcohol beers, lagers or cider and/or pub size glasses of low alcohol wine							

References

de Vous, D A *Surveys in Social Research* (3rd edition), UCL Press (1994)

Downie N M, Heath R W *Basic Statistical Methods,* Harper and Row (1965)

Holliday M, Cohen L *Statistics for social scientists,* Harper and Row (1982)

Mudge *Research Guide,* North Derbyshire Health Authority, Chesterfield (1993)

Rediguides: *Guides in Educational Research*, TRC-Rediguides Ltd, M B Youngman (ed), University of Nottingham School of Education, Nottingham (1978)

Rediguide numbers:

10 *Constructing Tests* (M B Youngman and J G Eggleston)

Acknowledgements

The publishers wish to thank the following for permission to use material:

Photographs
Action Plus: p 213 (3); Advertising Archive: p 331; Allsport: p 1 (4), 6 (3), 10, 11, 20, 205, 211, 212 (bottom), 240, 256, 271, 283, 288, 325, 329, 330, 334, 357, 366, 370, 379, 390, 396, 406, 409, 412; Author: p 142; Barnabys Picture Library: p 222 (right); Bridgeman Art Library: p 302, 344: Colorsport: p 205 (top), 207, 209, 216, (3), 222 (left) 294; Mary Evans Picture Library: p 303, 308, 311, 312; Hulton Deutsch Collection: p 297 (2), 299, 306, 307, 313, 315, 316, 317, 321, 323, 403; Image Bank: p 374; Jerry Mason: p 203 (2): Plas y Brennen: p 348; Popperfoto: p 148, 327, 290, 388a, 388b, 388d; Mile Powell: p 10; Gray Mortimore: p 11, 310; Science Photo Library: p 65; Sporting Pictures: p 212 (top), 386, 393; Stockfile: p 11; Tony Stone Worldwide: p 276, 339; John Walmsley: p 280, 254, 327, 388, 254, 327, 388b; Vandystadt: p 9.

Illustrations
Jeff Edwards and Andrew Bezear